THE PROBABLY TRUE ... ES OF S...

The following tale descri ... ong adventures of Sparky Malone, born in Ab ... otland in 1941. The writer would like to point out that any reference to him which identifies him as Sparky Malone, may probably be true. The name Sparky Malone has been used because the author found it easier to write about a third person, and anyway he liked the name.

Most of what you will read is actually true, but there will be occasions when poetic license has been used to either embellish the story because of a fading memory, or because it makes more enjoyable reading.

These adventures started very early in Sparky's life, and continued over many years, they cover his time in the British Merchant Navy, his new life ashore working as a marine communications service engineer, his progression into the life of a salesman. His many amazing adventures in the world of overseas sales. Being marooned in Baghdad during the first gulf war, and his escape across the Iraqi dessert in a taxi, with 15 English businessmen, ending with a hair-raising journey along 100Km of no man's Land to Jordan. Being greeted in Amman by none other than the famous BBC overseas correspondent Kate Adie.

All this is interwoven with his adventures in the mountains of the world, narrowly escaping with his life on more than one occasion. Sailing with various lunatics in the Irish Sea and other places, rock climbing, (with a passion) and fell running up and down big hills and mountains to feed his spirit of freedom.

It will be amusing, funny, occasionally serious, and sometimes sad. But hopefully enjoyable.

THE PROBABLY TRUE ADVENTURES OF SPARKY MALONE

MIKE BRIGGS

Dedicated to:

Billy, Nora, Pamela, Sharon & Lovisa
You are my Clan and my Ryhope
Family.

I love you all and hope you
enjoy Sparky.

Uncle Mike
xx

Author
Mike Briggs
Maghull
Merseyside
United Kingdom
email zen@w3z.co.uk

Contents

———◆———

PART 1

The Early Years

Shot out of his cot like a Jack-in-a-box
Cardboard wings and a leather helmet
Running away to Sea

———◆———

Sparky's story began at around 0300 hours on June 20th 1941, in Aberdeen Scotland. The Second World War was gathering momentum and his dad was stationed there with the Royal Army Ordnance Corps.

When Sparky was only a few days old he was catapulted out of his cot like a "Jack in a Box" by a German Luftwaffe bomber as it returned from its raid on the shipyards of Glasgow. It had jettisoned the remains of its payload on Aberdeen docks as it flew home to its base across the North Sea. Sparky landed on the bedroom floor with a dull thud, as his apprehensive mum rushed across the room to pick him up, but he appeared to be completely unhurt, still sleeping soundly through the whole proceedings. After that his mum always used to say that *he was never quite right in the head!*

As the months passed Sparky grew into a strong young lad, he always preferred to be outside exploring the world around him. When he was a year old his dad was moved to a secret

MOD ammunition depot in Sedgwick, on the edge of the beautiful English Lake district.

They stayed there for a while, renting a nice cottage just outside the village. During their first year it was a very hot summer, and as always Sparky wanted to be out side; the front garden was alongside the main road to the village, but it was a quiet place and his mum felt happy that Sparky was safe behind the garden gate. He was nearly two years old by now, with a chubby little face, and a mass of tight blond curly hair, he was a picture of health, his strong little body kissed by the sun giving him a lovely tan.

One day his mum was indoors keeping cool, having a cup of tea and a good old natter with her next door neighbour, who was known as aunty Vera. Sparky's sister Eileen came home from school, and as she approached the house she saw him playing in the middle of the road, the garden gate wide open. As she came closer she was horrified to see that he was covered in thick black tar from head to toe, happily pushing one of his little toy trucks in and out of the melted road surface whilst making vroom vroom noises, she shouted for her mum, who came running out with aunty Vera close behind.

To say Sparky was in a mess was putting it lightly, he was covered in tar all over his arms, hands, legs, face and worst of all in his lovely curly golden locks, which now looked more like Caribbean dreadlocks than hair, and by this time he was screaming the place down, most indignant that his play was being interrupted. It was a serious matter, but the three of them burst out laughing at the sight of their little blond "Tar Baby".

If Sparky had been yelling before, it was nothing compared to the noise he made as his baffled mum, Aunty Vera and his sister Eileen started to try and clean him up. Fortunately, for Sparky and his mum, Vera's husband used to own an auto repair garage near Kendal before he was called up to fight in the war with the Royal Engineers, and aunty Vera remembered that he had some special green cleanser used to get rid of the oil and dirt from his hands.

Together with lots of scrubbing and wiping they eventually removed most of the tar off his now very red and sore little body. His lovely golden locks however were a different proposition; and with no other option they reluctantly began to cut off his curls until most of his head was clear of tar. All the time this was happening Sparky was howling and screaming loud enough to awaken the dead, but after a lot of love and kisses he finally fell asleep in his mums arms; she put him down gently in his cot, sighed and said 'I wonder what's going to become of you my little angel', little did any of them know that this was just the start of Sparky and his adventures.

The war eventually came to an end, and he found himself living in Blackpool, Lancashire, along with his mum and elder sister Eileen. However his dad was not with them, and only appeared occasionally for short but rather stormy meetings with his mum. His parents marriage was falling apart and he remembered the words divorce and separation. They lived in an attractive, small, terraced house in the North Shore area of the town, and despite the austerity of post war Britain, life was comfortable and the young chubby Sparky began exploring as far afield as his little legs would carry him. Blackpool Tower, the Pleasure Beach with its House of Fun and huge roller coaster rides, miles of fantastic sandy beaches, donkey rides between the North and South Piers, all provided endless hours of fun, adventure and of course trouble.

Wherever he went Sparky was accompanied by his faithful dog Bruce, so named after a prize fighter called Bruce Woodcock, who was an English light heavyweight and heavyweight champion, winning Empire and European titles from 1945 to 1950.His sister Eileen was growing up fast, and wanted to become a dancer. mum had been on the stage as an actress, a vaudeville singer and dancer touring the music halls before the start of the war. She encouraged Eileen to try classical dance, and managed to get her enrolled with the Blackpool Tower ballet school of Madame Schultz. Eventually Eileen would become a professional dancer and whilst touring the country she was spotted by a talent scout and passed an audition to appear on TV's Sunday Night At the London Palladium, where she joined a line of chorus girls known as the 'Television Toppers'. This line of lovely girls used to open the show with a spectacular dance routine dressed in top hat and tails, their shapely long legs adorned with black fishnet stockings. Quite tame by today's standards, but certainly enjoyed by the male viewers back in the 1950's.

His sister continued her career on the music halls, eventually touring with the Irish tenor Joseph Locke, he had a powerful voice and was quite the hit of his day, he also had the reputation of being a 'bit of a lad' who enjoyed gambling, drinking and chasing young ladies. One day Eileen eventually reported him to the tour manager, accusing 'The great Joseph Locke' of behaving inappropriately towards her. The manager indignantly rebuffed her ridiculous accusation and sacked her on the spot. This heralded the end of her search for fame and and fortune on the 'boards' and she left the stage all together, and became a fashion model.

The famous Blackpool trams ran as far North as Fleetwood where the harbour was packed with fishing boats. Sometimes his mum would take the children there for a picnic and they would meet up with his Auntie Queenie and Uncle Aubrey who both worked the Fleetwood promenade. Auntie Queenie would dress as Gypsy Rose Lee and tell fortunes via her crystal ball, whilst uncle Aubrey ran a horoscope scam further down the beach, calling himself Professor Aubrey Grey. Their awestruck clients were mill workers from Lancashire and Yorkshire who hung on their every word, paying a few shillings to see what the future held in store for them! Sparky loved watching both of them in action and on one occasion Uncle Aubrey read the horoscope of a Birmingham butcher, and provided him with eight lucky numbers to take home from his holiday.

A couple of weeks later he read in the Sunday edition of the News of The World that the butcher had won £50,000 on Vernon's Football Pools, a huge amount of money in those days. The newspaper article claimed that Professor Aubrey Grey of Fleetwood, a world renowned 'psychic mathematician' had successfully predicted the correct numbers for the visiting holiday maker. The following day, uncle Aubrey caught a train down to Birmingham to see the butcher at his home, and he asked him for a share of the winnings; but the butcher promptly threw professor Grey out onto the street and threatened him with the removal of his lower appendages if he ever came back to Birmingham. Meanwhile back in Fleetwood Aunt Queenie was sitting in her 'kiosk' on the corner of the local bowling green opposite the Midland Hotel, busy foretelling births; deaths; marriages and divorces via her special magic crystal ball. Sparky's happy days continued uninterrupted.

However his greatest joy was to visit the fish quay and watch the trawlers unloading their huge baskets of cod and haddock. He loved to listen to the sailors talking about their trips to the Icelandic fishing grounds. There were tales of 30 foot waves, pack ice as big as houses, storms raging at 70 miles an hour day after day, and all the while they continued to trawl their nets before hauling them aboard full of shiny silver fish. The catch was then gutted and packed into ice boxes until the holds were full- there were no fishing quotas in those days! Sparky would sit at home dreaming of a life at sea; he saw himself braving the worst storms imaginable, whilst safely bringing home his crew and their valuable catch of Icelandic Cod. Little did he know he would be back a few years later.

However, life has a habit of changing and one day, his dad came and took him away from his mum to live with him in

North Wales, miles away from the sea and ships. The courts had decided in their wisdom that his dad would be able to offer him a better standard of life and education, a difficult and controversial decision for his mum to accept, this was something that haunted her for the rest of her life. For a while Sparky was very sad and unhappy, but his dad loved him and sent him to a nice school where he soon made new friends and settled down. Eventually he remarried to a lovely lady called Sheila, Sparky liked her very much. She was kind hearted and fun loving, they became friends very quickly. Sheila and his dad would have two children, Ian who was born in Altrincham Cheshire, and Diana who was born a few years later in Scotland.

Sheila had worked in an aircraft factory during the war and had lots of funny stories to tell. She was a progress chaser, checking on the various parts under construction for the airplanes. One day the foreman asked her to go to the fabrication shop and ask for a 'long stand,' it was a least fifteen minutes before she realised that was exactly what she was doing. It helped relieve the stress and boredom of the job, they were all under pressure to complete their work which was vital to the country's war effort. Most people often worked twelve hour shifts or longer. Sparky also liked his new Grandparents, especially his Grandpa, Mr. Neville or Nev as he was affectionately known, he was an auto electrician, with a workshop full of amazing stuff. Dynamos, armatures, accumulators, cable looms, connectors, crock clips, and hundred of other exciting things to learn about. Nev was a slim almost skinny man, he smoked Woodbine cigarettes, and wore an old trilby hat all the time he was working, even when he went in the house for a cup of tea. That is, until grandma Emily told him to take it off. Grandpa Nev turned out to be an excellent teacher, happily showing the young Sparky all kinds of wonderful things about the mystical art of *auto electricians*, remember this was 1948, and Sparky was only seven years old.

Around this time, his new mum's brother Noel came home from sea. During the war he had served in the Royal Navy sailing to Egypt, North Africa, Singapore and Australia. Sparky was in heaven, here was a real live sailor back from his adventures around the world, and from the start he got on really well with his new Uncle Noel, or little Nev as he was also known. He filled Sparky's young head with all sorts of fantastic stories which, as the years went by, contained more and more lurid details of a sailor's life. He mentioned things such as 'Dockside Bars and Juke Joints' where beautiful young ladies would throw themselves at the young sailor men, he omitted to mention that all this came at a price! The growing adolescent Sparky was completely entranced, this seagoing life was just the thing for him...but it wasn't to come easily.

At one point Sparky became interested in flying, after reading about the Royal Navy and its 'Fleet Air Arm' with ships called aircraft carriers. So he dreamed about becoming a seagoing fighter pilot. One day, in the Eagle Comic, he saw a detailed explanation of Leonardo da Vinci's early drawings showing manned flight using wings strapped to a man's arms and back. Sparky and his pals set about making some cardboard wings, they nicked the straps off his sister's roller skates and cut up a large box they rescued from the rubbish dump at the back of the local Co-op general store. They painted the wings silver and proudly put the Royal Air-force insignia on both sides. One of the lads pinched his dad's leather motor bike hat, goggles and a pair of leather gauntlets. The test flight was arranged and Sparky would be the pilot.

Close to where they lived was an old quarry with a 50 foot high cliff, and It was decided to launch him off the top. A runway was cleared and with his wings strapped on, wearing the leather helmet; goggles and gloves, he ran full pelt towards the cliff edge, and launched himself into space...The cliff face was mainly grey shale used in the local manufacture of household bricks.

Over the years it had eroded and formed a deep soft bank at the bottom; 50 feet below. With his pals cheering him onward to his doom, Sparky jumped off the cliff top, and finally free from the constraints of Mother Earth, he started flapping his little arms furiously. Almost instantly, they were forced vertically upwards with both wings shooting off into space, never to be seen again. Sparky plummeted downwards at 32 feet per second, hit the soft, shale bank, bounced up into the air, then rolled to a stop at the bottom of quarry. His ashen faced pals looked down in horror at the crash site with Sparky laying there motionless. Almost in unison,they screamed and ran off to his house to tell his dad that Sparky was lying dead at the bottom of the cliff. But when his dad arrived on the scene, accompanied by his tearful pals, Sparky was sitting up, holding his left arm and crying his eyes out.

His dad picked him up by the scruff of his neck dragging him to his feet. 'You stupid boy' he shouted, 'what on earth do you think your doing'? Then he clipped poor Sparky round the ear, kicked him up the bum and told him go straight home. When he got indoors, his distraught step-mum Sheila also clipped him round the ear, but then she noticed that his left arm was dangling at a strange angle. Realising it was broken they decided to take him to the local cottage hospital, five miles away in the small town of Mold. As it was Sunday, and in North Wales, there was no local ambulance service. It had to come from Chester some ten mile away, and since his dad didn't have a car, they strapped him to the back of his Uncle Noel's shaky old motorbike and clattered down the twisting road to the hospital, where they confirmed that his arm was broken.

Once back home, with his arm in plaster, Sparky decided that life as a seagoing flying ace was not for him. After a few weeks of enforced inactivity due to his plaster cast, he was getting really fed up. It was the summer school holiday time, so he asked his dad if he could go and stay with Granddad Neville for a while. They only lived a couple of miles away so his dad agreed. Off went Sparky with his treasured possessions stuffed into an old Royal Navy kit bag given to him by his uncle 'Little-Nev', at last he was free again and off on a new adventure. At the same time, Sparky's best friend Norman was staying next door with his own grandparents. Things were looking up already. The two of them had a knack of getting into trouble, but they promised their families that they would behave themselves. Norman was a bit younger than Sparky and normally lived with his parents in Manchester, but he loved to spend time with his Grandma, there were so many places to explore, open countryside, old farm houses and abandoned Kilns left over from a once flourishing brick manufacturing industry, not to mention disused railway lines, mine workings and bridges, just the sort of playground for a couple of lads like them. They spent the first few days doing harmless things like climbing up to the top of a huge oak tree, and chasing bulls up and down the fields. Spurred on by Sparky's recent aviation disaster, Norman pointed out to him that if he had been fitted with a parachute, he wouldn't have broken his arm. It was as if a magic light bulb had gone off in Sparky's head, and they immediately set about designing Para Mark 1.

They went to the local village paper shop and tried to find books or magazines describing what to do when bailing out of an air-plane if shot down by enemy fire. It proved to be an impossible search. Eventually, they got kicked out by the shops owner for putting their sticky little fingers all over his nice, shiny magazines. When they got home to Sparky's grandparents, he asked Mr. Neville if he knew anything about parachutes. Since his Grandpa Nev was so clever, Sparky was sure he would have an answer. 'An old bed sheet and a ball of strong string should do the trick' said Mr. Nev with sly smile on his face, he'd been a bit of a lad himself in his younger days, brought up in Llangollen, North Wales, he had an endless stream of stories about his young life and its adventures. He kept Sparky enthralled for hours on end, stories like the time Nev and his mate Bob drained miles of the Llangollen canal into the river Dee, after cracking open the sluice gates on the famous Pontcysylite aqueduct, resulting in tons of water cascading a hundred feet below into the river Dee. The boys were in terrified retreat, and ran back down the embankment towards the town of Llangollen. Reaching the bottom they were met by local lads rushing up to the aqueduct to find out what was going on, 'Come with us Nev,' they shouted, 'somebodies emptying the canal.' So Nev and Bob turned around and followed them back up to the scene of their crime.

Sparky went outside to his grandma's wash-house,which was also the privy, and there he found a large white sheet lying on the floor seemingly doing nothing, and obviously not needed by his Grandma Emily! He gathered it up and ran next door to show Norman, who was in his granddad's greenhouse unravelling lengths of string which were attached to bamboo canes. A few green things were caught up with the string but Norman soon cut these away with his trusty pocket knife, which he'd won in a game of conkers earlier that year. The boys were now in business, and went behind Nev's workshop to construct their ingenious life saving device. After cutting away more green things, which had small tomatoes growing out of them, they managed to salvage eight lengths of strong string which they knotted onto the bed-sheet at equal distances. They planned to attach four of these to each side of Norman's elastic braces which he wore to keep his over-sized shorts from falling down around his ankles. Norman was the obvious choice because Sparky didn't have any braces, he wore a naval webbing belt given to him by his Uncle Noel. It almost went twice around his little waist, but Sparky wore it with great pride, after all none of his pals had a belt that had been to a Singapore Juke Joint. Anyway Sparky couldn't do it, his arm was still in plaster.

Next day they were up with the larks and headed for their huge oak tree as soon as they had finished their porridge oats and honey. It was a lovely sunny morning as they climbed to the top of the tree and looked down at the lush, green grass thirty feet below. After some initial difficulty trying to secure the string to Norman's trouser braces, he was ready for his death defying leap into the unknown. Excitement was running high as he balanced on the edge of the tree branch, but suddenly, he froze, gripping the branch of the sturdy English oak with all his might. His bottom lip began to quiver and soon, great big tears rolled down his chubby little cheeks, as tendrils of mucus shot in and out of his nostrils, he sobbed his heart out. The trials looked doomed, even though Sparky tried to calm him down by telling him, yet again, about his own bravery when confronted with wide open spaces. Norman was having none of it and steadfastly refused to let go of the branch. His little hands were growing white around the knuckles, and his sobbing got louder and louder. It seemed to Sparky that they were destined to fail.

In between all the sobbing and snivelling, Sparky heard an even more disturbing sound. It was the voice of farmer Joe Fletcher who was standing thirty feet below them shaking his fist and holding a double barrelled shotgun in the crook of his arm. 'Get down here now you little sods or I'll have the police onto you'. Things couldn't get any worse, thought Sparky, but they did. As he told the petrified Norman to get down, he heard the quavering reply,'I can't let go'. 'You'll be fine,' yelled Sparky from half way down the tree, 'your parachute will save you.' For a long time afterwards Norman wondered why on earth he had taken any notice of Sparky in the first place. As the years rolled by, there were probably many other people all over the world who thought the same thing whenever they had occasion to remember Sparky Malone.

He had almost reached the ground when he looked up and saw Norman hurtling towards him, with a tangled white bed sheet trailing behind. But Just as he was about to hit the deck, the bed sheet caught on a branch higher up. Norman was yelling at the top of his voice and was heading straight towards Sparky. Suddenly, Norman's earthbound progress stopped abruptly, and he miraculously bounced back upwards as his braces caught on the edge of a rotten looking branch six feet off the ground. There was a split second of silence followed by a loud, ripping noise as the bed sheet tore in half. Norman fell head-first, bounced off Sparky's right shoulder then crumpled to earth like a sack of spuds, whilst landing hard on his left arm at the feet of farmer Fletcher. He rolled over, looked up at Farmer Joe, saw the shot gun tucked under his arm, screamed, then passed out. The next few hours were not the best Sparky had known during his short young life. Norman had a broken arm and suffered slight concussion, otherwise he was fine. But Sparky was reprimanded by the hospital staff, for drawing pictures of ships and maps of the world, all over his own plaster cast. They seemed particularly intrigued by words like *Shanghai Juke Joint* and *Hong Kong Lilly*.

The consequences of their parachuting exploits were not much fun either,they were both grounded and Norman's mum came over from Manchester to take him home. Sparky's dad was told to keep him away from their lovely little son, describing Sparky as being nothing but an uncontrollable little monster who should be sent to the nearest borstal. He asked his dad if that was a naval training ship,receiving a good humoured clip round the ear for his cheek. The remaining weeks of his summer holiday passed with Sparky feeling very gloomy, but his dad eventually relented and let him go back to Grandpa Nev's for a few days. As Norman had been taken home to Manchester, Sparky had no one to share anything with, let alone have the odd adventure. But Grandpa Nev came to the rescue, taking Sparky out on some of his service calls to fix trucks, tractors and cars with starting problems. He began to understand lots of things about electricity, batteries, coils, spark plugs and much more. By the time he went back to school, he considered himself to be quite the expert, as he explained all this amazing technology to his young gang of fascinated mates.

1953 was important year,on the 2nd of June Elizabeth was crowned monarch of the United Kingdom, Canada, Australia, New Zealand, Union of South Africa, Pakistan, India and Ceylon. Mount Everest was conquered by Edmund Hillary and Sherpa *Tenzing*. News of their success was delayed to coincided with coronation day. His dad was promoted to a senior position in Manchester, Sparky was 12 years old, and would run away to sea.

Due to his promotion, the family had to move house, but much to Sparky's horror, his dad enrolled him as a full time boarder at a private school for boys deep in the hinterland of the Vale of Clwyd in North Wales, which was even further from the sea than before. His dad thought it would bring discipline into his son's life and build some team spirit.

At first Sparky hated every moment of it, he was only small and was the butt of much bullying. When it came to playing his first game of rugby he was chosen as the hooker. During the scrum he was outraged at having his shorts pulled down and his private parts squashed and nipped, he retaliated by punching anyone who got in his way, the scrum fell apart and he was sent off the field,and was subsequently punished by the games master, who made him run twenty times around the school sports field. However he hadn't realised that Sparky loved running and was actually enjoying himself.

Eventually he made some friends, one of whom was the nephew of George Band who had been the doctor on the successful Everest expedition. The two talked of many things, one of which was the fantastic achievement of the Everest climbers. Sparky really was inspired and saw many exciting opportunities waiting for him in the high mountains of the world, but this was to come later, in the meantime all he could think about were ships and the sea.

Half term came round and Sparky went back to his new home in Manchester, he had no friends except Norman who lived on the other side of the city. Normans parents had not yet forgiven Sparky for the parachute incident but eventually agreed they could meet. The two pals had a great time catching up with each others adventures and they spent a day wandering near the Manchester ship canal where Sparky was once again mesmerized by the sight of all the ships, tugs and barges. When he got home he plucked up courage and asked his dad if he could go to sea as a sailor when he was old enough. His dad was having none of it and lectured him about looking towards his future, telling him to work hard and make something of himself instead of dreaming of a wasted life at sea.

Sparky was devastated and sat around the house being miserable but suddenly he had one of his bright ideas. There were a few days left of the half term holiday so he asked his dad if he could go to Blackpool and see his real mum. He usually visited her a couple of times a year, which was not as often as he would have liked. His dad made the phone call and that afternoon with his naval kit bag packed, he was sitting on the bus with a smile on his cheeky face and feeling much happier. His mum met him off the bus with lots of hugs and kisses, then took him home for a slap-up tea. They chatted away about what had been happening since his last visit.

He told her about his dad's refusal to agree to his seagoing life. She commiserated with him and said maybe his dad would change his mind.

That night in bed, he lay there thinking about the Fleetwood fish docks. It was only a short tram-ride away, and he could almost feel the power of the sea calling him and hear the sailors laughing and joking about their last trip. He knew what he had to do, but did he have the courage? Sparky was only small but he was very strong and confident for his age. He had the gift of the gab, inherited for sure from his paternal grandparents who were originally from County Cork in Ireland.

It was with some trepidation however, that he made his mind up and next morning, when his mum was out shopping, he packed his sea bag, and left a tear-stained note on the mantelpiece.

He really loved his mum and didn't want to hurt her but he knew that she would understand; she was also a free spirit. When he arrived at the fish dock, it was humming with activity, lots of noise and the strong smell of fish. He almost turned and ran back to the tram station but then a voice called out to him, 'Who you shipping out with mate?' Sparky turned to see a young sailor lad, probably a couple of years older than him, with a battered kit bag over his shoulder and his canvas cap perched cockily on the back of his head. 'I haven't made my mind up yet,' lied Sparky in a shaky, uncertain voice.

The young sailor knew that Sparky hadn't got a clue, but he went over to him anyway and introduced himself as Gordon McBride, deckie learner on the trawler Wyre Defender. They chatted for a while over a mug of strong tea from the dockside café. Sparky came clean and admitted he was trying to get a away on his first trip.

Gordon was sixteen and had already done three trips to the Icelandic fishing grounds. Sparky was in awe, he lied again saying he was sixteen and had already left school. It appeared that the Defender was short of a galley boy, the regular one having been taken ill that morning and they were due to sail in two hours on the midday tide. Gordon knew exactly what Sparky was about, he'd been there a few months earlier. It would be good for him to have another young lad on this trip, that way they could gang up on the regular sailors when they were making life hard for them. 'We can ask my skipper if he'll take you on,' said Gordon, 'the cook won't be happy without a skivvy to do all the messy work.'

He could see by the way he was dressed that Sparky had no proper sea going gear so he suggested he could use Bob's old kit. The previous galley boy wasn't going to need it whilst they removed his appendix at the hospital.

With time running out, they reported aboard the trawler and found the Skipper in his cabin. He looked very bad tempered and was swearing at the first mate about things Sparky had never even heard of.

'What the 'ell do you want Mac Bride?' he shouted as they stood outside the cabin. 'Beg pardon sir, but I think I've found us a galley boy,' he replied, pointing at Sparky. The big Skipper looked Sparky up and down, then glanced at the clock on the bulkhead. 'Can yer read and write lad?' he said, 'and how old are yer?' Sparky nodded his head and said, 'sixteen sir.' The Skipper mumbled something to the first mate who also looked Sparky up and down, then nodded. The Skipper told him to go with the first mate and get signed on. His pay was to be five bob a week and a small share of the catch, if he worked hard. Sparky was now almost shaking with fear, what on earth was he doing? It didn't seem like such a good idea now, but it was too late. The next thing he knew, he was signing a page in a large logbook, and was then taken by Gordon into a dark, smelly, cramped space below decks. He told Sparky to change his kit, and passed him Bobs sea bag.

The next few hours were simply terrifying as Sparky was engulfed in the sounds of shipboard life; engines growling, orders being issued and big winches clanking and banging.

As they cleared the harbour and thrust their way into the Irish Sea, waves and spray showered down all over the decks and the trawler began to roll and corkscrew as she settled into a force six head-wind.

Sparky found his way to the galley where he reported to the cook, who was a big fat man with a red face and monster hands, the biggest he had ever seen. The cook shouted something to him, and pointed to a huge tub of black-looking potatoes. He couldn't understand a word the cook was saying but realised he was expected to start peeling, and fast... Sparky was convinced he was going to die, and prayed for his mum and dad to forgive him. As often happens, things got worse. A deckhand told him to report to the Skipper on the bridge. He wasn't quite sure where that was but guessed it might be up top where he thought the ship's wheel was located. The look of thunder which greeted him on the face of the Skipper told him his game was up, and he fully expected to be thrown overboard at any moment. Sparky's life as a fisherman was over and a few hours later they were sailing into Fleetwood docks.

On the quayside he could see a police car, an ambulance, and his mum and his dad. At that point Sparky just broke down and cried. Eventually it was all sorted out with the police and the trawler owner, and they were allowed to go home, but these exploits were to have a dramatic and long reaching effect on Sparky's life.

His dad took him away from the boarding school in North Wales, and placed him in a private grammar school near their new home in Altrincham, Cheshire. His dad told him that this was his last chance to settle down and work hard.

Right from the start Sparky liked his new 'temple of learning.' It was located in open countryside but within easy walking distance of home. The boys in his grade were good fun so he decided to impress his dad and get on with it. His favourite subjects were: history, geography, English and science. He was not so good at maths, Latin or French' but excelled in all sports, especially running, tennis, and football.

To make things even more exciting, the history teacher, Mr. Joe Royal, was a keen rock climber and took groups of lads out to the Derbyshire gritstone crags for training once every couple of weeks.

So despite there being no ships in his life, Sparky was enjoying this new way of having fun. His dad also seemed happier, especially when Sparky decided to join the local Boy Scout Group, St Peter's 4th Hale. He really loved this with a passion and excelled in gaining all his badges. He was promoted to patrol leader, and eventually troop leader, before gaining his Queen's Scout Badge, which was presented to him in Gilwell Park, the home of world scouting.

Mr. Banks their Scout Master was an inspiration to all the boys, especially since he had suffered an accident in his school days, when an explosion in the science lab had severed his right hand.

This did not prevent him from becoming a senior draughtsman in a large, local engineering company, and despite having a prosthetic hand he could tie all the special knots required in scouting with one hand, and even had a special set of 'clip in' tools he used when the troop went camping, notably a hook which allowed him to lift boiling hot billy-cans off the camp-fire. All the lads thought he was just the greatest and best Skipper in the world.

Despite all this, Sparky was still not immune from more than the odd spot of trouble. His best friend at school was called Gavin and he was, without a doubt, something of a rebel. He and Sparky were almost inseparable. It wasn't long before they were brought before the headmaster for unruly and reckless behaviour in the school playground. Gavin had pinched a lad's cap off his head and flung it into the air. It was caught by a gust of wind and ended high on the uppermost chimney-pot of the main building. The lad started blubbering and threatened to tell the headmaster if he didn't get his cap back. Gavin just laughed but Sparky saw a way to redeem the situation and immediately climbed up the very long drainpipe which led to the apex of the school roof. He straddled the slates and inched his way towards the cap, which was precariously perched on a big red pot, but when he reached the stack, he had to stand up in order to retrieve his prize, it was a precarious man-oeuvre.

By this time, he was high above the school yard, all the lads, and some masters were down below, open mouthed, looking up at him.

Disaster struck when the Headmaster came out to see what all the commotion was about. Sparky looked down and saw, rather than heard, the Headmaster shouting at him to come down. The wind was gusting strongly and as he reached upwards for the cap, it was caught by another strong gust, and shot off towards the girls convent school next door. (Another reason Sparky liked this school). There were cheers and shouts from down below as he reversed back along the roof tiles and tried to gain a handhold on the drainpipe, which had helped him to get up there in the first place. He looked down at the growing throng of people forty feet below, and suddenly felt very scared. Meanwhile In the school yard, masters were ushering the boys inside, as Sparky clung on desperately to the roof. He was beginning to loose his grip, and his feet started slipping.

Just as he thought his lot was up, he heard a clanging bell, and saw a beautiful red fire engine racing up the school driveway. It pulled up below him, and in no time at all, a ladder was winding its way upwards complete with a fully kitted out fireman gripping the top rungs. Sparky thought he heard the fireman telling him not to panic but he was far too busy holding onto the drainpipe to take much notice. Minutes later, he was back on ground with the fireman, and being confronted by a very angry, red-faced headmaster. 'In my study now boy,' he said. When Sparky got to the heads gaff, as the boys called it. Gavin was already standing in the corner looking completely unconcerned. The enraged headmaster droned on for what seemed like hours to the two lads, it was no use making excuses, they were caught red handed and there was no escape from this one. They both received six of the best on their left hand with the head's wicked looking Malacca cane, then sent home to be further tormented by their respective parents.

Meetings took place with both sets of parents, their errant children and the headmaster. They were excluded from school for a week with severe warnings about the consequences of any further breaches of school discipline. Sparky thought he heard both Gavin's dad and his own discussing the unlikely prospect of the boys being expelled from school, due to something they called, the lost revenue of two sets of fees. Life was certainly grim for at least a week or more, but eventually the terrible duo returned to the fold, silently cheered and revered by large sections of the third year. The whole school had been warned by their respective form masters, not to show any sympathy towards the pair when they returned, or they themselves would be introduced to the dreaded Malacca whiplash. However, some of the lads were made of sterner stuff and immediately formed a secret S and G admiration society. Summer term holiday came and went, with the pals being separated due to family commitments and visits to relatives. Sparky at least was trying to make amends for his actions, but Gavin was unrepentant and when the new term started, he seemed to be more mischievous than ever.

One day the snow arrived and the playground, which was on a slight incline, was full of long ice slides with great fun being had by all.

Around this time, Gavin was getting a lot of grief from Mr Eccles his science master. Mr Eccles did not like Gavin at all and was constantly making him stay behind for detention, whilst the rest of the boys were out having fun in the fresh, new snow. Mr Eccles wife was the school's French teacher, she was in fact from Paris, and very much adored by most boys of a certain age, on account of her rather voluptuous body. Gavin in particular, was convinced he was in love with her and he thought that Mr Eccles suspected the same, hence the reason for the excessive detentions. One break time, whilst the snow was still around, Gavin decided to push some up the exhaust pipe of Mr Eccles' 2CV motor car, working on the theory that the minus temperatures would freeze the snow and prevent Mr Eccles from starting his car when it was time to go home. Unfortunately, or not as the case may be, sharp eyed Mr Eccles spotted the rather large icicle sticking out of his car's exhaust pipe and with the help of a stick and some magic solution he got from the science lab, he was able melt the blockage and drive away much to Gavin's disappointment.

The dreaded mock exam time was looming and the conscientious students were working hard to gain good results. Sparky was doing his best and thinking of the future, asked his dad again if he could go to sea but the answer was still a resounding NO! Once again he went into a bit of a black period and was not very happy. When the mocks we're over his dad was asked to attend a meeting with the headmaster. Later when Sparky got home, his dad sat him down for a serious talk. It appeared that he had done quite well with his exams but had not reached the grades the school expected of pupils who were aiming for a place in University. It was thought therefore, that it would be better for Sparky to leave school at the age of sixteen and apply for an apprenticeship with one of the many engineering firms in the Manchester area. Sparky was horrified, he could think of nothing worse, he and his dad had reached a total *impasse*...

Back at school the next day, he told Gavin about his dad's decision. Gavin agreed that parents were useless, and suggested it would be better if they both ran away and joined the French Foreign Legion.

That afternoon, they had stayed behind to play a quick game of tennis, and on their way past the building works being carried out on the schools new science laboratory. The contractor's large red crane which was being used to demolish a wall, it was parked just outside the newly built section of the lab. The crane had a long chain hanging from its jib, with a huge and very heavy looking steel demolition ball attached to a swivel. Without hesitation Gavin jumped in the cab followed by Sparky. Gavin pressed a green button and suddenly the crane's engine burst into life. Both lads started to panic and tried to get out of the cab door at the same time. Unfortunately Sparky's satchel strap became entangled with a lever, which then clicked forward as he struggled to get out. The crane cab suddenly began to move around whilst its tracks remained stationary. The horrified boys scrambled back inside the cab pulled another lever hoping to stop it from revolving, but this made things even worse and the cab began to turn faster. The panic stricken lads watched in horror as the steel ball began to swing further and further away from the vertical, with an ark which was getting closer to the newly constructed wall of the science lab as the cabs speed accelerated and the steel ball drew closer and closer until it.

Inevitably crashed into the wall, smashing a great hole through the bricks as it continued on its circular path of destruction.

The boys escaped from the scene and ran down the school driveway as if the devil himself was after them. On the main road they separated and rushed home until they reached the sanctuary of their respective bedrooms. Neither of them had much sleep that night and dreaded going to school the next morning. They met at the school entrance and walked slowly towards the main building. As they approached, a number of lads came running down the drive waving and shouting, apparently they said, the big red crane had mysteriously demolished the new wall of the science lab sometime during the night! 'I wonder how that happened' shouted Gavin as he ran up the drive with a big smile on his face.

A few days later, Sparky's Dad sat him down yet again and told him that his Grandma Emily had been to see him. She had persuaded him that the best thing he could do was to agree to

Sparky's request for a life at sea. Some time later he found out that what Grandma Emily had actually said was, that if his dad didn't let him go to sea, Sparky would probably only run away and go anyway. Having now made his decision about Sparky's future his dad was great, and went about doing everything he could to help his son achieve his dream. He went with him to attend interviews with various shipping companies, hoping to secure a position as a cadet. Eventually he was offered a place with Manchester Liners, and a five year deck apprenticeship. Sparky could already see himself strutting up and down the bridge of a ship in his captain's uniform and cap.

However on the way home from the successful interview, their bus stopped outside The Brooks Bar Radio College for the training of Marine Radio officers, his dad suddenly took Sparky by the arm, and said, 'come on son lets have a look at this place'.

They went into the college to make enquiries about what it could offer his son as a career. They were welcomed by a very nice friendly secretary called Mrs Spark who gave his dad the full prospectus and details of the course and fees. It was half term and there were no students in attendance, so she took them around the various training and lecture rooms , which were full of interesting looking radio equipment, and various photographs of ships radio rooms, Sparky was fascinated, and very excited. When they arrived home he had a long chat with his dad, and together they decided that a career as a ship's radio officer would be an excellent opportunity, providing Sparky with a worthwhile job, and good prospects. His dad offered to fund his college fees and enrolled as a full time student in 1957.

The amazing turn of fate which took them to that bus stop in Mosside Manchester, and his dad's uncanny foresight would prove to be the start of a long and eventful career. His best pal Gavin was devastated when Sparky gave him the news, but also pleased that he had finally got his wish to go to sea. Gavin in fact left school at the same time and spent the summer months messing around trying to get into some sort of mischief, but it wasn't the same any more without Sparky.

Gavins parents were quite well off, and his Dad had been a career soldier, attending Sandhurst as a cadet officer before joining his regiment, where he eventually reached the rank of full colonel. He served with distinction in the war, and travelled extensively during Gavin's early years. It was no secret that his parents were not impressed with Gavin's errant ways, they couldn't understand why he seemed to rebel against nearly everything put before him. Just before Sparky was due to start at Radio College, he and Gavin met up to compare notes, then they swore an oath of undying allegiance to each other. Gavin said he was going to join the Royal Navy as a boy sailor and was due to start training in a few weeks time at HMS Ganges. His father was furious with him, but eventually relented signing the consent forms in the hope that the Navy could instil some discipline into his son's life, and maybe make something of him in the end. Alas it was not to be, Gavin failed to complete the full training course due to his newly acquired interest in women, he apparently found himself in some sort of bother with a young Wren, who happened to be the daughter of a very senior submarine commander stationed at HMS Dolphin in Gosport Hampshire. Gavin was released from his commitment and sent home to Cheshire. Sparky heard later that Gavin omitted to tell his parents what had happened, he took his dad's car and cheque book and left in disgrace for an uncertain future... it was rumoured that he had taken up a career as an actor, eventually working in Television as a producer, but the boys never met again.

Sparky however was now about to start out on a completely new adventure, one which was to provide him with a life full of travel, excitement, danger, failure and success. During these early years, he had further developed his passion for the outdoors, embracing the world of climbing and high mountains. He was a natural on the rocks and loved running, favouring long distances rather than sprinting. All these pursuits would provide him with lots of adventures in the future, but for now Sparky was about to achieve his lifelong dream of going to sea, all he had to do was work hard and pass his exams at the Radio College...

PART 2

The Sea Going Years

All that Jazz and Espresso coffee
Living in a brothel
His sister leaves for America
Getting his ticket

————◆————

With his dad's change of heart, brought about by the intervention of his Grandma Emily, Sparky had finally been given approval to pursue a career at sea, and his somewhat chequered life as a schoolboy was over. Not that it had been without incident, he'd had lots of fun, and often sailed very close to the wind, which was something he would do for many years to come. However new horizons now presented him with the chance to fulfil his dream of a life at sea in the Merchant Navy, and in autumn of 1957 he began his new life as a full time student at the Brookes's Bar Radio College for the training of Marine Radio Officers in Manchester.

The course was intensive and required the students to learn the theory and practical applications on the principles of radio communication, they also had to learn the international Morse code, and how to transmit and receive messages over radio using a Morse key. In 1957 this was the only way of communicating with merchant ships sailing the oceans of the world. However on passenger ships radio telephony equipment had been introduced, providing the opportunity for those who could afford it, the luxury of making very expensive telephone calls from ship to shore. In those early days these conversations were not two way, or duplex as it became known, whilst one person was talking, the other had to listen and wait their turn to speak, each person saying the words 'over' and then release the 'press to talk button' on the handset when they wanted to hear the reply. Needless to say this often caused confusion, but it was still an innovative technology and moved communications at sea another notch forward. It would be a while however before radio-telephony became widely available to merchant ships.

Safety of life at sea using radio communications was in a state of continuing development, the sinking of the Titanic on the morning of the 15th of April 1912 was the catalyst which forced the international maritime community to agree to a whole new set of regulations, structured to help safeguard the lives of seafarers and passengers alike. The world economy was frantically working hard to recover from the ravages of world war 2. International trade was dependent on ships to carry their precious cargoes of manufactured goods, timber, grain, raw materials coal and oil, in order to fuel the global economy. Ship building was intensive as the merchant fleets of Great Britain, Europe and the USA began to rebuild themselves and recover from the massive losses they had incurred due to enemy action.

Many thousands of tons of shipping and seafarers lives had been lost; and a new era for the marine radio officer had begun in earnest, as international maritime regulations required all ships over 2,500 gross tons to carry a fully equipped radio station and a trained officer to operate it. As the course unfolded Sparky soon realised how important his role would be on board ship, he began to take it very seriously and was excited at the prospect which lay ahead. For the first time in his young life he could see a way forward and applied himself eagerly to the task ahead. To his surprise he found the technical lectures easier to understand than some of his course mates. It wasn't long before he realised that the time spent in his Grandpa Nev's auto electrical workshop had been time well spent. He already new about accumulators, coils, relays, armatures, voltage and current, plus a lot more.

Just before starting the course his dad moved the family home once again when he was promoted to the companies Liverpool office. So Sparky went to live in lodgings close to the college, together with a couple of other lads who had enrolled at the same time. This was his first real taste of freedom away from the family circle, but to begin with his dad insisted that he came home at weekends rather than staying in Manchester. He settled down quickly and worked hard, making friends with Dave and Taffy who shared the same lodgings.

It wasn't long before the trio started to explore the night-life of big city Manchester, and there was plenty of fun to be had. Espresso coffee bars were the 'in' place to be seen, they stayed open late, sometimes all night, Jazz clubs were all over the city, and although they were under the age to be served with alcohol, they looked older than their years and got away with it most of the time.

Dave came from Kendal in the English Lake district, he was a good looking lad with a cool relaxed attitude about most things. His Dad was a builder, and had served in the Royal Navy as a gunner during the war, but was keen to give his son a chance to make something of himself, and travel the world. Employment prospects in the Lake District were not so good at that time, mainly farming or working in one of the many tourist shops or hotels which were still trying to recover financially like everyone else. Taffy, or John as he was also known lived in Barmouth North Wales, his family had been offshore fishermen for five generations, but it was a hard life and Taffy couldn't see much future for himself, especially since he was the youngest of three sons. His share of the family fishing business was not going to amount to much. His cousin Glynn had been a ship's radio officer before the outbreak of world war two, serving mainly on Tramp Steamers which by the nature of their trade spent many months and sometimes years away from home. Built to take a wide range of cargo, which could be anything from coal, farm machinery, grain, iron ore, timber or rice they would deliver it to wherever it was needed. Often after they unloaded their goods, the ship would anchor off the port and wait for the Captain or the ship's owners to secure another cargo. This sometimes took days or weeks, or they may be lucky and sail off to some other distant port and load a lucrative cargo destined for the other side of the world. They were as the name implies, tramping the Oceans of the world looking for work.

Glynn liked the life, and never seemed to be short of money whenever he came home to Barmouth, that sounded pretty good to Taffy. He was an easy going lad, always up for a laugh, he a had a great sense of humour and kept the trio amused, especially after a few pints of beer. But being a typical Welshman he nearly always burst into song, usually the Welsh National Anthem which he would sing over and over again.

The wonderfully circular design of the Manchester Central library was a great place to study in the evenings, it was warm and exciting, with amazing acoustics. (Drop a coin on the desktop and listen to it echo all round the building until it reached its starting point). The library was always full of university girls, and there were lots of places close by to meet up and make friends afterwards. The young trio enjoyed themselves working hard at college, and at night during their free time. Being away from home had given them a wonderful feeling of freedom, and they took full advantage of it whenever they could. Everything went well for the first term, but at the start of the second the boys found themselves ejected onto the street late one night, after the landlady caught them entertaining some girls in their cramped attic accommodation at the top of the house. In the 1950's moral attitudes were still rather strict, and this sort of thing was just not tolerated.

The boys had to crash on their mates sofas and arm chairs for a couple of weeks, but eventually wore out their welcome until they were on the street again. Eventually they found a small but affordable flat in the dubious red light district of Mosside, only a mile away from the college. They pooled their resources and moved in. The flat was owned by Stan, who also ran a greasy spoon café close to the college, all the lads used this as a meeting point, they could buy cheap mugs of tea, and huge toasted bacon butties for breakfast. Ron's Café also boasted a great Jukebox box with a mixture of 200 rock and roll, blues, and jazz records. After the boys had been in their new accommodation for a few days, they realised that the rest of the house was occupied by young working ladies of a somewhat dubious reputation, and that Stan the greasy café man was their benefactor. Half way through the new term the trio fell behind with their rent due to spending it all on espresso coffee, beer and university girls. Stan was not a happy man, but he quite liked the three boys, so suggested they could help their situation by collecting the money from each of his 'working girls' until they could afford to pay him back. It was a great arrangement, and the boys fought over who's turn it was to collect it. The girls were really friendly and would often invite them in for a drink when they weren't busy with clients.

Sparky eventually told his dad that he had moved to another flat, but didn't disclose where it was. By this time he was not going home at weekends, and often escaped into the Derbyshire Peak District or North Wales to go rock climbing with the Manchester University Mountaineering club. One Saturday when he was off climbing his dad came to Manchester on business and decided to pay Sparky a visit. He went to the college and asked if anyone knew where his son was staying, and was directed to the luxury hovel in Canal street. Sparky's dad was a tall handsome distinguished looking man, he prided himself on his appearance and wore expensive suits, even though he couldn't always afford them. He looked at the rather seedy surroundings and eventually knocked on the door. He was greeted by Rita, a very voluptuous nineteen year old who naturally thought his dad was a punter, so she smiled and asked him in. Sparky never really knew the full story, because Rita said she gave his dad *a cup of tea and buttered scones*, before waving him goodbye. Strangely enough Sparky's dad never did mentioned that he had been in Manchester on business that particular Saturday.

After just over a year of full time study all three lads passed their exams and gained a 2nd class Certificate of Competence in radio-telegraphy with the authority to operate granted by The Postmaster General. The celebration lasted three days, then it was time to look for a job. Sparky however stayed on for another term and converted to a First Class Ticket of competence (as it was generally called), in the hope that this would help his career prospects. The year was 1958 and it was the end of an exciting time in Sparky's life. Dave joined a Cunard passenger ship in Liverpool, and Taffy did his first trip on a Reardon Smith Cargo ship bound for Buenos Aires out of Cardiff, they kept in touch for a while, but then as happens in life they drifted their separate ways.

Qualified Radio Officers almost exclusively found employment in the Merchant Navy, but their qualifications also offered them opportunities to work in other interesting areas, one of which was with the British Antarctic Expeditionary Force, as communications officers in the various scientific bases around Antarctica. Sparky was quite tempted to apply for a position, as the call of the wild really appealed to him. However his Dad put him off by saying that it was all men and no women, then tapping the side of his nose he said 'and you know what that means don't you son?'His dad was of course completely wrong, especially with his veiled inference that 'funny things went on down in Antarctica.' But Sparky realised that he needed to get to sea as soon as possible, after all this was the whole reason for his existence on the planet.

The main options of employment at sea were found by joining one of the four marine radio manufacturing companies, the largest of these was Marconi who at that time had the most number of radio stations contracts with ship owners, they were followed by Siemens Brothers of Woolwich, Redifon of Wandsworth and the International Marine Radio Company of Croydon, or IMRC as they were better known. Another but more difficult option was to join one of the shipping companies who had set up their own radio department, managing their own officers, but purchased, or rented radio station equipment direct from one of the companies previously mentioned. At that time there were not as many opportunities for direct employment, but over the next few years things changed as the shipping industry continued to expand.

Another option for ship's radio officers, or Sparks, were called, was to hire themselves out on a freelance basis to foreign flag vessels on short or long contracts. This paid better money than the rather poor salary grade British ship owners were prepared to offer. However it was less secure, and some of the early ships were old rust buckets that had tramped the oceans of the world for decades, and many of them were on their last sea legs. However our Sparky hedged his bets and applied for, and was accepted as a junior RO with Marconi Marine. All newly certified RO's were required by maritime law to serve six months as a junior on a ship with one or more senior officers. Usually-cargo ships or tankers only had one permanent senior officer, and they would undertake to train the junior in the complex business of radio traffic operating procedures, watch-keeping, and marine telegraphic accounting, which involved keeping a record of messages sent and received from the ship to shore. All these messages were charged for by the radio operating company. On busy ships such as passenger liners there was a considerable income to be made, providing a nice profit for the radio supplier.

Assuming the junior proved reliable, sober, diligent and hard working, his chief would then recommend that he was competent to operate a ship's radio station of his own, his employers would then assign him to a ship. This 'berth' as it was known, could be on anything from a tramp steamer, an oil tanker, a general cargo vessel, (which in those days often had accommodation for up to twelve fee paying passengers), a deep sea ocean going salvage tug or a UK coastal vessel above 2,500 gross registered tons. Some of these coastal ships were called 'Colliers' and were purpose built to carry coal, plying their trade from the coal-ports of South Wales and the North East, mainly Sunderland, Seaham and Newcastle. There was an never ending demand for coal to fuel the power stations of southern England such as Battersea, located on the South side of the mighty river Thames.

Battersea continued to provide electricity to the capital until 1980, but with the introduction of alternative oil fired stations, it no longer became viable and was closed down. A national campaign to save the building resulted in it being awarded the status of a national heritage site, and was eventually awarded grade 2 listed status. Redevelopment of the whole site began in 1986 and has continued over the decades, despite surviving a string of economic and contractual problems.

In addition to the 'Colliers' there were small oil tankers of similar tonnage which delivered fuel oil for domestic consumption into small ports around the UK. The oil companies installed huge storage tanks in their depots, and together with fleets of road tankers, distributed fuel to petrol stations and smaller sub-depots around the country. It was a lucrative business, which undoubtedly contributed to the economic expansion and recovery of post war Britain.

In the 1950's and 60's the road and rail networks of Britain were in desperate need of modernisation and investment. The coastal cargo vessels were an economic way of transporting goods around UK coastline. In addition the ships delivered British manufactured products across the Channel to Europe, discharging their cargo in such ports as Amsterdam, Hamburg, Copenhagen, Oslo and many more. With some financial help from his dad, Sparky was kitted out with his merchant navy uniforms, and all the things he needed to cope with the various conditions he would encounter at sea. From the cold of the North Atlantic to the tropical heat of West Africa and beyond. (He eventually repaid his dad out of his monthly salary). Sparky was really proud of his uniform, which displayed a single wavy gold braid on the sleeves of the jacket, and epaulettes to signify his rank as a junior radio officer. Once he was promoted this would change to double wavy gold braids with a diamond in the middle.

The world was now his oyster and the young fresh faced Sparky decided he looked just fantastic, 'I bet those university girls in Manchester would be queuing up for a date with me now,' he thought. In fact he was so pleased he took himself to Jerome well known photographers in London road Liverpool, where he had some pictures taken to send to his mum and sister Eileen in Blackpool. In the final months of his time at radio college his sister had met and fallen, in love with an American GI called Jim Ruckert. Jim was stationed at the Burtonwood Air base near Warrington Lancashire. It was a whirlwind romance, typical of the day, with Eileen and Jim spending all their spare time together. One day Jim broke the news to Eileen that he was being repatriated back home to the USA. On the night before he was due to leave he proposed to her and she accepted on the spot. Jim said he would send for her as soon as he got home to Pittsburgh, where they would get married with his families blessing. The next morning Eileen excitedly told dad, he was rather taken aback by the news, and said. 'You can forget all about that, you won't hear from him again, these Yanks are all the bloody same.'

Yet again his old dad was completely wrong, and within a few weeks of his departure Jim sent Eileen a registered letter containing enough money to pay for her passage on a Cunard liner out of Liverpool to New York. He also sent photographs of all his family, and of the house he was going to buy for them to start their lives together. It has to be remembered that this was 1958 overseas telephone calls were very expensive and difficult to arrange at the time. It was not possible to make a direct dial call, few people could afford such a luxury as a telephone, and even if they could it was likely it would take months before being installed. Airmail letters and telegrams were the quickest way to make contact. Contrary to his dad's prediction Jim and Eileen were to remain married for many years until Jim's untimely death of a heart attack in 1996.

Even from the early days as kids, Sparky and Eileen were always very close, they often scrapped and fell out, especially when she used to pinch his bike so she could go off and see one of her many boyfriends, but at the end of the day they were inseparable, and loved each other very much. Woe betide anyone who upset his sister, they would have Sparky to deal with. Despite him being happy about Eileen's news, he was very upset at the thought of her going to live so far away, but realised he may possibly get the chance to visit her if one of his ships went to America. It never occurred to him that the USA was a vast country and the chances of that happening were remote. Eileen eventually booked her passage on the Cunard Liner 'Corinthia' which sailed from Liverpool's pier head on a dismal rainy day in November 1958 bound for New York.

Sparky and his dad went to see her off, but their mum was too upset to join them. Eileen boarded the ship with her suitcase and found her way to the upper decks, where she lined the ships railings along with all the other passengers. Eventually they spotted her and waved like mad, it was impossible to hear one another above all the noise. At the appointed sailing time the ship's steam whistle blasted out over the Mersey, scattering the seagulls and immediately bringing tears to the eyes of hundreds of people both on and off the ship. In his quiet moments over the intervening years Sparky often remembered that day, he felt utterly desolate and immensely sad at losing his sister. It was a cold grey windy afternoon, with the rain lashing down on them. Eileen stayed at the railings all the time, moving to the aft part of the deck as the ship moved away from the berth. Sparky and his dad stood in complete silence, soaked through to their skin, both with their own private thoughts, until the ship was too far away to see any sign of Eileen. His dad put his arm around Sparky's shoulder and they walked off silently together to catch a bus back home. It would be fifteen years before he saw her again.

PART 3

Sparky Goes to Sea

Gets Stranded in Cristobal
Home in disgrace on a Danish Freighter

———————◆———————

With his seagoing gear already packed, Sparky waited eagerly for the Marconi telegram to arrive with its joining instructions for his first ship. It seemed like it would never come, so he spent the time catching up with old pals, and thinking hard about the journey which had brought him to this point in his young life. Before him lay the complete unknown, a world mainly dominated by older men, all living together within the confines of a floating steel home. He had no real idea of what it would be like, he wondered if he would be able to do the job which he had worked so hard to secure, were the seas really 30 feet high, (as the Fleetwood Fishermen had boasted all those years ago)? What if he didn't like it once he got there, his mind was full of conflicting emotions. Then suddenly it was all over. His dad came into the room holding the eagerly awaited 'Marconi telegram' containing the instructions for him to join his ship in Liverpool two days later. All his previous fears and concerns disappeared and were replaced with last minute panic whilst he checked all his gear, and put together the paperwork as instructed on the telegram from Marconi. All Sparky's dreams were about to come true, but he was blissfully unaware that they were almost to come to a disastrous end before they had really begun.

The events which are about to unfold over the next few paragraphs took place some 57 years ago. The story which surrounds them has been told many times to many people, in many parts of the world. Most of the time it has been received with lots of laughter and some considerable degree of amazement, as well as comments of derision. The author has decided to change some of the names of the people and ships which form a central part of this episode. It is one thing to use the power of the spoken word to describe events of the past, but expressing them in the written format presents a different dimension. The author has no desire to embarrass or belittle anyone who may have been involved at that time, and who like him, are still around to remember. There will no doubt be some 'Old Salts' who may be able to identify the real ships names and owners, so be it!

In July 1959 having just turned eighteen years of age, he was instructed to report to the Marconi office in Liverpool where he would then be taken to sign on the SS Salamander as junior RO. His ship was due to sail within 24 hours, bound for Valparaiso via the Caribbean and the Panama Canal. Just those few words written 'in ticker tape strip' fashion on the telegram, transported Sparky into a combined state of ecstasy and fear, his biggest adventure so far was about to begin. Once again his dad did him proud, giving him the money for a taxi to take him to the Liverpool. Having first reported his arrival to a pretty blond receptionist, he sat alone in the waiting room for some time. Eventually he was joined by a few other people, whom he assumed were also radio officers. Every now and again morse code signals were emitted from a loudspeaker on the wall, and each time this happened somebody would stand up and go through the door labelled 'Depot Manager'.

Sparky wasn't yet skilled at reading Morse code in his head, that would happen with practice once he put some time in at sea. But for now he was rather confused about what was going on. The atmosphere in the waiting room was not very congenial, some were reading newspapers and others were sitting there looking a bit scared, just like he was. They watched as a steady stream of people went in and out of the dreaded office door. He was beginning to get a bit impatient, after all here he was ready to report for duty and was seemingly being ignored. Then to his great surprise the words "Malone" bellowed forth from the loudspeaker, he looked around the room as if seeking confirmation that it was actually him the voice was summoning. Before he could move his now semi paralysed legs, the speaker spoke yet again, only this time more forceful than before "MALONE" it said... Sparky shot up off his seat and nearly fell over as he rushed towards the dreaded office door, he turned the handle and stumbled into the room.

'Malone I presume?' said the voice behind the desk. 'Yes Sir,' quaked Sparky. The voice looked him over carefully, then in a calm and friendly manner told him to take a seat. By that time Sparky was almost bereft of the power of speech, he just sat there and listened to the 'voice' as it welcomed him to the great Marconi Company, and then went on to explain what would happen next, and what would be expected of him once he joined his ship. The voice emphasized how important it was to uphold the traditions of the 'Great Marconi Company' at all times, and to act with the decorum and bearing befitting a ships officer... Little did they both know that this encounter was to be re-enacted a few weeks later, only with far more dire consequences.

A Marconi technician was detailed to run him over to the Hornby dock where his ship was berthed. Alf, the technician, chatted away as they approached the docks, 'What did you think of our stick of rock then?' he asked Sparky, 'I'm sorry

I don't know what you mean,' he replied 'Oh that's OK, it's what we call the boss,' smiled Alf 'If you broke him in half he'd be like a stick of Blackpool rock, only, instead of Blackpool it would say Marconi all the way through it.'

As they approached the Salamander Sparky was amazed at how big she looked, he'd never been this close to a cargo ship before. It also appeared to be well maintained, and in his untrained opinion, was not very old, (it was in fact only 13 years since she was completed in 1946). Then he was suddenly was standing at the bottom of the ship's gangway, and with his sea bag clutched tightly in his hand, he clattered his way up the metal stairway to his temporary new home. He was taken to the ship's dining room where the Shipping Master from the Board of Trade was seated at a large table signing on new crew members into the ships log.

Sparky presented his identity papers and his unused Seaman's Record Book, then he signed the articles of engagement, and in that one action he was now officially recognised as a 'British Merchant Seaman.' With the formalities over he was introduced to the ships purser, who handed him a set of keys, and directed him to his cabin, which was on the same deck as the ships engineers. The purser also told him that the senior radio officer would be back on board in a couple of hours. Sparky opened his cabin door, stepped inside, dropped his bag on the deck, then let out a huge yell, 'I've made it at last' he shouted. It was a nice airy space with a bunk along the starboard bulkhead, a comfortable looking couch, a large wardrobe, and a wash-hand basin. He was delighted, and for the first time in a long time, he started to feel confident and happy, so he unpacked his things and sat down for a rest to await the arrival of his 'Chief'.

A knock at the door disturbed his daydreaming, and as it opened he saw a smart, fair haired young man in blue uniform, who immediately introduced himself as Grenville Hughes senior Cadet. Sparky stood up and they shook hands. 'Its tea and tab-nab time,' he said, 'fancy a brew and a spot of grub then?' Sparky realized he was famished, he hadn't eaten anything since breakfast, and that was hours ago. 'Follow me then and we'll see if there's anything left after those *Ginger Beers* have been at it.' Later Sparky realized Grenville meant *those engineers,* and he was to find out that all sorts of rhyming slang names were allocated to various departments, people and places, it was a thing at that time on board British ships.

Two flights of stairs led up to the aft end of the boat deck where the officers ward room was located, Sparky saw the brass name plate above the doorway, and suddenly felt a bit overawed, it sounded a bit posh to him and he suddenly felt nervous. Then he remembered what the Marconi 'stick of rock' had told him about always conducting himself in the manner befitting a Marconi Radio Officer. So he pulled himself together and stepped into the room.

It was full of smoke and noisy chatter, filled with people dressed in greasy white overalls, work trousers and battle dress tops. There was lots of laughter and good humoured banter as 'Gren' introduced Sparky with a wave of the hand. They were met with comments like 'You'd better eat as much as you can mate, this is the best it gets from now on,' or 'You'll be sorry you signed on this slave ship.' It went on for a bit longer as people stepped forward and shook his hand. A powerful looking man with huge black beard thrust his hand forwards and said 'I'm Gordon O'Toole second Engineer, just make sure you've always got a few cans of McEwans in yer cabin and you'll be fine.'

So, that was his introduction to some of his shipmates, all very friendly and convivial, they'd made him feel at ease, and after scoffing down a few cakes with a cup of strong sweet tea he made his excuses, nodded an acknowledgement to 'Gren' and went back down to his cabin to wait the arrival of his boss. He was sorting out his personal belongings when there was a knock at the door, followed by the entrance of a slim man, around five feet seven, with a slight stoop and greying hair. 'Malone I presume'? said the man, 'I'm Jimmy Jay your chief for the next few months.' Sparky stood up and reached out with his hand. 'Yes sir,' he said 'that's me.' Jimmy shook hands with a firm and steady grip. 'Welcome aboard, let's go up to the radio shack and have a wee natter then eh lad.'

The *Shack* as they were known was bigger than he had expected, but casting around at all the equipment he hardly recognised anything familiar, nothing like the radio college back in Manchester, a slight moment of panic must have shown on his face, Jimmy had seen that look before. 'Don't worry lad, it probably looks terrifying at the moment, but you'll soon get the hang of things.' His Chief was a pleasant quietly spoken man, with a strong Northern Ireland accent, there was a nervousness about him, but he appeared to have a good sense of humour, and Sparky began to relax a bit. Jimmy Jay had been a radio man most of his life, working mainly freelance on Scandinavian ships before the war, sailing the seven seas on all types of vessels. The day war broke out he was working in a radio station on the Canadian side of the Great Lakes, but transferred to a seagoing berth as soon as one became available. He spent the majority of that time on the North Atlantic run, sailing on tankers, freighters and later in troop ships. During that time he he also served in Liberty ships.

The Liberty ship was a standard design cargo vessel, built in the USA and developed to meet British orders to replace the increasing numbers of ships being torpedoed by German U boats. Eighteen shipyards throughout the USA mass-produced a total of 2,710 Liberty ships between 1941 and 1945, an industrial output on a scale never seen before. The contribution which these provided to the eventual winning of the war cannot be understated.

Sparky's chief was not a regular Marconi man, having only just joined them prior to taking over the Salamander after her annual dry dock on on Glasgow's river Clyde. During his service in the North Atlantic Jimmy had survived being torpedoed three times. Sparky was well impressed. They spent some time going through the operation of the radio transmitters, and listening to the rhythmic staccato of morse code signals from short wave stations around the world on, the Salmanders powerful communications receiver. He heard signals from Canada, the USA, South Africa and beyond. Sparky's morse receiving skills were no match for these operators but, that was only a matter of practice, and in time he would develop this skill and become very adept. Eventually he was able to read morse and hold a conversation with somebody, whilst typing an incoming message.

The Salamander cleared the Liverpool dock system at 2300 hours that evening, leaving the Canada dock behind as she joined the mighty river Mersey. With the Pilot on board to safely guide them up the Queens channel to the Bar Light and pilot cutter. This was finally it, Sparky was actually at sea, a junior radio officer, on his way to the start of his biggest adventure of his life so far. He was in awe of everything that was going on around him, but tried his best to keep calm as his chief explained the various procedures required by the radio department during departure.

To his untrained eye the darkness around them seemed impenetrable, he wondered how on earth they could see where they were going. He was soon to understand the importance of the ships radar, echo sounders, Decca Navigators, Radio Direction Finders, fairway lights, port and starboard buoys, with red and green lights. But at this precise moment in time he was just too excited and, a little nervous. Jimmy's cabin was next to the radio shack, with an interconnecting door. The main entrance lead directly onto the boat deck. After a few more minutes, Jimmy then handed over the watch to Sparky, and told him to send a TR to Anglesey radio. Then left and closed the door to his cabin behind him.

Sparky was in panic mode, send a TR, his mind went blank and he couldn't for the life of him remember what to do. He frantically read the admiralty radio signals books looking for a clue, eventually he took the traffic receipt file from the book shelf and found copies of TR's sent by Jimmy on his way down from Glasgow to Liverpool. Then he wrote out the message advising his nearest coast station, Anglesey Radio, that they were leaving Liverpool bound for Bermuda. His next problem was to actually power up the transmitter, tune in the receiver and call Anglesey using his morse key. He spent a few minutes listening to the radio traffic on 500Khz, trying to write things down on a clipboard, and after a while he began to under stand what was happening on the airwaves. After a shaky and hesitant start he finally managed to send his TR. Anglesey was very patient with him, they were well used to first trip operators, and they wished him all the best.

He signed himself off watch in the radio log book, and sheepishly went down the two sets of steps to his cabin. He'd made a bit of a botch of that one all right, but things should only get better with practice. Jimmy had given him instructions to attend breakfast at 0700 in the main saloon, dressed in full uniform. He was awake early, too excited to sleep much. When Jimmy met him, he smiled and said 'Don't worry lad, things will improve the more you do it...' And of course they did. He was bound for Valparaiso Chile on the west coast of South America, via Bermuda and the Panama Canal, and he was ecstatic. All his dreams were coming true, he was at sea at last. Sparky settled into the routine of ship-board life very quickly, Jimmy kept him busy in the radio shack showing him how to complete all the paper work, and use the comprehensive list of admiralty radio signals. It was also vitally important to keep the emergency radio batteries in a fully charged condition. In a serious situation like fire on board, or the prospect of having to abandon ship, the batteries may make the difference between life or death. It was a job Sparky enjoyed, he knew all about lead acid accumulators, he seen dozens of them before in his grandpas workshop, when his just a lad all those years ago.

So Liverpool was left far behind, and as they sailed further south and westwards the weather became warmer by the day, they would soon change their uniforms from dark blues to tropical whites. He had made friends with other junior officers from both deck and engine room, Sparky was fascinated with everything to do with the ship, from the fo'c'sle-head to the depths of the engine room. Over a period of time he was shown how to navigate and lay off a position on an admiralty chart by Gren the senior cadet. He talked to the Bosun and the carpenter, or chippy as he was know, asking them about the cargo hatches, wire splicing,and winches. He asked questions about the daily maintenance required to keep 'Salamander ship shape'. The chief engineer gave him permission to go down the engine room, and Gordon his next door 'alleyway' neighbour took him on several visits, explaining the steam turbine engine, fuel pumps, main electrical switchboard, and the massive generators which provided all the power. Sparky just loved it, however there were those who criticised his interest, and told him he shouldn't fraternise with 'grease monkey engineers' But he didn't care, as far as he was concerned the more he knew the better, after all it may come in handy one day!

He was completely at home on board the ship, the noise of the engines were his sleep-time lullaby, the sound of the sea rushing along the hull outside his cabin porthole was a comforting and mesmeric reminder that he was on the ocean, miles away from home and dry land. The constant movement of everything around him, the roll from port to starboard and back again, the pitch as the bows plunged down into the deep Atlantic were all feeding his senses, making him feel alive, and at the same time peaceful. This is where he had always wanted to be, it did not disappoint him. It was wonderful.

After clearing the islands of the Azores they ran into a south-Westerly gale, a full force eight touching nine. The sea was transformed from a gentle rolling slumber to a raging maelstrom of crashing water, shooting upwards from the bow as Salamander cleaved her way into the white topped crests, parting the huge mass of ocean, sending it howling and crashing over the top of the forward hatches until it slammed against the wheelhouse windows. The ship shuddered then rose again out of the cold Atlantic, ready to deal with the next encounter. It was a battle she would win every time, but only because the sea was not ready to take her, and because the skill and experience of the Captain and his crew were watching over Salamander, always alert, always ready, showing the respect the ocean deserved.

Sparky was alive, he was buzzing, adrenalin charging through his body as never before. He was not afraid, he trusted the ship, but the awesome power of the ocean made him shiver as he held on tightly to the varnished wooden top of the wheelhouse bulwark, waiting for the next lashing spray to sting his face. They had been on passage for three weeks now heading for their first port of call, Hamilton Bermuda. Off duty time was spent reading, or sunbathing around the makeshift swimming pool knocked together by the chippy. It was on the foredeck between two hatches, and was made from canvas and old bits of timber, or dunnage that had salvaged during the loading and discharge of cargo. It was filled with cool sea water, and was good fun for everyone.

He had made friends easily with the young apprentice cadets and engineers, some of whom had been at sea for a few years, they all had ambitions to become captains or chief engineers. In their off watch time they would sit around drinking beer and talking about their various escapades ashore. Their stories were sometimes hard to believe, but he was soon to discover that a sailors life ashore can be fraught with all kinds of pitfalls and dangers, you had to learn to take care, and look out for yourself and each other. There were many temptations to be wary of thieves, pickpockets, con artists, and attractive young working girls. All very eager to relieve a sailor-man of his money. He was yet to go ashore in a foreign port, and his excitement was mounting as the prospect of shore leave in Bermuda was imminent. They approached Hamilton harbour in early morning sunshine, it looked just fabulous, sandy beaches, white villas and a beautiful clear blue sea. The ship was only to stay for a few hours, offloading some cargo, which included a new Morris Minor car for the Island's Governor. However there would be no shore leave for him this time, he was required to work alongside his chief helping to repair one of the ships long range radars. Sensing his disappointment the chief consoled him by explaining that Bermuda was an expensive place, and there wasn't much time available anyway. So Sparky put that behind him and busied himself with helping to repair the radar, it was a skill he became very good at over the years, and one he enjoyed.

Ten days later they were berthed alongside the quay in Cristobal,the Atlantic entrance to the Panama canal. The passage of which would take them into the Pacific ocean on their way to Valparaiso. They were unloading transatlantic telephone communication cable into the Mercury, a British cable laying ship which was tied up just ahead of them, the transfer was expected to be completed by the following morning.

There was lots of excitement on board ship, the prospect of going ashore was very appealing after nearly five weeks at sea. In the evening the crew could be seen strolling along the quayside heading for their favourite bar or 'pleasure house'. Knowing he was a 'first- tripper' and almost certainly new to the ways of a seafarer's world, they invited him to join them. 'Come on Sparky, we'll show you how to have a good time'. He was apprehensive and a little scared, it was still very warm with a high level of humidity. The air was full of the sound of chirping crickets and other insects he had never seen before.

The heat rising from the concrete surface of the quay went through the soles of his 'flip flop footwear' making his feet sweat, as he carefully dodged his way around the huge brown cockroaches, that were feeding off surface debris left over from the recent unloading of cargo ships.

Sparky filled his lungs with the sensation of the shimmering heat, he wondered at the rich mix of smells that were completely new to him. The memory of this first exotic sensually tropical sensation, would stay with him for the rest of his life. The crew were in high spirits, and pointed out various bars and cafes which were all highly recommended as being safe places to drink and enjoy life. Eventually they turned off into a side street and headed for one such establishment.

The flashing neon lights of the Doghouse Bar welcomed them as they went through the cowboy style saloon doors. The air-conditioned interior felt wonderful after the hot and steamy walk from the ship, and Elvis Presley was singing *Heart Break Hotel* on the Juke box.

Sparky had never experience anything quite like this before, it was exciting, and just a little daunting, but he was really starting to enjoy himself now. His thoughts suddenly took him back to younger days, when his uncle Nev had told him about 'Dockside Bars and Juke Joints where beautiful young ladies would throw themselves at the young sailor men,' Sparky realized that this was his sailor uncle had been talking about. However, he had no idea that this was probably the beginning of his slide downhill and big trouble.

The taste of Bacardi Rum and Coke, with ice, began to hit the spot. Things became more frantic and rowdy the more they drank. The Juke box blazed away, creating an atmosphere of excitement and rhythm he had never experienced before. The Doghouse was full of scantily clad young women, with dark flashing eyes and pure white teeth which seemed to glow in the blue lights of the bar. Gradually the sailors began to leave with a girl or two on each arm, heading for the not so discrete rooms at the back of the bar. He had been dancing with a succession of 'lovely' girls all of whom told him they had to support their families with the money they earned, one even said she was saving up to get married. But he couldn't bring himself to take the plunge, so he tottered unsteadily over to the bar and ordered another Bacardi and Coke. Just audible above the noise of the juke box, a cultured English voice said, 'I say old chap aren't you off the 'Salamander?' He looked through the haze towards a good looking man, and for a moment he thought it was Errol Flynn, the Hollywood film star. He was dressed in KD slacks with a short sleeved uniform shirt. 'Your discharging telephone cable into our forward hold.' He said with a relaxed smile, and holding out his hand, he introduced himself as James Edwards, first mate of the Mercury. The complete downfall of Sparky's shore leave was about to escalate very rapidly. Errol told him he had only come ashore for a quick drink, and post some mail. 'There's a party on board if your interested,' he said, 'we have some nice nurses down from the American hospital, your more than welcome to join us.'

At that precise moment the saloon doors were flung wide open by a crazed, drunken looking man holding a pistol. 'Bastido' he shouted looking straight at Sparky, 'You mess with my woman eh,' he said, as he fired shots in the general direction of the bar. The sound of breaking glass and the screams of the local girls created pandemonium, Errol Flynn grabbed Sparky's arm shouting 'lets get to hell out of here.' They ran out through the back of the bar, past the rooms where his shipmates were enjoying their shore leave. The madman running behind them firing off his gun. They ran down alleyways, through peoples rooms, in and out of brothels and shops onto the main street. They grabbed a taxi back to the docks, laughing all the way to the Mercury. The final stage of his downfall was now cast in stone as he walked up the gangway with Errol Flynn. The officers ward room was jumping with rock and roll music and the sound of laughter, he took one step inside and was immediately pulled into the room by a buxom young nurse. Sparky just knew he was going to enjoy himself...

As the sun beat down on his face, he thought he was going to die. Forcing open his eyes with some difficulty, he saw that he was lying on the deck, underneath a ships lifeboat, apparently, still on board the Mercury. With mounting panic, and a feeling of dread, he staggered to his feet, and looked around for his ship, it was nowhere to be seen. The Mercury had moved to a new berth on the other side of the dock. 'What the bloody hell are you doing here?' said Errol Flynn' I thought you'd left hours ago.' Then he looked at him and said, 'Christ mate, you've missed your ship, she entered the canal ages ago, looks like your on the beach.' Errol Flynn's words just wouldn't sink in. How could this be happening, how stupid, how irresponsible, what was he going to do now? He felt physically sick. To make matters worse Errol said that his ship was due to sail for it's Atlantic station in around two hours time. Errol could see how retched Sparky looked, he felt sorry for the lad, and in some small way perhaps he felt responsible, if he hadn't asked him on board then maybe this would not have happened.'Come with me' he said, 'lets see what we can do.'

The Mercury was using Gonzales and Co, the same shipping agents as the Salamander, and the representative, Miguel Ortega was still on board sorting out the ships papers before she could sail... After explaining the situation to Miguel, he agreed to take Sparky back to their offices as soon as he had concluded his business. A very subdued and downhearted Sparky shook hands with Errol and thanked him for his help. Errol responded by saying he was sorry he'd invited him on board in the first place, adding 'it's not the end of the world lad, you'll get over this and have a laugh about it over a few beers with your mates, when it's all sorted out.' An hour or so later he was sitting in a rather hot and stuffy shipping agents office, there was no air con, just a couple of tired looking ceiling fans slowly going round, hardly disturbing the air at all.

After a while Miguel came over and sat beside him, evidently the Salamanders crew had been sent ashore to look for him. They had searched the dockside bars and dives but eventually reported back that he was nowhere to be seen. Little did any one know that he was only a few metres away, on the Mercury, having a great time with his buxom American nurse. Salamanders purser handed over Sparky's personnel details, and a kit bag with some hurriedly put together possessions to the ship's agent. There was no chance of them being able to get him to the Pacific side of the canal in time to rejoin his ship, it was too late, she had cleared the canal system and was making ready to proceed to Valparaiso.

In the kit bag were Sparky's discharge book and some other relevant papers, together with an envelope containing $20.00 US dollars and a note from his chief which simply said '*hope this reaches you and that you are safe and not injured or ill*'. The Gonzales manager came out to see him and told him they had sent a message to the Captain of the Salamander, confirming that he had been found safe and well. The ship had replied, and asked that they try to secure him a berth as a supernumerary on any UK bounds vessel at the first available opportunity. An hour later, he was sitting in his rented room at the Cristobal Flying Angel Mission to Seamen. Life was pretty miserable, but at least he had a bit of money and a few personal effects. After spending a quiet and contemplative six days on the 'on the beach' he signed on as a supernumerary on board the Danish freighter Norse Viking bound for Glasgow with a cargo of South American Hardwood.

He was received cordially by Captain Olson and the officers, they new his circumstances, it did not appear to bother them. They allocated him a bunk in the ships small hospital, it was in fact it very comfortable, with the added luxury of his own bathroom and shower. As they sailed further east the weather became colder, and the ships first mate, realizing that he had no warm clothes gave him a sweater, a warm shirt and an old U.S. Navy Pea Jacket donated by a members of the crew.

Gunter, the ships radio officer, welcomed Sparky into the his 'shack'. He was a veteran of many Atlantic convoys during the war, and entertained him with hair-raising stories of his close encounters with the German Wolf packs. He had been at sea for a long time, and was now looking forward to retirement. His plan was to go and live on the South Pacific Island of Aloha, Sparky got the impression there was someone waiting for him there, but he didn't press Gunter for more details, instead he decided it sounded like a great idea, and left it at that. Norse Viking had been built in 1920 at the German shipyard of Krupp Bremen, She had a water cooled steam reciprocating engine, which made the characteristic clonking and thumping sound each time the crankshaft revolved, pushing the huge pistons up and down. Sparky found this quite a comforting rhythmic sound, but as was normal with this type of engine, once they hit any bad weather or headwinds the old girl would shudder and almost stop, then surge forward as she picked up more power.

Despite her years the ship was well maintained, but Captain Olson told him this would be her last transatlantic passage, she would be sold for scrap when they reached Copenhagen. He had been captain of her for nearly ten years, and told Sparky that they had sailed all over the world together, mainly 'Tramping', picking cargoes whenever and wherever they could. This was the passing of an era, and Sparky felt pleased to have been on board, but wished it had been under better circumstances. Their Atlantic passage was generally uneventful, with reasonable weather. But as they sailed north past the Antrim Coast of Ireland some squally showers welcomed them into the Irish Sea, and the following morning they entered the river Clyde berthing alongside in Glasgow docks. It was a miserable day, raining hard, with gusty blasts of wind stirring up the landlocked water around the quayside.

PART 4

Home in Disgrace

Looking for a new Job
A second Chance
Confronting his parents

————◆————

Sparky's mood was also somewhat miserable, he knew what he had to do, but wasn't looking forward to the consequences. He thanked Captain Olson, his officers and crew for all the kindness they had shown him. He picked up his duffel bag, and was about to head down the companionway, when the bosun came forward to shake his hand, at the same time giving him a roll of money saying, 'Best of luck lad, try not to worry too much, worse things happen at sea.' They both smiled and Sparky headed off into Glasgow to catch a train for Liverpool.

The crew had donated nearly £20.00. Sparky was very moved by their kindness and generosity, it was a godsend to him, and for a while it lifted his sagging spirits. The train journey was slow and uncomfortable, it seemed to stop at every station, further delaying the dreaded encounter with his fate. At last he was walking down Lime Street heading for the Stella Maris mission to seamen. He paid for three nights accommodation, then went in search of a place to eat. He wasn't ready to face his family just yet, preferring to wait and see how things worked out before going home as the prodigal son, to confess what he'd done. After a sleepless night, he showered and dressed as smartly as his depleted possessions allowed, then walked out into a cold and misty day, dreading the short journey to the Marconi Offices and the fate that awaited him. Upon arrival he reported to the same young lady receptionist he had seen only a few short weeks before, she smiled at him and said 'we've been expecting you, please take a seat, by the way your looking nice and sun tanned she added.' 'I wish I was feeling as sunny as I look,' he replied returning her smile.

The meeting with the 'Stick of Rock' was short and to the point. He was given a lecture on how not to behave whilst in the employment of the great Marconi Marine Company. He was told to pick up the balance of whatever money was due to him, and advised that his future career with them was over. Sparky left the office of doom and reported to the staff clerk, where he was handed an envelope containing nearly £18.00 and a letter confirming his termination of employment. Well at least he had some more funds, but he was now without a job and maybe even a career in the merchant navy, he felt absolutely awful.

As he passed the receptionist desk she looked up and gestured him to come closer. '*I think Siemens Brothers are looking for more RO's,' she whispered. 'Their office is in Rumford Place, just at the back of the Liverpool Echo.*' 'Thank you very much,' he said forcing a smile. 'Good luck,' she replied, 'It'll be alright, you'll see.' He wandered into the street, suddenly feeling dizzy, and realised he was very hungry, 'No good hunting for a new job on an empty stomach,' he said to himself as he headed towards the city. At least he could now afford to buy a decent breakfast. He paid the bill, and the waitress gave him directions to Rumford Place. He was now feeling a lot better and strode off confidently towards his next hurdle, a job. It took a little while to find Rumford Place, it was in a narrow lane, flanked on either side by office windows reaching upwards five or six floors towards the daylight.

Near the top of the lane he saw a man who was obviously doing some sort of work on a vintage Rolls-Bentley coupé, a very posh car indeed he thought. 'I'm looking for the Siemens Brothers offices,' he said to the man, who, without lifting his head from under the car bonnet said 'down the stairs behind you, first door on the right.' Sparky thanked him and headed downward towards his fate...

As he entered the offices he was struck by the light and airy atmosphere of the place, despite it being below street level. Sitting at the reception desk was a cheerful looking young lady in her mid twenties. 'Can I help you?' she said looking straight at him and smiling. 'I'm looking for a job as an RO.' He stammered out the words, feeling embarrassed and not at all confident. 'Well you've come to the right place then, we're looking for more seagoing staff.' His spirits raised a bit as the young lady said 'I'm Joan,' and handed him some forms. 'Could you please sit over there and fill these in, the boss will be down soon, he's upstairs at the moment tinkering with his old Bentley.'

'Yes I think I've already made his acquaintance.' said Sparky. Then without even being prompted he said. 'Before I complete these forms, I should tell you that I've just been sacked from Marconi for missing my ship on my very first trip as a junior.' Joan put her glasses on the end of her nose, moved slightly forward over her desk, and with a smile she said 'Well, well, that's very interesting, you'd better tell me all about it, it's not every day we have a VNC applying for a job, sorry VNC, voyage not completed.'

Before he could reply the 'Boss' came down the stairs,and wiping his oily hands on a rag he walked into the reception area. 'Ah, Mr Hatchard' this young man is looking for a job,' said Joan 'Indeed,' said Hatch, 'come through to my office, would you like a cup of tea or coffee?' He added. 'Tea please,' said Sparky. 'I've got that.' shouted Joan. Sparky was amazed at the relaxed and friendly attitude, but he knew he would have to come clean with his tale of woe. Hatch, as he was known listened carefully to Sparky's detailed account of his 'Cristobal' demise. There was a silence, and Sparky was convinced he'd blown it. Then Hatch stood up and walked round his desk to open the door for Joan, as she struggled with a tray of coffee and biscuits. He looked carefully at the young man sitting rather awkwardly in front of him. 'Not a good start to your seagoing career eh?' he said, as he walked back to his to his chair. 'No pretty lousy really,' he replied Sparky.

After completing the application forms he sat in the reception for about fifteen minutes, then Hatch came to his office door and asked him to come in.'Well, you will be pleased to know that we can take you on our seagoing staff, we don't have a ship for you at the moment, but don't think it will be too long. Once you receive the letter of confirmation from head office, you'll be on salary and expected to be available for sea going duty, are you interested?' Sparky was almost lost for words, could hardly believe his ears. 'Er, yes sir- thank you, that's wonderful.' Hatch looked across at him, the room seemed to have suddenly gone very quiet. Then he said 'It's a damn good life at sea these days, three meals a day, a cabin of your own and a chance to travel the world whilst doing a worthwhile job, keep your head down, learn everything you need to know, *and don't let me down.'* He stood up and put his hand out as if to seal the offer. Sparky raised himself on jelly like legs, and in a croaky voice said 'I won't Mr Hatchard, thank you very much.' He left Hatches office feeling a bit dizzy, and, as he walked past her desk Joan said 'welcome aboard, and take care of yourself.' 'I will he replied'.

Outside in Water Street it was lunch time and very busy, office workers were heading for the café and sandwich bars, he suddenly felt very hungry. He could hardly believe what had happened to him over the past couple of hours, out of work at breakfast time, employed by lunch. It all seemed like a dream, but it wasn't, he was now being given a second chance. It was now time to confront the next hurdle... His dad. He finished his lunch, went back to the seamen's mission and collected all his things. The manger was kind enough to give him a refund, he'd only stayed for one night but paid for three. Things are looking up he thought, let's hope the next few hours will have a similar happy ending. As he went through life, Sparky was confronted on many occasions with difficult situations, some of his own making, others which were out of his control, in the end he always seemed to win through, maybe this was all part of his apprenticeship.

He walked down to the pier head and caught the Mersey ferry to Woodside, Birkenhead, and as he sat on the bus heading for Mold he dreaded the forthcoming encounter with his dad and Sheila. The thought of admitting that he had been drunk and out of control, let alone the distraction of a buxom American nurse and his adventures with Errol Flynn just terrified him. There was however no alternative except to tell the truth, as it happened, warts and all. The bus didn't go past his home, but dropped him at the bottom of Kelso Hill. He then had to walk nearly a mile to the house, it seemed a long way; it was raining slightly and a chilling wind added to his feeling of gloom and despondency. As he crunched his way up the gravel path to the front door his dog Togo started barking, well at least he would have one friend who wouldn't pass judgement on him. The door opened and Sheila came out to greet him with hugs and kisses, stuttering her words, so surprised to see him, 'why didn't you tell us you were coming? are you OK? you look lovely and tanned, a bit skinny though. Wait till mum, (grandma Emily) hears your home.' His old dog Togo was wagging his tail and lifting his upper lip, smiling, and barking with excitement. He ran around the house as if to tell everyone the news. Sparkys dad had been in the back garden, but came through the French doors into the lounge just as he put his kit bag down, more hugs, not so many kisses but a warm reception anyway.

Sheila came from the kitchen with tea and biscuits, setting them down on the small table by the settee. His dad smiled and said 'Well son how was it then, your first trip to sea, you're home earlier than we expected?' Sparky seized the opportunity and slowly told them his story, he left out the bit about the crazy man with the gun in the 'Doghouse Bar.' His tale was bad enough without introducing the spectre of a mad Panamanian chasing their son, and new found friend Errol Flynn, through shops, front rooms and brothels. Whilst telling his story Sheila sat listening wide eyed, and with her head slightly to one side, trying to take it all in. His dad was silent and impassive, looking directly at his son, his thoughts hidden behind a rather stern looking expression.

He finished his tale with the good news that he had secured employment with another radio company, and could expect to ship out again in a couple of weeks. The lovely sweet Sheila leaned over and gave him hug, saying 'What an adventure that was love, anyway your home now, and it's wonderful to have you here.' Then she looked over at dad, stood up and left the room, sensing that there was need for a father to son moment. His dad took the whole thing more calmly than he had expected, there was no blistering recrimination, no moral judgement or condemnation of his son's actions, after all he had been in the army during the war and saw action in both France and Italy. But he was clearly not pleased. They sat quietly for a while, then Togo came in and put his head on Sparky's lap, looking up at him with a curled upper lip. Sparky wanted to cry, but forced back the tears, then gave his dog an affectionate rub around it's ears instead. The silence was broken, and his dad simply said 'I'm glad your home safe and sound, it could have been a different story.'

Sparky had weathered the storm, he began to feel happier than he had for a number of weeks, so he settled down to a few days of catching up with his friends, telling them a more colourful and somewhat exaggerated version of his exploits. Most of his pals were well impressed, and a few wanted to have the more lurid details of his buxom American encounter. However he declined to engage them with such things, telling them to use their own imagination. His uncle Nev, Sheila's ex royal navy brother however, was not so easy to fob off, as they sat having a beer in the Boars Head pub, he insisted on having the the real unabridged version, guns, film-stars, and passionate Americans; So Sparky gave him the *probably true* account of his Cristobal adventure.

PART 5

The Second Chance

A cruel Twist of Fate
Deja Vu
Charlie wins £75,000.00
Coming Aboard in a Cardboard Box

————◆————

A couple of days later the letter arrived confirming his establishment with Siemens Brothers, it detailed his pay scale with conditions of employment, and wished him well. Now back in funds he went into Liverpool to replenish his somewhat depleted personal possessions, having left most of them on the Salamander. He didn't expect to see them again. Once back home he set about sorting out his sea going gear, packing all his things in readiness for his next, and most important appointment. Ten days later the eagerly awaited telegram arrived, it instructed him to report on board the SS Nevis in East India Dock London, sailing in two days time, bound for passage through the Panama Canal, then sailing up the West Coast of the USA to Los Angeles, San Francisco, Seattle, and finally Vancouver Canada, before returning home.

His nemesis had raised its ugly head, he was stunned at the cruel twist of fate that was to take him back to the scene of his previous dubious adventure. At first he thought that maybe it was a mistake and that the telegram was meant for somebody else. Sitting on the edge of his bed he read it again, it was his name, his radio officers company number and his home address. There was no mistake. Sheila saw him as she passed his open door, and could see he was looking unhappy, she lightly tapped the on the door, walked over and sat by his side. Without lifting his head he handed her his written instructions, shrugged his shoulders and let out a big sigh. She put her arm around him, read the telegram and said 'well love, this is your chance to show that you are worthy of holding this position, all you have to do is remember what that nice Mr Hatchard told you, work hard, learn everything you need to know, and above all don't let him down. It's time to pay him back for the opportunity he has given you.' With that she stood up, kissed him on the top of his head, and said 'come on then lets have a cup of tea, and you can tell me what you think about sailing off to all those lovely places.'

He would leave for London the following morning, catching a train from Liverpool Lime street. Uncle Nev offered to take him through to the station, it would be a far more enjoyable journey than the one he had taken a couple of weeks previously. After breakfast he said his goodbyes, everyone seemed a little subdued, even Togo wasn't smiling, he just mooched around with his tail down, occasionally looking up a Sparky as much to say 'your off again then.' Nev was outside in the car and blew the horn anxious to get going. His dad came to the door with him, and just as Sparky turned to go down the path, he pressed something into his hand, it was a white five pound note. 'Make sure you book into a nice hotel tonight.' he said with a smile 'not like those places in Panama.' Sparky didn't know what to say, so he just nodded and got in the car. Uncle Nev dropped him outside Lime Street station, and helped him with his sea bags, they shook hands and Nev said 'watch out for yourself, and be careful.' Once out of the station the train picked up speed, and

Sparky sat back in his seat closed his eyes and thought about the madness of the past few months. He was very lucky to be on his way to join another ship, his second chance had now started. It did concern him that he was bound for the Panama canal once more, but as Shelia had so rightly told him, now was his chance to redeem himself, and show his new employer he was worthy of the position.

His instructions were to join the Nevis the following morning so he decided to use the money he'd been given to find a decent hotel. He took a taxi to the Ritz, thinking to himself that his dad couldn't complain about staying there. As he stepped out of the taxi, a young hotel porter rushed over and took his kit-bag before he even had time to pay the driver. 'This way Sir.' said the lad, his cockney accent showing through his attempt to disguise it. The hotel foyer was very imposing, thick carpets, leather settees and chairs, with chandelier's gleaming brightly, highlighting the impressive colours of the elaborately decorated ceiling. He wondered if this was a good idea after all, a moment of doubt caused him to stop and look around him. He'd never actually been inside such an opulent looking building before, the place was quietly busy, with well dressed men and woman sitting in small group talking or moving back and forth towards the lifts.

'Yes sir, can I help you,' said the very pretty young lady behind the reception desk, 'do you have a reservation?' For a moment he froze, she really was very attractive, her inquisitive and sparkling blue eyes seemed to be surveying him from top to toe, he realized she was checking out his merchant navy officers uniform, she seemed to approve. He dismissed the thought of going to the Seaman's Mission down on the dock road. This would do fine, he thought. 'Unfortunately I haven't.'He replied, with more confidence than he actually felt. 'Well, lets see what we have available, how many nights will you be staying Sir.' She purred. 'Just the one please, I have to join my ship in the morning.' This last phrase just slipped out, but It made him feel quite mature,adding just a touch of excitement to what he'd said. As she checked through the bookings register she looked up and smiled. 'Going somewhere exotic Sir?' 'Bermuda, Panama, and up the west coast of the USA, to San Francisco, Los Angeles and eventually Vancouver Canada.' The words just rolled off his tongue as if he'd done it dozens of times before. Suddenly he felt a rather embarrassed, but she simply said 'how wonderful sir, it must be very exciting.' He thought of telling her that in fact he hadn't made it through the Panama canal to the Pacific ocean, so he hadn't been to these exciting places yet. But he thought more of it, he wasn't telling any lies, so he just left it like that.

'We have a nice room for single occupancy on the fourth floor, which I can let you have for two pounds twelve shilling and six pence, *(the equivalent in today's money of more than fifty pounds)* inclusive of full English.' she said looking straight at him, smiling. He had never heard of full English, but it sounded good to him, and he would still have change out of his dad's white five pound note. The nice young lady called the cockney porter who brought his bag and escorted him to his rather smart room. The boy put the bag down and then stood there with his hands folded in front of him, Sparky said 'Thanks,' but the lad still stood there, with an expectant look on his fresh cheeky face. 'Beg pardon Gov but gents like what you is, usually cross me palm, so to speak.' Suddenly it dawned on him what the lad meant, 'Oh, sorry how much do people usually give you?' he said. ' I wish it were ten bob Gov, but to be honest it's usually a shilling if I'm lucky.' Sparky dug deep into his pockets, but there were no coins, he'd given it all to the taxi driver. 'Look,' he said, 'I'm really sorry, but I have no change at all.' I'll see you a bit later when I get back from a walk around town.' 'Very well sir, thank you.' He replied and then walked off out of the room. Sparky felt a bit awkward about what had happened, but there wasn't much he could do about it now

He took a stroll in the late afternoon sunshine, it was a bit chilly but he hardly noticed, he was too busy looking at all the shops and the hundreds of people going about their business. Lots of men in dark suits carrying brief cases and wearing bowler hats. Smart, young and older ladies walking briskly, sometimes in pairs, arm in arm, chatting away ten to the dozen and laughing a lot. London was certainly an eye opener for him, he had always thought Manchester was a big busy city, but London was in a different league. He bought some postcards and decided to go back to his room, his mum and sister were well overdue a letter, they had no idea about his disastrous first trip, but he would leave writing a full account of what happened until he arrived in the Caribbean.

Down stairs in the hotel restaurant he looked at the menu, but could hardly recognise some of the items. He decided to go back into Piccadilly street where he found a bar selling chicken with chips, and a nice pint of beer. Back in the hotel, as he took the lift to the fourth floor he was followed, almost as the doors closed, by the cheeky cockney porter. Sparky smiled and gave him one shilling and sixpence. The lad touched his cap and said 'I knew yer was a gent the minute I saw ya, thank you kindly sir.' When the lift arrived at the second floor he opened the doors and walked briskly down the corridor humming a little tune.

After breakfast, he called at reception to pay his bill, hoping to see the young blue eyed beauty from the previous day, but she wasn't on duty. Then, as he put the change from the five pound note into his wallet,the young porter appeared at his side picked up his sea bag, and said 'would sir be wanting a taxi?' Sparky nodded, 'To East India Docks please.' By the time they had walked through the foyer and out into the street, a black cab was waiting for him. Wiser now than when he had arrived, Sparky gave the young porter one shilling and some copper change, winked at him and said, 'Thank you, and take care.' The lad touched his pill box shaped cap in mock salute, 'And the same too you sir.' he replied. The Nevis was busy loading cargo, but the taxi driver managed to drop him off quite close to the gangway. The quayside was alive with activity and noise, dockers shouting instructions, directing cargo pallets, creaking under the weight of sacks and crates as they were loaded into the ships holds. He made his way to the pursers office, situated on the aft end port side working alleyway. Inside was a uniformed, slightly built man with dark hair and horn rimmed spectacles, he was talking with a fair haired young deck officer, probably a cadet.

The horn rimmed face turned and looked at Sparky, 'Ah you must be our new junior radio officer, we've been expecting you.' he said in a somewhat cultured scouse accent. 'I'm John Wyatt, purser, and this is Chris Jones, our senior cadet.' Sparky stepped over the weather board sill into the office and shook hands with both of them in turn. After a last minute set of instructions, the cadet left, and the purser said, 'leave your gear there.' pointing to a large settee covered in files and cardboard boxes of various sizes, 'let's go up to the officers mess and find the shipping master to get you signed on.'

Inside the room was a rather large, red faced man sat at a table with a small stack of merchant seaman's discharge books in front of him. He and the purser spoke for a while, then the Shipping Master asked Sparky for his papers. As he handed them over he was already expecting some sort of reaction, and wasn't surprised when the red faced man, looked up from the table top and said,'VNC eh, not had one of these for a while, especially from an officer.' Then with a smile he looked at the blue covered discharge book, lifted his head and said 'looks like you're bound for the scene of your last shore leave, hope it was worth it.' With that he pushed an official looking set of papers across the table and indicated where he should sign, then with a flourish one would expect to find behind the desk of an immigration officer at the boarder post of a less than friendly country, he took the all important rubber stamp and thumped it down on the page of Sparky's book. 'Next please.' he shouted. The purser nodded, and said 'Right then, let me show you your cabin.' It was located beneath after end of the boat deck on the port side. It was similar to his previous berth, but Sparky thought is was a bit bigger and brighter. Outside his cabin door was a stairway leading up to the Radio Room. Having collected his possessions on the way past the pursers office, he put them on the bunk, checked himself out in the bulkhead mirror, feeling slightly apprehensive, he climbed up the stairway to the radio room and his new boss, the chief.

Geordie Miller was a jovial round faced man, with shock of white hair, he stood up from the radio room operating desk and extended his hand. It was a strong positive grip, Sparky liked that, and rightly or wrongly it made him feel comfortable. The radio room was spotless, all the equipment was polished and shining, looking round he then realized that it was all completely new to him, and looked nothing like the Marconi rig at the wireless college or that on his first ship. They sat down, went through all the various company procedures, and the operation of the station. His boss told him he was aware of what had happened to him in Cristobal, he didn't dwell on it, but simply said he hoped that Sparky would settle down quickly and enjoy a life at sea.

The following day they cleared the dock system and made their way down the river Thames. With the Meadway Pilot safely on board his cutter, they set a course through the English Channel for Lands End and onward to the West Indies. Here they would discharge some cargo and be joined by four passengers in Kingston Jamaica who would stay with them until they reached Los Angeles. Sparky soon settled into shipboard life, the rhythm of watch keeping, the feel of the ship as it rolled gently in the remaining sea swell left by a recent storm in the Bay of Biscay. The sounds of life aboard were now not exactly new to him, and he felt at home again. The constant hum of the engines and generators added to his sense of well being. He felt relaxed and eager to improve his knowledge of marine communications, whilst at the same time hopefully impress his new boss the jovial Geordie Miller. It wasn't long before the warmer weather was being announced with the arrival of flying fishes, and schools of Dolphins, then confirmed by orders from the captain that uniforms would now be changed, it was time for 'Whites'. Many British shipping companies at that time, conformed to an officer's uniform code, some had traditions reaching back to the great East India company, where different uniforms were required for particular times, the Pacific and Orient shipping line for instance required ceremonial swords to be worn with full regalia for dinner each evening when serving on passenger ships. However this tradition was gradually dying out in favour of a sensible and more practical set of clothing.

The weather was set fair as they left Kingston Jamaica and set course for George Town, where they picked up four more passengers who would disembark in Vancouver. With the arrival of warm sunny days, life on board settled into a comfortable routine, and some off duty hours were spent doing a bit of 'bronzy,' the sailors word for sunbathing. The crew were constantly kept busy with regular ships maintenance, a never ending battle against the ravages of sea and salt water. Scraping rust, painting the decks, and varnishing the woodwork. The crew were soon stripped down to shorts and working boots, or sometimes flip flops, as the days progressed their bodies became tanned with the sun. Sparky was born in the month of June, and loved the sun, he did his fair share of 'bronzy' it suited him, he was a strong fit young man, and took care to keep it that way. Arrival and departure in George Town was, a short lived affair, just enough time to hand over the bags of Royal Mail from England, and discharge a few items of cargo. Sparky had written the account of his ill fated first voyage to his mum and sister, both on airmail letters. This was a popular and economic way to send mail in those days. His sister's would wing its way to Pittsburgh USA, and his mum's to Blackpool in Lancashire, England. He considered the poignancy of these two different destinations, he knew he would see his mum again soon, but when would get the chance to be with his sister, that was impossible to predict. It would be a number of years.

As they sailed away from the Windies towards Cristobal and the entrance to the Panama Canal, Sparky couldn't help but reflect on the consequences of his wayward escapade the last time he was there. This time he resolved to be more responsible, he could not afford to make a mess of his second chance; there were too many people who cared for him, and had provided him with the opportunity to keep his career on track, not to mention those on board who would no doubt be quietly watching and waiting to see how he coped.

He decided not to tempt fate by going ashore, instead he caught up with some work in the radio room, checked the emergency batteries, a duty he would continue to diligently carry out during the rest of his time in at sea. In circumstances of imminent peril, where the ship may be on fire or in danger of sinking, the batteries were 'potentially' the last chance to use the ships radio equipment, and send a distress message containing their position, nature of distress, and a request for assistance. A life saver for those on board, and it was his responsibility to make sure they were not let down.

A few days later they arrived at the entrance to the canal, a magnificent engineering achievement, an example of man's ability to overcome extreme adversity created by the natural environment. Started in 1881 by the French their work was abandoned due to many factors, but mainly because of insufficient funds, and the extremely high worker mortality rate. In 1904 the USA took up the challenge completing the work and opening the canal in 1914. Including both phases of construction, an estimated 27,609 workers lost their lives to win the challenge of forging a passage linking the two greatest oceans on the planet, the Atlantic and Pacific. Many people died from the extremely harsh working conditions, exacerbated by tropical diseases such a dengue fever, dysentery and many others. The project was a magnet for people desperate to work, they came from the Caribbean Islands, from North and South America, Canada, Ireland the UK, Europe and the Orient. It has been described as the greatest human achievement of all time, and the eighth wonder of the world.

As the dawn light bathed the ship in its early glow, Sparky was already out on the after end of the boat deck, excited at the prospect of the next few hours. A team of local long-shore men were on board to assist with the handling of ropes and lines during their entry and exit of the impressive canal lock system. A few of them had slung their hammocks around the ship, under the handrails, between davits and stanchions, anywhere in fact which afforded them somewhere they could rest. It was not long before the Nevis entered the canal and powerful pumps flooded the basin with thousands of tons of water.

For a young man, only just eighteen years old, it was a very special and exciting experience. The Captain wore his well battered Panama hat, and handed the responsibility of their passage to the highly experienced canal pilot. It was a day to remember for the rest of his life. Once clear of the canal and out into the Pacific, the Nevis headed north along the western coast of Mexico. The weather was beautiful, the temperature on board made pleasant by an offshore breeze and passage of the vessel itself. Sparky was feeling pleased with himself, his self restraint had paid off, and he was bound for Wilmington California, a commercial port of Los Angeles. Panama was slipping away behind them, that was fine with him. Little was he to suspect that his return there in a few weeks time would bring him perilously close to performing an encore.

They were to stay five days in Wilmington, discharging a cargo of British made products for sale throughout the U.S.A. It was time for Sparky to stretch his sea legs, one of the cadets loaned him a local map and he set off along the dock side towards the town of Wilmington. It was a very warm morning, there were many ships loading and discharging, commerce was obviously thriving. The smell of molasses was new to him, it wasn't unpleasant, but it seemed to get everywhere, and the memory of it stayed with him as one of those early experiences of something new. A twenty minute walk from the docks brought him into a small shopping area, with a variety of stores, restaurants and bars it was hot now so he sat for while at a side-walk café and ordered a cold fruit juice, followed by an ice-cream. Then he strolled around the shops marvelling at the huge range of products available, clothes, leather goods, food stores and much more, even the prices seemed to be very reasonable.

Then out of the corner of his eye he noticed a shop on the corner of the street, in the window appeared to be a large display of firearms and knives. A closer inspection confirmed, and amazed him, he had never seen anything like this in his life before. Inside the store were even more guns, rifles, pistols, automatic shot guns, hunting knives, crossbows, assault rifles, well that's what it said on the labels. A smart young salesman cornered him as he was about to leave the shop. 'Is there nothing we have that takes your fancy sir?' he said looking him directly in the eye. ' To be quite honest, I wouldn't know what to do with any of them,' he replied. The salesman seemed genuinely amused, and at the same time surprised. Sparky told him that back home in England the only people who openly displayed firearms were farmers, soldiers and very occasionally policemen, but only with a special warrant issued by the appropriate authorities. It took Sparky some time to try and convince the salesman that life back home in Britain was very different, but he wasn't sure if he had succeeded. It was mid afternoon now as he walked slowly back towards the docks. It had been an interesting day, leaving him with a lot to think about. Once on board he went up to the officers ward room to see who was there and have a beer. A number of people were off duty and sat relaxing and talking about all manner of things, lively debate was never far away. Everything from football to philosophy, things sometimes became heated, but the unwritten rule was not to allow them to get out of hand, and discussions concerning religion or politics were not welcome.

The second engineer Andy McDonald and third mate Denis were planning to eat ashore,the ships agent recommended a newly opened steakhouse called the 'Top Cut Beef Bar.' It had a special deal on that night which sounded like a bargain. They invited Sparky, who despite having just arrived back on board, accepted and went off for a shower and change of gear. The heat of the day had given way to a warm close evening, and the humidity made them sweat as they walked slowly towards the bar. Once inside they were greeted by a welcome cool blast from the air-conditioning system, but a really warm welcome by a very cute waitress. She was dressed in short shorts, and a well fitting T shirt emblazoned with the slogan 'Top Cut Bar'. 'Hi you guys, I'm Marlene, table for three OK?' 'Yes please' replied Sparky, hardly able to take his eyes off her T shirt. 'Oh my, are you guys from England?' she said with a coy smile. 'Well I am, but Andy here is a Scotsman, and Denis is from Yorkshire, but they can't help that,' retorted Sparky. His little joke was probably lost on her, but she laughed anyway, then took them over to a table. They ordered the Top-cut Beef house special, and a large jug of draught beer. The bar was filling with people and on the stage a country and western band started playing. When the meal arrived they were very impressed, it was huge, the steak was superb and everything was well presented. They had another jug of beer, and sat back to enjoy the atmosphere. The whole place was buzzing and becoming very loud, so they decided to pay the bill and walk back to the ship.

Andy collected everyone's share and went to settle up, they stood around waiting for him. Suddenly, near the stage, a fight broke out and people moved away bunching up around the bar. There was the sound of braking glass and lots of foul language, things were becoming ugly. Andy turned to the man standing next to him and asked what all the fuss was about. ' Well hell mate its Saint Patrick's night, and that's always a good excuse for a bit of action,' he said with a wide grin spreading across his somewhat battle scarred face.

There was a lot of shouting, people wading into the affray, with chairs crashing to the floor as bodies locked in combat. Sparky was vaguely aware of something hurtling through the room towards him, it was a bottle and it caught him on his forehead just above his right eye, bounced off and shattered as it hit the wall behind him. Blood trickled down his face as his raised his hand to explore the damage. It became very confused, and for a moment Sparky lost sight of his shipmates. Then Andy came pushing through the sweating, heaving mass of St Patrick's drunken revilers towards him. 'Come on mate lets get out of here,' he said grabbing his arm and pulling his towards the door. They spilled out into the street, it was quiet and hot, Denis was already waiting, and cursing the fact that his nice new Hawaiian shirt was ripped down the front. 'Only bought this bloody thing yesterday,' he complained. 'Look lads lets get away from here,' said Andy as the sound of police sirens rent the air,'we don't want Sparky to get arrested, he's under age for drinking alcohol in this town, you've got to be twenty-one in California'.

As they walked quickly away from the the chaos at Top-Cut bar, two of LAPD's finest black and white police cars screeched to a halt outside. Sirens wailing and strobe lights casting strange stuttering patterns over the façade which was the front of the bar. A few minutes later when they were clear of police, Denis said 'let me have a look at your face Sparky,' he pulled his bloody handkerchief away and Denis had a good look. ' I'll probably have to give you at least six stitches, and you'll be scarred for life,' Sparky gave him a concerned look, and then realized he was joking. But you will definitely have a black eye in the morning,' he smiled. As they walked back to the docks Andy suddenly uttered forth in his best Glaswegian accent. 'St Patrick eh! Ye would nay find any respectable Scot celebrating that heathens birthday.' Denis and Sparky looked at each other and burst out laughing, it had been a strange night ashore, they were pleased to be back on board and the security of their ship.

After two days they cleared Wilmington harbour Los Angeles and set sail for San Francisco. The sea was flat and calm, with clear blue skies, almost perfect conditions. They arrived off San Francisco Bay just as dawn was breaking. Sparky came up onto the boat deck, leaned on the railings and looked ahead towards the Golden Gate Bridge and the island of Alcatraz, he felt he should pinch himself, was this a dream, or was he really just about to sail underneath this iconic structure. He had seen pictures in books, and sometimes in Hollywood films, but as they passed beneath it, he looked upwards. The size of the steel girders amazed him, and their height above his ship, confirmed to him the enormity of this engineering marvel. Once they had passed underneath, he looked back following the trail of the ships wake, the strong currents made it seem like a snake winding it's way into the distance. It also gave him the true perspective of how small his ship was when measured against the backdrop of the bridge in the gradually increasing daylight.

The custodial island of Alcatraz looked almost picturesque with the bay mist clinging to the rocks around its shoreline, it didn't look very far from the mainland, but many prisoners had perished in their vain attempts at swimming to freedom across its treacherous tidal waters. They made fast on Fisherman's wharf, an iconic location, within easy walking distance of the city. By now the sun was up, highlighting the San Francisco sky line, and spreading its golden rays over the seven famous hills of this amazing city. To Sparky it looked for all the world like a fantasy drawing. He picked out a tall slender tower on the skyline, it's presence benignly keeping watch over the bay. Later he would discover that this was the famous the Top of the Mark restaurant, located on the nineteenth floor of a world renowned hotel, first opened in 1938. As he turned to go down to his cabin, he looked back again towards the bridge, it was now bathed in stunning light, and he understood why it was called the Golden Gate.

After checking with his chief that there were no jobs for him to do, he decided to go ashore on his own, and explore Frisco. He wanted to just wander around the streets and shops. After a while of he found himself in a large park area which went all the way down to the shore line. The Golden Gate bridge dominated the skyline. He sat on a bench and looked around to get his bearings, not far away were a group of some dozen, or more people sitting on the ground, there was the sound of singing and a guitar. He decided to go over and have a closer look, they were a collection of men and woman, nearly all the men had long hair and beards, and every one was wearing beads, jeans and headbands. At first, for some odd reason he thought they were native Americans. But what he was looking at, was his first ever introduction to Beatniks, he knew very little about them, and what they stood for, except for what he had read in magazines and newspaper articles.

As he moved towards the them the music stopped, and one of the men stood up and started reciting a poem. Sparky tentatively grew closer, almost to the edge of the group. He didn't really understand what the poem was about, and as he stood there thinking about it, a pretty young woman said, 'Hi there, how ye do-in man?' 'Er, I'm doing fine thank you,' he replied,feeling a little embarrassed. The poet who was still standing up, smiled at him and said, 'Come over and join us, peace be with you.

The next few steps Sparky took would introduce him to a completely new life experience. He would hear and see things which would have a lasting influence on him for the rest of his life. The group were very friendly, inviting him to sit down with them. They offered him a beer and some food, he declined the food, but gratefully accepted the beer. They were interested in who he was and why he was in San Francisco. For the next couple of hours he sat with these unconventional people, they drew him into their conversations, asking him about where he lived what he did for a living, and how did he spend his spare time. Occasionally they would listen to some poetry or sing a song. It was a lovely warm day, all very relaxing, and at no time did he feel threatened. He was in fact intrigued and strangely in tune with his surroundings, although he did not quite understand some of the things being discussed.

There was a lot of talk about freedom of the spirit, love and peace. It was all new territory for him. He had never actually thought about such things, but he found it very interesting. One of the men, called Conrad, asked him if he was interested in Buddhism. Sparky had been looking deeper into religion for a couple of years. He wasn't sure he believed in God, even though he was brought up in a conventional christian environment, he had attended church, especially when he was in the Scouting movement, but there was something missing, and he was trying to understand what it was. At one point he had enrolled in a correspondence course about Catholicism. He had quite enjoyed the first few lessons, but as he continued reading, he became more and more uncertain as to whether or not he could embrace all the discipline required. The constant affirmations that God would provide him with happiness and well being, bothered him.

It was after he had left school, and had just started at the radio college, that he met up again with his old English teacher, Joe Quinn. Joe was one of his favourite people, always helpful, always encouraging. So when they met at an, 'old boys' cricket match, he asked Joe, an Irish Catholic, for his opinion about whether or not he should convert to the Catholic faith. Joe looked at him, paused, then said 'Unless you feel your absolutely certain that this will be right for you, then don't do it, if you get your mind on the wrong side of the faith, then you will just spend your life in a state of perpetual guilt. Get yourself out into the big wide world, and just see how things work out for you.' Those wise words helped him, and he felt better for having asked Joe the question. Now he was being asked about Buddhism, a subject he had been thinking about for a while. He could not explain why, but he had always been interested and fascinated in south east Asia, China, Japan,and Indian.

Conrad and others talked for a while longer, with Sparky contributing as and when he felt confident to pass an opinion or share a thought. They all listened to what he had to say, he actually felt excited and pleased. Up to a couple of hours ago he did not know any of these people, and yet here he was, thousands of miles away from home,eighteen years old, sitting in the middle of a San Francisco public park, talking and learning from others, who appeared to value his opinions. They did not dismiss what he said, or try to change his mind. Eventually the gathering began to break up with people saying their farewells, wishing him all the best, telling him to go peacefully and with love. It was time for return to his ship, and Sparky's mind was working overtime, from his encounter with these unusual people, and anyway he was feeling hungry and dinner would soon be ready o board. Conrad and some of the others walked with him in the general direction of Fisherman's wharf.

As they approached the wharf, Sparky said his farewells to everyone, and shook hands with Conrad who handed him a slightly dog eared paper back book, 'please take this, hope you find it interesting,' then as they turned he said, 'maybe see you around, hey go in peace, and love.' He looked down at the book, it was 'The Way of Zen' by Alan Watts. Sparky nearly ran after them, but decided to savour the moment and everything that had happened him. He turned towards the quayside and went aboard his ship. Back in his cabin he opened the pages of his recently acquired gift and read the following message, written with a strong neat and confident hand inside the front cover.

It was nice to meet you, I hope you like the book. Check out some of these; On the Road and The Dharma Bums by Jack Kerouac. Poems by Allen Ginsberg.

Go in peace and love

Conrad

This brief encounter with its spontaneous communication, and tranquil attitude, was a revelation to him. He felt that something special had happened during those few short hours in the park. The amazing events of that day would remain with him, sitting comfortably in the vault of his memory, and often revisited.

He read the 'The Way of Zen' over a two day period, some things he could not understand, some thing's he never understood, but it hardly mattered, he gained enough insight into Buddhism to whet his appetite. It seemed to him that it showed a way forward, encouraging people to try their best to be good human beings, thoughtful, kind and compassionate. Not always succeeding but not being challenged or judged and made to feel guilty if they failed. There was also no mythical holy spirit, no worship of a God. The Buddha had been an ordinary man, who as far we know was a real flesh and blood member of the human race. The teachings of Buddha were much more in tune with the way Sparky felt about life, and the universe. It had been an interesting and eventful visit to San Francisco, and to top it all he'd met some Beatniks, a very different group of people indeed

At 1600 hours the next day they set sail northwards for Astoria on the Columbia river in Oregon to load a cargo of tinned Tuna fish. At the entrance of the Columbia, a river a pilot boarded the ship, navigating them through a series of small islands, and eventually to a tuna canning factory with a rather dilapidated looking wooden jetty sticking out into the river. It was a cold but beautiful sunny day, and they were rewarded with stunning views of snow covered mountains to the east, and at 2549 metres high, Mount St Helens dominated this impressive panorama. Sparky was to remember the view for a long time, it was his first real sighting of big snow covered mountains. As they approached the jetty an icy squall from the east picked up intensity. There was no tug boat available to assist with the berthing procedure, and the pilot approached the rather sad looking wooden structure with caution. Bow and stern lines were thrown ashore, but due to the strength of the gusting wind they were unable to secure them on the first attempt. With tide and wind working together to push the ship's bow towards the jetty, the pilot asked for half astern from the engine room, and full port rudder from the helm, the manoeuvre almost worked, but the bow slowly collided with the corner of the jetty, and the sound of creaking, splintering timber confirmed contact had been made. There appeared to be no real damage to the ship, but evidence of it's encounter with the jetty was rather obvious.

That night he went ashore with some of the crew, they were looking for a game of pool and somewhere to eat, it was quite a small town but eventually after slipping and sliding through the snow they found a diner with a pool table. They ordered burgers and fries American Style, then set up the table for a few games. They started talking to the locals, who asked them if they were Limey's who had half demolished their ancient jetty that afternoon. They of course confirmed that this was true, at that point the bar owner stood up and shouted 'OK you guys the beers on the house.' When they asked why, the owner said 'the town's fishermen and tug boat owners had been trying to get a decent jetty for years'. Now, thanks to the Nevis they were confident a new one would be built with money from their ships maritime insurance. They had a fun night, even though they had lost every pool game against the locals. The following afternoon they completed loading their cargo of canned Tuna and cleared Astoria, bound for Seattle,leaving behind a happy maritime community.

Seattle was hosting their first, 'World Fair,' it was a huge event involving countries from all around the globe, a showcase for American products, and technologies. The world was opening up and beginning to recover from the legacy of World War 2. There were exhibitors from Great Britain, Canada, France, India, Australia, New Zealand, South America and many more. Sparky had never seen anything like this before, and was fascinated by the size, and the wide range of products on show. Admission was free, and he took full advantage of it. Before setting off on this latest trip Sparky's Dad had bought him a Kodak Retina 2B 35 mm sport camera, with a built in light metre and some semi automatic functions. It was a great bit of kit, taking photographs using Kodak 35mm slide film. He had purchased four rolls of film, which would provide him with 36 images per roll. These had to be posted to a Kodak processing lab, and when they were ready they were posted back in small plastic boxes which contained 36 slides mounted in cardboard frames, all this was included in the purchase price. The digital camera age was a long way off, and it must now seem inconceivable to people that photographers had to go through such time consuming, and expensive procedures, before they could even see the results of their efforts.

From his very earliest recollections Sparky had been interested in photography, his Grandpa Foy was a professional before the outbreak of WW2, with a studio in the seaside town of Blackpool. He earned a steady living as a freelance press photographer, but his main income came during the summer months when Blackpool was full of holiday makers. He had a stall, or a pitch as he called it on Blackpool's famous seafront known as the golden mile. He would set up there each day, exhibiting his work for all to see. When crowds of happy factory workers walked down the sea front promenade with their 'Kiss Me Quick hats', and candy floss, grandpa Foy would take their photos and transfer them onto a large badge which they could pin to there jackets or shirts.

The badges were available for collection two hours later. This was quite an innovative thing to do in those early days, and together with studio shots of happy newly weds or family groups his grandpa was doing very nicely. This was almost certainly an influence on his young grandson, and Sparky's love of photography was to grow and stay with him throughout his life.

Since the start of his second trip to sea, and with his resolve to make sure he was successful in completing his junior training, he had kept a low profile. There were so many things to learn about on board ship, he used his camera to take images down the engine room, on the bridge, out on deck with the crew when they were working, in fact just about anything that took his photographer's eye. The World fair was just teaming with things he had never seen. On the afternoon of their second day in port the Padre came aboard from the Flying Angel Mission to Seamen. He brought with him boxes full of books which were exchanged for ones on the ship. There was always an interest from the crew and officers, reading helped to fill in the time between watches, or simply just to enjoy a good yarn.

The Padre invited them down to the Seaman's mission that evening, a local Country and Western band were playing, and there would be the chance to meet some of the locals, and maybe a few nice young ladies.

The evening was a great success and enjoyed by almost everyone. It was customary, but not compulsory to attend the mission chapel for a short sermon before returning to the ship. Many sailors were not devout Christians, but out of respect for the services the mission provided to the seafaring communities all over the world, most people were happy to attend. During the evening Sparky had a met an American coast guard called Gary Halvorsen, he was there with his sister, and younger brother. Gary was training to be a ships cook, and was stationed in Alaska. Each tour of duty was three months, then home for two weeks leave. They hit it off right from the start, Gary was keen on photography and in the summer months would go backpacking in the mountains around Washington State. They agreed to keep in touch. Leaving Seattle behind, bound for Vancouver Canada, they received a message from head office advising the Captain that as a result of the collision in Astoria, the company had arranged for them to enter dry dock for an inspection by Lloyd's Marine Underwriters.

They would then discharge remaining outward bound cargo, before loading Canadian and American goods bound for the UK and Europe.

The dockyard tugs manoeuvred the Nevis into the floating dry-dock, it was an impressive sight, and was carried out with a cool air of calm and efficiency. Standing on the boat deck Sparky looked around longingly at the snow covered hills and mountains which stretched for miles along Vancouver's northern skyline. Later as he wandered past the chartroom the third mate Dennis Brown was working on various chart corrections issued by the admiralty. This work was essential for the safety of navigation, and was carried out on a regular basis. 'Those snowy mountains look great,' he said to Dennis. 'Yep, they sure do, we could have a go at walking to the top of this one,' he said as he pointed to the chart he was working on. Sparky moved closer and saw that within a couple of miles of the dock was a ski lift which eventually terminated at the top of a peak called Grouse Mountain.

To the eastern side of the lift was a trail which wound itself through the forest and up to the top. Dennis measured this off with his dividers and and proclaimed, ' It's about three miles with a rise of just over 1200 metres.' They both looked out through the wheelhouse windows, it was a beautiful sunny, but cold morning. 'If it's like this tomorrow morning, how about having a go at it?' smiled Sparky, 'Yer on mate,' replied Dennis. Sparky was excited, there was the prospect of going up a mountain, the next day, and the main business of dry docking the ship was happening as they spoke. Dennis put away the charts, and reported for duty on the ships stern together with the second mate, where they would oversea the management of the various lines and hawsers which would be sent aboard from the dock yard team, stationed on the side of the basin.

The ship slowly entered the flooded dock and was manoeuvred carefully into position until it was aligned with the various markers on the dockside. All this was carried out with a quiet unhurried skill by the dockyard superintendent, his shore gang, and the crew of the Nevis. Once they were inside the dock, the huge lock gates were closed behind them. Then the orders were given to raise the dock, and huge pumps emptied thousands of gallons of water out into Vancouver Harbour.

As the 8,500 ton Nevis gradually settled onto the massive blocks underneath her keel. The dockside crew positioned long wooden poles between the walls of the dock and the sides of the ship. The whole operation went like clockwork, and Sparky was impressed.

Life on board ship went on normally, it was hard to believe they were not floating on the sea. All essential services, electrical power, water and waste disposal were connected from shore to ship, and by lunch time the dock was completely drained of water. One of the cadets loaned Sparky a pair of overalls and waterproof boots, and together they walked ashore across the gangway, then down the massive steps built into the walls of the dock, leading to the floor of the basin.

When he finally reached the bottom, Sparky was in awe of the true size of his ship, now sitting high and dry. With his camera fully loaded, he walked around from stem to stern taking photographs of anything which took his interest, and there was a lot of it. The ship's propeller looked enormous, as did the diameter of the shaft which turned it, and looking up underneath the rudder he felt quite small and insignificant. His most cherished shot was taken looking forward from the stern post, along the ship's keel as it rested on ten foot high blocks, it gave him perspective and was dramatic with it's dark shadows, the occasional glare of floodlights and arc welding torches. He felt very lucky at being able to see such amazing sights. Pete the cadet admitted that after two years at sea, this was his first time down the bottom of a dry dock.

Sparky and Denis both received permission to go ashore next day for their attempted trail walk to the summit of Grouse mountain. They spent a quiet night aboard, sorting out some gear and something to eat on their trek. Once again the cadets helped Sparky out. A pair of good working boots, thick socks, a warm balaclava and some woollen gloves sorted out the essentials. They didn't have suitable backpacks to carry things in, so their oilskin waterproofs were rolled up then slung over their shoulders on some nylon cordage from the bosun's locker. The assistant cook made them some ham and cheese rolls, and a couple of empty plastic bottles were filled with water. Dennis thought it would be a good idea to take some emergency food, so he procured, from somewhere, a large tin of ham, which protruded outside each end of his rolled up oilskins. It was 'rum' looking pair that left the ship early next morning, Dennis hadn't got any boots, so he was wearing a pair of waterproof 'wellies'.

On the advice of the ship's agent they had a booked a taxi to take them to the start of their walk, which was known as the 'Grouse Grind Hiking Trail'.

After leaving the taxi, the road soon led upwards via a series of red and white markers painted on the trees, which the ship's agent had told them to look out for. There was a very slight covering of snow on the ground, and foot prints indicated that people had been that way already. For a while the trail wound easily upwards through the pine trees. It turned back on itself now and then giving them a pleasant walk. It was nice to be off the ship for a change, enjoying some exercise and fresh air, despite the temperature being close to zero they soon warmed up. The clear blue sky was now giving wayto darkening clouds, and a brisk wind whistled through the forest pines. After an hour the trail began to steepen, the markers were further apart and not so easy to spot. Looking back occasionally they could see Vancouver Bay through gaps in the forest. Their sixth sense told them they were heading in the right direction, but then it began to snow, light and spasmodic at first. As the tree line thinned out the snow abated and they could make out the what appeared to be the shape of a building on the horizon, a little further on they spotted the cables and towers of the ski lift, they nodded to each other and put some extra effort into the climb.

After an hour and a half of steep trail they reached a wide semi circular terrace, at one side of which were ski lift gates and various items of machinery. The main lodge was to their left, and Sparky spotted a light from one of the windows not far from what appeared to be the main entrance.

They opened the door and stepped inside to a wide reception area, 'Anybody home?' shouted Dennis. A door opened to their right, and out came a well built tanned man with a big bushy beard. 'Gidda'y Mates, can I help you?' said the beard. His accent was obviously Australian, and took both Sparky and Dennis by surprise, almost in unison they stammered and said

'Hi, err well.' Then Sparky explained saying 'We just walked up the trail from the shipyard.' There was an awkward silence then the Oz voice said, 'Well pleased to meet yer lads, I'm Malcolm, come inside and have a seat.' Oz was employed as the resident Ski- Lift engineer, and was up at the lodge checking things out in preparation for the forthcoming weekend invasion of ski crazy town's people. He offered them some coffee whilst they sat around talking. Oz told them he had been travelling round the world for the past seven years, but was currently saving his money to fly back home to Brisbane where he planned to get married and settle down. Dennis and Sparky explained where they were from and why they had come up the mountain.

He asked them if they would like some 'tucker' adding that there was lots of stuff in the fridge and that they were more than welcome. He soon put a slap up meal together, which they washed down with a few beers. The story telling continued, with Malcolm and his adventures taking prime place. He was very entertaining and time flew by quickly. Dennis suddenly looked up and said ' Hey, it's snowing like mad out there!' All three went to look out of the window, a thick mantle of snow covered everything in sight. Oz told them that this would probably go on for an hour or so, but with a bit of luck should stop by nightfall, then hopefully it would freeze overnight. Just right for the start of the weekends skiing. 'Don't fancy your chances of getting down the trail in this though,' he said, and they couldn't help but agree with him, they were concerned with the consequences of not arriving back on board their ship that evening.

Sensing their obvious distress, Oz said, 'Look guys why don't you kip here for the night, there's lots of spare bunks, and in the morning I can send one of the lifts down to the third level, from there we can get you down to the road.' 'That's a great offer, but the ship will be worried if we don't report on board tonight.' Oz thought for a moment then explained ' 'Look I can phone the lodge at the bottom of the run and ask one of the guy's there to have someone drop by your ship and let them know you're safe and sound.' There was really no alternative, they were stuck there like it or not.

Oz phoned, and half an hour later they rang him back to say the message had been delivered to the First Mate, Peter Shepherd. He confirmed that was all acceptable, adding that they must be back on board by midday. The ship would be preparing to leave dry dock ahead of schedule, and Dennis would be required on duty. With a sense of considerable relief Sparky and Dennis thanked Oz for all his help. Sparky in particular was keen not to miss his ship, even though it was only moving across the bay to load cargo. They spent a warm and pleasant evening up the mountain, drank a few more beers which they washed down with more stories of past adventures.

At day-break Oz woke them with a mug of strong fresh coffee, then cooked them a great breakfast. They offered to pay for everything, but he would hear none of it. Instead he just said, 'No worries mates, buy me a couple of beers next time you're in Brisbane, it's been great having some company for a change, I've enjoyed the crack mates, even though you are a couple of Pom's.' They all laughed, it had been an interesting and lucky encounter. Thinking about their accent up the trail, and the snow which fell when they reached the lodge, it was a good job Oz was on duty, otherwise a forced retreat would have been a very tricky business. Even allowing for Dennis and his tin of Spam, they might have ended up very hungry. Although Oz had declined their offer to pay for the night lodgings, Dennis gave him the tin of Spam anyway, 'You never know,' he said it may come in handy one day, so long as you've got a tin opener.' Sparky looked at Dennis, his eyes wide open and said 'You mean you didn't have one?' 'Nope, he replied,' with a sheepish grin, 'It might have been a bit of a problem if we needed it in an emergency.'

Outside the first rays of the sun began to highlight a winter wonderland of pristine snow, it was thick, and had a sparkle which told them it was frozen. The phone rang and Oz reported that level three were on duty and he could send down the service car as soon as he was ready. They shook hands, then made their way to the cab, the dry cold air outside almost took their breath away, the temperature gauge in the cab was showing a cool minus sixteen degrees. With a thumbs up sign Oz activate the electric motors and the cab pulled away from the platform to begin its journey down the mountain. By now the sun was above the horizon, the sky was a clear and faultless azure blue, with not a whisper of a cloud to be seen anywhere.

The descent to level three only took fifteen minutes, but in that short time they were treated to the sight of breathtaking scenery. They could see for miles over the snow covered pine forests and the Ski runs below them. The city of Vancouver was bathed in golden sunshine, contrasting with the emerald green waters of the seaway in the bay. Their ship was clearly visible, sitting comfortably in the cocoon of the dry dock below. Sparky wondered how many other seafarers had been fortunate enough to look down from a frozen mountain at their 'sea-going' home.

The staff at level three greeted them in a friendly manner, and after logging their details in the station day book, they arranged for them to be driven back to their ship in one of their half track snowmobiles. Even down at sea level the snow was quite thick, but the ever ready ploughs had been busy clearing the roads in time to allow the army of commuters access to their jobs in the city. All this was carried out with a quiet efficiency, Canadians were well used to these conditions, it's a normal part of life. Back on board the Nevis, Dennis was soon changed into his working gear, and 'turned to' with his various duties, preparing the ship's departure from dry dock, and transfer to the commercial cargo berth. They were to load Canadian goods for export to the United Kingdom and Europe. These were heady days for shipowners, a full cargo of 8,000 tonnes outwards bound from the UK, and loading a full cargo for their return. World trade was booming, and they were playing their part, helping to bring wealth and prosperity back to the nation.

Sparky's chief was keen to carry out some maintenance once they had berthed alongside. Batteries, paperwork, aerials and a full check of radar scanners and displays. Vancouver was a lovely city with some fine buildings, parks, bridges and highways. It had a vibrant atmosphere, and appeared to be a very prosperous place. He went ashore on the mail run to the general post office, taking with him more than twenty pre stamped airmail letters collected from officers and crew. These were an excellent way to keep in touch with people back home, it was the only practical way to communicate with seafarers in the 1960s. Long distance phone calls were very expensive, not everyone had a home telephone, and it would be many years before the cellular telephone revolution and the internet was to change people's lives for ever.

Most seafarers looked forward to receiving mail upon arrival in port. The letters were usually brought on board by the ship's agent, but it was not unusual to have letters eventually catch up after missing the ship in previous ports. This sometimes meant the news they contained was well out of date by the time it reached the recipient, but it was always a welcome sight.

With cargo loading completed the Nevis set sail from Vancouver on its homeward bound trip, calling briefly at the lovely Vancouver Island before clearing Canadian waters and steering south down the western seaboard of the USA and the Pacific Ocean. Sparky was feeling very pleased with himself, apart from the Saint Patrick's day bang on the head, he had settled down, worked hard to impress his chief, kept out of dockside bars, and above all kept out of trouble. But life has a way of taking many unexpected twists and turns, and despite his good intentions and best behaviour, his Panamanian nemesis was waiting for his unguarded arrival, threatening to plunge him once more into serious trouble. But for now they were south bound for Seattle, and he was looking forward to meeting up again with his new friend Gary Halvorsen, the US Coast Guard cook.

During this second visit he had a fleeting romance with Gary's sister Rachael. She was attractive and intelligent, with natural fair hair and lovely blue eyes. Her Scandinavian ancestry was very evident. Apparently Rachael had been quite taken with Sparky when she met him during their northbound visit. She especially liked his good manners, and was most impressed with his sartorial elegance. (which was most certainly influenced by his Dad's attention to smartness and nice clothes).This was the era of the Italian look back home in England and Europe. The trendy men wore smart Italian suits, with slim trousers, jackets with four buttons down the front, and small high lapels. This was completed with shirts displaying cut away collars and slim necktie's. The whole ensemble was finished off with a pair of extremely pointed toe shoes, known as winkle pickers. Sparky topped this off with a felt hat known as a Pork Pie, so called because of its rounded shape, and inspired in his case by photographs of the singer Frank Sinatra, who was often seen wearing similar types of headgear. At that time, and for many years afterwards old blue eyes, Sinatra was a big favourite of his.

The Italian look had not yet caught on in the USA, and Rachael wanted to show him off to all her friends. They thought he was a real neat guy, some may even have called him cool. Sparky spent as much time as he could with her. She was working in a bank, and earned good money, enough to allow her to have her own car. They packed as much as possible into the six days his ship spent in Seattle. She drove them out into the countryside of Washington State, visiting mount Olympia. They topped this off with his first ever visit to a drive in movie, Sparky was enthralled, he just loved sitting in the car with a loudspeaker on the window. The last films they saw were Ben-Hur and Rio Bravo.

It was a pleasant and enjoyable interlude in his life, they were young, and romantic, but they knew it had to end. On their last night in port Rachael's parents gave a party at the family home, inviting Sparky' and his shipmates. They were treated to down home American hospitality at its best. Lots of BBQ Chicken, huge home-made beefburgers, more salads than they had ever seen before, with Coke a cola and none alcoholic beer. Gary's Dad gave a prayer of thanksgiving at the end, and wished them all a safe voyage home to there families and loved ones. The kind and open hospitality was very different to what Sparky and his shipmates were used to. Although Gary and his family were ordinary working class people they appeared to have an affluence which was not to reach the shores of Britain for some time. At the end of the evening Sparky and Rachael stayed out on the back porch. They both new he had to go, and it was probable that he would not return. They had enjoyed each others company and agreed to keep in touch. Then, in silence, she drove him back to his ship, stopping at end of the jetty. A final kiss, a lingering embrace, then he turned and walked slowly towards the ship's gangway. He stopped at the bottom, turned and looked towards Rachael, but she was gone. On board the ship the master at arms had been watching the romantic drama unfold, he'd seen it all before. 'Evenin Sparky,' he said in a quiet voice ' You comin aboard or jumpin ship?' he asked, as Sparky made his way slowly up the steps.

Two days later they were back in Wilmington LA, to load the last of the cargo before heading home via the Panama canal. Sparky went ashore to the outfitters close to the docks, he bought ten pairs of Wrangler denim jeans at four US Dollars a pair. It was very difficult and expensive to buy these back home, and he was hoping to a least double his money, providing the Customs men didn't find them in his sea bag. They had cleared Wilmington and were heading south once again. Six passengers had joined the Nevis, happy to take a more leisurely trip home to England on a cargo ship. Twenty four hours before reaching Panama Sparky was on watch in the afternoon, receiving regular traffic from Portishead radio. As the fourth telegram started to unfold he could hardly believe his eyes. As soon as he had completed receiving the rest of the radio traffic he went to his chiefs cabin and showed him the message. It was addressed to Charlie Watts the bosun's mate, and was from Charlie's brother. Basically it gave the amazing news that Charlie had won £75,000.00 on Vernon's football pools, the equivalent today of more than a million and a half pounds.

Apparently he was in the habit of leaving the stake money and his choice of numbers with his brother, who then made sure it was posted to Vernon's every week. Charlie didn't trust his wife to carry out his wishes, fearing that she would spend the money on something else instead. Still in a state of disbelief Sparky asked the chief what he should do. They went back into the radio room and the chief sat down and typed the message onto a special telegram greetings form, and then placed it in a gold coloured envelope. Then he turned to Sparky and said. 'Here then lad, you took the message, it's up to you to deliver it to Charlie, but don't forget you must not divulge its contents to anyone. Remember you have signed the secrecy of correspondence act, and its against the law to break it.

It was 'smoko' time and the sailors were out on the forward hatch having a brew and a smoke. Charlie was sitting with the bosun and some of the other lads puffing away on his pipe. As he approached the hatch, with the telegram in his hand, Charlie looked up and realized he was heading towards him, a concerned expression came over his face. 'Hope that's not bad news you got there my lad?' mumbled Charlie. 'No,' said Sparky as he handed the golden envelope into the sunburned hand of the bosun's Mate.

By now Charlie's shipmates were showing a lot of interest, and gathered around him to see what it was all about. Charlie looked at the telegram, then turned to his mates, and in a croaking voice said 'I've won the fecking Vernon's pools lads, seventy five thousand fecking quid.' There was a split second of astonished silence, then all hell broke loose as everyone started jumping up and down, howling and shouting. Some were even rolling around on the fore-hatch laughing like crazy men. Sparky smiled and walked up the steps back towards the radio room. 'Hey thanks Sparky,' shouted Charlie, 'It was my pleasure,' he replied, and he meant it. Up on the bridge, first mate Pete Shepherd had been watching the antics kicking off on the fore hatch. 'What's going on down there Sparky?' he shouted, and with a mischievous grin on his face Sparky tapped the side of his nose and replied 'Sorry chief can't tell you,secrecy of correspondence and all that.' Which of course was quite true. All ships radio officers were required to sign the declaration which prohibited them from divulging the content of any telegram they received, unless instructed to do so by the ships master, or if they felt in their own judgement that the contents were subversive, or likely to be a threat to life or limb.

It was a beautiful day, clear blue sky, flat calm sea, and excellent visibility. The Mexican coast line could be seen off the port side, the ship was sailing effortlessly south towards Panama, life was pretty good, three square meals a day, a nice comfortable bunk to sleep in and the feeling of having done a worthwhile job. Sparky was feeling very contented. But his nasty little nemesis was lurking around the corner, just waiting to trip him up. Upon arrival in Panama they tied up alongside a holding berth, where more cargo was to be loaded prior to entry into the canal system, scheduled for 1500 hours the following day. This gave the passengers the chance to sample the dubious delights of Panama city, and the crew were granted shore leave until 0700 hrs. Sparky had no plans to go ashore, deciding instead to stay and write some letters home, and one to Rachael in Seattle. But the hand of fate was never very far away, when, just as he was settling down to write, a very rich Charlie Watts knocked on his cabin door and invited him to come ashore for a celebration drink.

Charlie had been to see the Captain, and told him of his good fortune. He also confirmed that he did not wish to sign off the ship and fly home, but would rather sail back with his mates. This he said, would give him time to think about how his dramatic turn of fortune was going to affect his life in the future. He was a steady and reliable seaman and was in line for promotion to full bosun; he had a lot to think about. Like many seafarer's he enjoyed the freedom from domesticity which a seagoing life offered. *It could have been Joseph Conrad who said, all those who go down to the sea in ships are running away from something.*

Sparky thanked Charlie, and told him he wanted to finish his letters, but would come ashore later and find them. 'The Blue Moon Bar then,' said Charlie, 'right okay,' he replied. A couple of hours later he had finished his letters, and gave them to the purser. These, along with any others, would be handed to the ships agent for posting. It was a warm calm evening, as he walked along the wide palm tree lined Panama City street looking for the Blue Moon Bar. Sparky was feeling relaxed and pleased with himself. The air was filled with chirping crickets and the squawking of brightly coloured parrots, occasional taxi drivers would beep their horn touting for business, and the local working girls offered him the best time of his life for ten US dollars. He smiled and walked on unknowingly towards his fate! Dressed casually in lightweight khaki pants and a loose fitting shirt he had no intentions of staying ashore for long. The Blue Moon was only a short walk from the docks, less than ten minutes, and was not unsurprisingly, close to the red light district of town. As he walked into the bar, the noise and excitement struck him like a thunderbolt. It was a huge elaborately decorated room, with Roman Columns and a stucco ceiling. The walls were adorned with large painting of scantily clad voluptuous woman, posing in overtly exotic fashion, there was no mistaking their message.

Suddenly, Sparky had an overpowering feeling of deja vu. His instinct screamed at him to turn round and high tail it back to the ship. He was half way through the door when Charlie Watts grabbed his arm and pulled him back inside. 'Where do you think yer going young fella?' slurred Charlie,'come on lad, the gangs over here, we've been waiting for yer.'

There was no escape, the gang consisted of all the off duty sailors, catering stewards and quite a few engineers. Charlie was very well known by the owner of the Blue Moon, he'd sailed through its welcoming doorway many times over the years. But this time it was different, he was a very rich sailor-man. The owner and all his lovely young girls were going to make sure this would be a night to be remembered for years to come, a night that would be talked about all over town, and It seemed to Sparky's sober observations that everyone in the bar had suddenly become Charlie's best old friend. But he was overwhelmed and out gunned, Charlie hung round his neck telling everyone that this was the lad that brought him the golden envelope. Despite all his best intentions Sparky was unable to escape, so he decided to keep smiling, have a few drinks, and then make a tactical exit as soon as the opportunity presented itself. But his nemesis had other ideas. Before long he was fully immersed in the noise, the mayhem and the madness. Images flashed before his eyes, groups of people merged into unrecognisable shapes, voices beckoned him to 'come this way sailor' as he stumbled upwards, laughing, as they fell into a spinning cavernous space, and landed on the cool white sheets of a huge circular bed.

The sound of dogs barking, and someone shouting loudly in a strange falsetto voice made him open his eyes, he looked carefully around at his surroundings, for a few seconds, he had no idea where he was, and then it dawned on him like a crashing crack of thunder. He shot bolt upright, a feeling of terror and panic overpowered his reasoning, then he looked at himself and realized he was stark naked on top of a large circular bed. Falling off onto the floor he searched frantically for his clothes, the room was empty, apart from a pair of old flip flops, one red and the other black. He staggered over to an open window and looked down onto a silent empty street, it was still dark, but above the roof a thin line of golden light told him dawn was breaking. His clothes, shoes, money and wristwatch were gone, and despite his feeling of dread, he new he had to leave the room and find someone to help him. As he entered the corridor outside he shouted at the top of his voice, 'Help, is anybody there?' there was no reply. Looking back into the room he saw the flip flops again, rushed over and tried them on, one was bigger than the other, but at least they were opposite feet. Back in the corridor he saw a glimmer of light and cautiously walked towards it. There was a staircase heading downwards, at the bottom he found himself in the citadel of his downfall, the bar of the Blue Moon. Chairs and tables were scattered all around the room, some upended and broken.

As he stood there almost paralysed with fear and embarrassment, a door opened to the left of the bar, and an old woman carrying a pail of water and some long handled brooms stepped into view. She looked straight at him and almost screamed, but suddenly stopped and said something to him, in what sounded like Spanish. He held his hands up in the air and shook his head, and then by using various gestures he tried to tell her that he had lost all his clothes. 'Si Si Señor compendia,' she smiled.

Then putting her bucket and brushes down she left the room. Sparky panicked, he was convinced she had gone to fetch the police, but in truth there was little he could do, and anyway he'd been robbed so it wasn't his fault. A few minutes later the old lady came back smiling as she waved a T-shirt at him, then opened it up and proudly showed him a picture of Brazilian football sensation Pele. He immediately put it on, it was on the large size, and covered his torso just beyond his nether regions and past his backside. With this one action his spirits rose, he looked around the room and on the wall above the bar he saw a large ornate brass clock, the second hand was moving round, so at least it was working. The time was five minutes past six, and he rightly assumed that was AM not PM. His ship's shore leave was due to expire at 0700 hrs.'Thank you God,' he mumbled to himself.

Feeling somewhat more composed, and not so embarrassed he thanked her by smiling back and nodding his head. But his troubles were still not over, he could hardly walk back to the ship wearing just a T-shirt and odd coloured flip flops. He made gestures indicating that he needed some shorts or a pair of pants, she understood what he meant but shook her head as she left the room again. More than five minutes passed and he was now convinced she wasn't coming back, then suddenly she re-appeared through the front door of the Blue Moon, but instead of shorts or pants, she was holding a cardboard box with the words Fray-Bentos Corned Beef, written in large red print all over it. Realising it was time for drastic action, he took the box and gave her a gentle hug around the shoulders, he slit open the bottom, stepped into the sanctuary of its four sides, then holding it up with both hands, he blew her a farewell kiss and tripped rather than walked outside into the street. There was no sign of life, save for a couple of scruffy stray dogs sitting in the middle of the pavement, and a black cat with its legs akimbo, taking slow and deliberate rasping licks with its tongue, along the full length of its right leg. It stopped, it's eyes met his, and he was sure it was saying 'what the hell are you doing in that box?'

Mustering all the confidence he could find, he retraced his steps in the general direction of his ship. It wasn't easy walking properly within the constraints of a cardboard box, he had to take small shuffling steps, and felt more like a Japanese Ghysher girl than a bizarrely dressed ships radio officer. Further along the street a number of side alleyways opened up a view of the docks, and he caught sight of his ships bow and mooring lines. He turned right down the next alley and could see the ships companion way. So far so good, apart from two mangy dogs and an inquisitive black cat, no one had seen him. Just a few more shuffles and he could be making his way on board. He stepped out from the gloom of alley and into the brightness of the quayside. For a brief moment he thought the coast was clear, then his heart almost missed a beat as a voice said, ' I say George, isn't that our junior radio chappie down there on the quay?' He knew then the game was up. 'By Jove my dear I do believe your right,' replied George.

Sparky had no options open to him now, he reached the end of the companionway, gripped the edges of his cardboard pants, looked straight ahead and made a beeline for the top step and the astonished gaze of the master at arms. As he put his first foot on the deck two more passengers came round the corner. They didn't blink an eye, but just nodded, said 'Good morning gentlemen,' and continued walking down the starboard side with their heads held high. Fortunately for him Sparky's cabin door was unlocked, just as he had left it when he went ashore the night before. He fell over the threshold into a haven of peace, security and freedom from ridicule, he'd made it, against the odds, but not without the help of an unknown Panamanian cleaning lady. He knew there would be consequences, but for the time being he was safe on board, and before the expiration of shore leave. They were not due to enter the canal system until 1500 hrs. He had plenty of time to sort himself out.

Since he'd been seen coming abroad by some of the passengers he decided to forgo breakfast, and instead he had a shower, changed into his uniform and arranged for the officers steward, known as the *Tiger* to bring him a pot of strong coffee and a couple of large bacon, egg, and sausage sandwiches. Now feeling much calmer he sat quietly trying to piece together the events of the the previous evening, how did he managed to end up in such a difficult situation? In the end he gave up, and reasoned that he'd just been swept along with mood and enormity of a very unusual event. He also reflected that he was actually quite lucky, he'd lost his clothes his wristwatch and a few US dollars, but it could have been much worse, it could have been his life. About an hour later one of the cadets came to his cabin and told him the Captain would like to see him on the bridge. He knew very well what it was about, but in essence he'd actually done nothing wrong. However as he walked up the port side steps to the bridge his heart was pounding, and he certainly wasn't looking forward to the encounter. The Captain was standing at the chartroom table sorting through a number of documents spread out before him. Panama Joe, as he was known, was a big man, both in stature and reputation. He had been with the company for over thirty years, sailing the Atlantic and Pacific seaboard's of the Americas since his days as a first trip cadet. During World War 2 he had commanded a number of Atlantic convoys, helping to guide merchant ships through the treacherous attacks they encountered from German submarine Wolf Packs.

'Well young Sparky, what's all this malarkey I hear about you coming aboard this morning, dressed in a cardboard box and not much else eh?'

Sparky knew there was no point in denying it. 'Yes sir, I did,' he replied. Panama Joe drew himself up from the chart-table, looked down over the top of his spectacles and said 'Why?'

Without stopping, Sparky told him the whole story from the time he'd left the ship the previous night, right up to his bizarre arrival back on board a couple of hours ago. His Captain was clearly trying his best not to allow even the slightest hint of a smile pass his lips. 'Your damn lucky to have got off without losing more than your gear and your dignity. Your chief tells me you've worked hard since you joined the ship, and he's pleased with your progress, make sure you continue to do so, and keep a weather eye out for trouble eh, you might not be quite so lucky next time.' Sparky was about to reply, but Panama Joe simply said 'That's all for now.' 'Thank you Sir,' he said, as he turned and made a shaky retreat towards the bridge stairs and the radio room. It was time to go and see his boss.

PART 6

A Ship of His Own

Whatever happened to Charlie Watts
Ships with folding masts and funnels
Shore leave

———•———

Sparky walked down the boat deck towards the radio cabin, which was located on the aft-end. The door was open and his boss Geordie Miller was sitting in the operating chair with his headphones on, obviously taking messages from a commercial radio station. He acknowledged Sparky's arrival with a nod and indicated he should sit in the spare chair. After a few minutes Geordie took off his headphones and placed them on the stowage hooks at the side of the communications receiver. 'Well son, tell me what happened, warts and all,' then he sat back in the chair, folded his hands in front of him, and looked expectantly towards Sparky, who took a deep breath, and basically repeated what he had said to the Captain half and hour before. There was a brief silence, then his boss burst out laughing. 'That's amazing,' he spluttered, 'What a tale eh?' I mean I've been around this old world a fair few times, but it's one of the best yarns I've heard for ages. I can't fault you lad, I mean a cardboard box, thank god for Fray Bentos eh! Even

Sparky had to laugh. 'Right then,' said the boss, 'we've got work to do, so lets get on with it.'

By now it was past 1100hrs, and not all the Blue Moon revellers had made it back on board, in fact Sparky had been the first one to arrive. As the morning wore on, taxi's deposited various crew members on the quayside. Most of them looked very much worse for wear, weaving and stumbling up the gangway with their heads down, whilst a few of the passengers on the boat deck looked on with considerable amusement. Gradually the Master-at-arms checked off the arrival of the remaining crew, but there were two men still adrift, Charlie Watts, the very rich bosun's mate, and a junior engineer called Harry Jones. The tempo of shipboard life continued as preparations were made to make passage through the canal. Once clear they would head home across the Atlantic Ocean. Anxious crew members kept a look out for Charlie and Harry. Then with less than an hour to departure they arrived in a police car, the driver got out, opened the door for his occupants, and as Charlie stood up the policeman shook his hand, then extended it to Harry, then saluted them both.

On-board the Bosun and others watched the scene with mixed feelings. The extravagant night ashore had certainly left its mark, and potentially put the ship in a difficult situation. He looked forward to hearing what the 'deal' was with the Panama Police Force, but in the meantime he needed to get his sailors organized for departure. With impressive efficiency, the Panama Canal Company managed the daily passage of ships, large and small through its system. The maritime pilots had a considerable responsibility, and the Nevis along with five other vessels bound for the Atlantic Ocean that day, eventually cleared the port of Cristobal without incident. Their destinations were in general north-eastwards towards the UK, Europe and Scandinavia. World trade was booming.

As the Nevis said goodbye to its Pilot the crew squared away the cables, ladders, and other items from the deck of the ship. There were a few sore heads amongst the sailors, but they were ready for their homeward bound passage, none stop to the port of Avonmouth. Captain Panama Joe stood on the bridge of his ship, he rang full ahead on the engine room telegraph, the instruction was acknowledged and the large steam turbine picked up power propelling them on their way. The age old rhythms of shipborne life created a peaceful atmosphere of good order, a gentle Caribbean roll added to that special feeling of being free of the land. Whilst astern the sun sank slowly behind Panama and its western horizon. As Sparky stood on the aft end of the boat deck, he wasn't the only one on board who wanted to hear what else had happened, in the now infamous 'Blue Moon' house of pleasure, ill repute and circular beds.

It wasn't long before the story began to unfold, filtering its way along the working alleyways of the ship, eventually reaching Sparky via the officer's steward 'Tiger' . Apparently not long after his departure for the delights of the circular bed, of which Sparky remembered very little, the downstairs bar of the 'Blue Moon' erupted into mayhem and madness. News of the evolving carnival spread like wildfire throughout the *night people* of the red-light district. The bar was besieged by working girls, pimps, and sailors from other ships, together with anyone else who could force their way into the throng of drunken sweating humanity. The bar staff were overwhelmed, it became almost impossible to serve the drinks and satisfy the demand. Gonzales, the bar's owner phoned his brother who owned a restaurant closer to town, he agreed to send help, saying he wasn't doing much trade anyway. So eventually the flow of liquor and profit was restored. It's not quite clear at what stage things got out of hand, but it had something to do with Charlie Watts deciding to start a *Conga line*, the jukebox was hammering out a Cuban beat, and once it got going it became an unstoppable force. Dozens of people joined in with the staggering, wandering snake of drunken revellers, shouting, 'Hi Hi Conga, Hi Hi Conga.' With Charlie in front they left the bar and headed down the street moving deeper into the even more shady enclave of strip joints, brothels and eager bar owners.

It was always destined to end badly, all that mad mass of crazy people were bound to disintegrate. With offers of free booze and special carnal delights, it was too much to control. Fights broke out all over the place, bar fronts had chairs and people crashing through onto the street. It was like a wild west cowboy film bar room fight, only this was real.

Eventually the sirens wailed and the Policia Nacional riot squad arrived in force, breaking up the Conga line, along with the heads of anyone who failed to get out of the way. The paddy wagons and ambulances rounded up the mob and took them away for processing or treatment, or indeed both. The various crew members of the Nevis scattered in all directions, with the older hands escaping into the sanctuary of those houses of pleasure which had not been caught up in the madness.

Unfortunately Harry Jones, first trip Junior Engineer became embroiled in a scuffle with the Policia, he was a big lad, well used to a bit of rough and tumble, he'd played rugby union for Wigan Town before deciding on a life at sea. Harry was giving as good as he got, but was eventually overpowered and thrown into the back of the wagon, which by this time was getting rather full. Charlie Watts, instigator of the wandering Conga, and benefactor to the Blue Moon Bar, was trying his very best to extricate himself from the scene without getting arrested. As he pushed his way through the mob he caught sight of Harry as he was hurled into the back of the van.

When he slowly opened his eyes, Charlie realized he was in hospital, and not back on board ship. His head was throbbing due to the lump on the back of his skull and he had a large plaster on his forehead. But worst of all he was handcuffed to the bench he was sitting on, and looking around him he could see a number of other individuals in similar states of containment and distress. A white coated doctor was talking with a police officer who pointed at Charlie, the doctor smiled and walked off towards a side ward. The policeman came over to Charlie and said a few words in Spanish, but the only thing Charlie could understand was *amigo* and señor Watts. 'Si Si,' said Charlie, taking a chance. 'Ven conmigo,' come with me,' the officer said, unlocking the handcuff from the bench, and placing it around his own wrist. They walked down the corridor and eventually out into the street, where, much to Charlie's surprise he was greeted by Gonzales, owner of the Blue Moon Bar, or at least what was left of it. 'Oh my God Charlie are you Okay?' asked his friend. 'My head feels bloody sore, but I'll be alright, I've had worse than this in my time.' The policeman then took Charlie's cuff"s off, saluted Gonzales said 'Adiós Señor Gonzales' then walked over to a police Jeep and drove off.

'What's going on?' asked Charlie. 'Come,' said his friend, 'I think we need a good strong drink.' Once Inside the cool and orderly surroundings of a quiet bar,Gonzales brought Charlie up to speed. Most of his shipmates had avoided the cells, some were suffering with more than just a few bumps and lumps, but they were OK, and could be found licking their wounds in his brothers restaurant-bar, assisted by more than one of the local girls. Harry Jones was not so lucky, and was locked up in the cells, he had not capitulated easily causing quite a bit of damage to a police car and the station detention room.' Well that's bad news,' said Charlie, 'it's the lads first trip, if he's kept in the clink he'll miss the ship, she sails tomorrow afternoon.' Gonzales smiled, 'Don't you worry my old friend, I'll have him out of there in time for breakfast.' Charlie took a long pull from his glass of dark rum, 'Come on then, spill the beans what have you been up to you old alligator.'

The station commander was Gonzales son in law, and could be very accommodating in matters concerning *friends* of his wife's father, providing that the right amount of *accommodation* could be agreed, they would keep Harry in the cells until the shift changed at 0700hrs, then he would be released to join his ship. The two old friends then examined the cost of the past few hours mayhem. His Blue Moon bar was a mess, but it was mainly broken furniture and a couple of windows. 'It looks worse than it really is,' sighed Gonzales, 'but it was one helluva damn night wasn't it amigo?' 'I guess so,' replied Charlie'.

'Then there is the matter of getting you and Harry released,' continued Gonzales. After some discussion they came to an agreement, and shook hands. Charlie knew that paying up was a better option than rotting in a Panama jail for a few months. The trouble was he didn't have that kind of cash available, and he could hardly go back on board the ship and ask the Captain to advance him a large sub against his wages.

Charlie's younger brother Ian, owned a successful car dealership in London's West End. He was selling loads of motors to up and coming legitimate, and none-legitimate business people, as well as Stock market traders, and a few dubious characters, who always paid with ready cash. They went back to the Blue Moon and into Gonzales office to place a telephone call with Charlie's brother. It was around 11 pm UK time when his brother Ian rather tentatively picked up the phone. It rarely rang at such a late hour, unless it was trouble. After a quick exchange of greetings, Charlie gave him the full story, nothing left out, then asked him if he would agree to transfer the money to Gonzales Panamanian bank the following day, and under no circumstances was he to mention any of this to his wife Betty, or Charlie's wife Kay.'Thick as thieves them two,' he added. It was no problem, and the amount was small beer in comparison to the current state of Charlie's bank account. The money was to be transferred in US Dollars, Ian seemed quite happy with that, saying he knew where to get a good rate of exchange. Charlie decided not to quiz his brother further, best to leave him to get on with it, and they arranged to send a telegram with the banks details. So the deal was done, and before saying goodbye his brother said, 'I've got a very tidy Rolls Royce lined up for you when you get home my son.' 'Get off yer cheeky little sod,' replied Charlie with a smile.

The validity and truth about what went on that mad Panamanian night will never be known, but at the end of the day, Charlie rescued young Harry from serving time in prison, all the ships crew managed to make it back on board, and the ship sailed on time. The Captain doled out suitable punishment as appropriate, no doubt giving stern warnings about the foolishness of such shore-side activities in the future, knowing full well that it went in one ear and out of the other. It was a beautiful balmy evening and they were sailing the Caribbean on course for home. There were no other ships in sight, and the weather was set fair, with no major storms brewing. But once in the Atlantic you can never be too sure. In those days ships participated in a scheme known as Weather Observation, the navigating officers recorded wind speeds, direction, sea state, temperature barometric pressure, and cloud formations on a daily basis. Then together with the ships daily position, they produced a coded message which was passed to the radio room for onwards transmission, to the World Weather Service. These transmissions were called WX- or Weather Obs, and those ships who provided regular information could win prizes from the Meteorological Centre, in recognition of the effort they put in to this very valuable service. There were no satellites, no computers, no GPS or mobile phones, the sea could be a lonely place, no matter if it was the English Channel of the South Pacific, vigilance and safety were paramount. It would be awhile before technology advanced enough to enhance the lives of seafarers, but it was on its way. The Nevis cleared the *Windward Passage,* with Port au Prince-Haiti to starboard, and the eastern tip of Cuba on their port-side. Guantánamo was still a number of decades away from it's eventually infamous reputation. This was 1959 and terrorism as we know it in the 21st century had yet to be defined.

They were now in the Atlantic Ocean and the ship settled down to the easy rhythm of watch keeping and off duty routines. The days passed without incident, Sparky was very happy, he loved the sea in all its moods, and he was feeling confident that his career was now back on track.

As they drew closer to the Bay of Biscay the weather changed and so did the mood on board. A phenomenon known to seafarers as the 'channels' was gradually gathering pace. All the ships company, including officers, were affected to some degree or other by this strange feeling. To some, it was the excitement of seeing family and loved ones again. For others it was the uncertainty of what they would find back home after months away at sea. The excited ones were happy, and a sometimes reckless, drinking and gambling, occasionally losing all their pay on a game of poker. For those who were uncertain of what they would find, they probably wished the voyage would never end. Whatever camp you were in everyone knew it wouldn't be long before they docked in Avonmouth. They had been away from home for just over three months, some crew members would 'pay off' the ships articles and go their various ways, others would stay to man the ship, and probably complete another voyage. The 'channels' affected people in different ways, some couldn't wait to see family and loved ones, they were the ones who got it in a big way. They were excited and walked round with a permanent smile on their faces. There were others who had no such shore-side strings pulling them away from the security of ship board life. With its three square meals a day, a place to lay your head at night, and the camaraderie of your shipmates, it took some beating. Whichever berth you were in, it was always an exciting time for a sailor to see the shoreline of his own homeland.

Sparky signed off on the 21st of December, and would be home for Christmas. He was keen to get back and show his Dad and Sheila the photographs of his voyage, and spin a couple of yarns into the mix. He felt proud of himself and hoped they would feel the same. He was due just over three weeks leave before re-joining the Nevis on the 19th of January for another trip. It was one of the best Christmas holidays of his young life. All his mates wanted to hear about his latest adventures, and girls who had never given him much attention before, were flocking round him in the local pub. Invitations to attend parties came fast and furious, he felt quite a celebratory. To top it all he sold all the Wrangler Jeans he'd bought in Wilmington California. He more than doubled his money, and took orders for another twenty pairs. He was loaded with cash, some of which he spent on nice Christmas presents for Sheila and his Dad, the rest he put away in a savings account.

Despite having such a great time, Sparky was keen to get back to his ship, and on the 19th of January 1960 he signed on the Nevis again in Victoria Dock London. Geordie Miller was still his Chief. All he needed to do now was successfully complete this trip, and hopefully he would be assigned a ship of his own. Life was certainly pretty damn good, and with the prospect of new adventures waiting for him over the horizon, he couldn't think of a better way to start the new year and a new chapter in his eventful young life. His next trip on the Nevis, was to him, one of consolation. He was feeling much more confident about his future, the familiar surroundings, the friends he had made during his previous voyage, these all added to his sense of well being and hope. He had also taken well to his actual job as a radio officer, enjoying the whole experience of communications via wireless transmissions, and his trusty morse key. With the radio equipment available at that time, contact using the various marine operating frequencies allocated to ships, was not always a simple matter.

There was an particular skill to be learned, it was necessary to choose the correct frequency bands, which changed depending on the time of the day, the time of the year and their position on the oceans of the world. Sparky loved all of that, he was very pleased if he cleared his outgoing radio messages quickly. It wasn't always like that though, it sometimes took a couple of hours or even more. He was also keen on the technical aspect of servicing the communications equipment, and the ships radar. The things his old Granddad Nev taught him in his auto electrical workshop remained with him. The best bit of advice he ever gave him was, *'When starting to look for a reason why some piece of electrical or electronic equipment wasn't working, then before doing anything else, always start by checking the source of supply. In other words the battery, the mains power or whatever it is that makes it operate, and in the simplest example, find out if it's actually switched on, or has it blown the fuse? This all sounds rather obvious, but it wasn't always the case'.*

Some years later when he was working as a service engineer, Sparky was sent, at great expense, travelling for three days in a battered old Jeep on unmade roads, to a land based, long range radio communication station in the heart of darkest Africa. Their powerful and essential transmitter had stopped working, and when he got there he found a fuse had blown.

His second trip was very enjoyable from the start, he got on really well with his Chief, and continued to improve in all aspects of his job. The dreaded Panamanian nemesis failed to catch him out. His second passage up the west coast of the great American continent, was generally without incident. On the northbound leg he went back to the clothing store in Wilmington, and purchased another twenty pairs of Wrangler Jeans. The owner was delighted to see him again, and discounted the total by 25 percent, then threw in a couple of nice sport shirts for Sparky himself. It was a nice gesture, but they were not really his sort of thing, so he sold them along with the Wranglers when he arrived back home. In Seattle he met up with Gary his US Coastguard friend, unfortunately Gary's sister Rachael was away in New York State visiting her grandparents. The two had kept in touch by letter, and he was not surprised, but never the less disappointed to have missed her. Gary was home on study leave, enrolled in the Seattle Coast Guard Training College preparing for his final exams to become a fully qualified chef. With time available Gary and Sparky went off on a short backpacking trip to the Snoqualmie National Forest, north of Mount Rainier. He fixed Sparky up with suitable boots, clothing and sleeping bag. Seattle has a Mediterranean climate with dry warm summers and mild winters. It was late February, and although forecast to be dry, the nights could be cold, so they agreed to use hiking lodges rather than a tent.

It was a superb three days, they drove up in Gary's Ford Colt pick up truck, a real American dream machine of the day. Sparky was well impressed that Gary could afford such a nice set of wheels. It had a powerful engine, 4 x 4 traction, and consumed fuel at the rate of 15 miles per gallon. To top it off he fitted a fantastic push button radio, tuned into all the local stations, offering everything from country and western music, to blues and rock and roll. They sang all the way from Gary's house to the trail-head at Snoqualmie. Sparky Knew no one back home in his peer group, who even owned a car, let alone something like a Ford Colt with massive wheels and push button radio. If they had any wheels at all, they were lucky to have a BSA 125 cc Bantam motorcycle or a push bike. The hiking lodges were excellent and very cheap, costing three dollars a night. They were fully fitted out with cooking facilities, a proper communal eating area and comfortable bunk beds. There was a network of lodges along all the trails, or you could pitch a tent on a proper camp field if you preferred. As it was midweek there were very few 'hikers' to be seen, but at weekends Gary said the trails and lodges were well used. They completed two full days of walking in the forest and foothills of the local mountains, arriving back at the Colt on the third day. The scenery had been superb, they had laughed a lot taken loads of photographs, and talked rubbish way into the night. But all good things come to an end, and Sparky had to rejoin his ship.

Gary passed his exams with distinction, and continued to sail with the US Coast Guard service for another five years. He served on ships patrolling from Alaska to Hawaii in the Pacific, and on the eastern seaboard of Americas Atlantic coast. He eventually married his childhood sweetheart, opened a restaurant in Portland Oregon, after which Sparky lost contact with him, he was a nice young man. His lovely sister Rachael went on to qualify as an accountant, then moved to New York after securing a good job with one of Americas largest financial corporations. She was a nice young lady, and Sparky was pleased to have known her.

The voyage continued along without incident to it's turn around point at Vancouver. Lots of work for the deck officers, checking the off-loading and loading of cargo, making sure it was stowed correctly in the holds, watching for damage caused by pilfering, especially cases of Scotch Whiskey and Gordon's Gin. When the stevedores picked the right cartons or crates to be broached, there would be an accidental spillage of the pallet containing the chosen bounty, usually down in the area known as the 'tween decks'. The cases or crates would fall and break open, with quantities of the prized liquid suddenly disappearing from view. The remaining smashed bottles were cleared up, and unloading would start again The Cadets and Mates had to keep a constant vigil on such cargo, but it was an impossible task to prevent this sort of thing happening. A wise Ship's Officer on cargo duty, would turn a tacit blind eye to these activities, better to say nothing, rather than have the stevedores down hooks and walk of the ship in mock indignation, if accused of such goings on. But the trick was to pass the word that 'things' had been noticed, and that moderation in all things was the name of the game.

Because Sparky was intensely interested in everything to do with his ship, he often worked tallying cargo, this involved checking the quantity of items being loaded or unloaded against a manifest or cargo log. It was an important way of helping to prevent losses. It was also necessary to log and report any damaged cargo, as the customer or shipper may claim against the company for loss of goods and profit. After all they had paid the shipping company to transport their goods, and expected them to arrive safely. It was also a function of the young cadet officers to tally cargo, but if things were a bit hectic, then extra help was always appreciated. Sparky received no remuneration for this work, but occasionally a bottle or two of amber nectar would mysteriously appear in his cabin.

The cost of stealing items from ships cargo was enormous, and was endemic all over the world, it had been happening for centuries. The high cost of insurance premiums reinforced what a problem it was. In the mid 1950s 'the shipping container' was introduced, and containerisation became the way forward. Modern container shipping celebrated its 50th anniversary in 2006. Almost from the first voyage, use of this method of transport for goods grew steadily and in just five decades, container-ships would carry 60% of the value of goods shipped via sea.

The effect of this radical change to the way cargo was carried at sea would eventually see the end of the type of cargo ships Sparky was sailing in during the 1960s, and indeed it saw the end of many small and medium ports around the world, favouring instead vast container handling terminals, linked to road and rail networks which could load and deliver right from the quayside to the customer's own premises. But all this had yet to affect young Sparky, he was unknowingly witnessing the end of an era, but it took a while before he could look back and acknowledge that he had been part of a wonderful period of world maritime trade, history, and development.

At the end of April 1960, the Nevis arrived back in UK waters and safely tied up alongside in Victoria Dock, London. It had been a very successful trip for all concerned. Geordie called Sparky to the radio room, and congratulated him on the completion of his statutory six months service as a junior. He then handed him a copy of the letter he had written to their Head Office. This confirmed that in his opinion Sparky had performed extremely well during his time on the Nevis. That he had understood all the accounting and operating procedures, had maintained the ships emergency radio batteries to a high standard, that he was punctual in his watch-keeping, capable of maintaining all the equipment in the radio room, that he was of sober character, and he had no hesitation in recommending him for taking charge of his own station, confident that the equipment and company's interests would be in good hands.

When Sparky finished reading the letter, his Chief shook his hand and wished him the very best of luck for his future, no matter where that may lead him. Although he'd had no reason to suspect that he would not pass muster, his relief was almost palpable, he gave a big smile and thanked Geordie very much for all he'd done, and for having faith in him. Silently, in his own head he thanked Mr Hatchard in the Liverpool office for giving him another chance. Many of the crew and officers, including himself were to sign off articles that day, and make their way back to their respective homes. Days like this on board ship were a mixture of happiness and slight feelings of regret. Despite all the promises of, 'I'll give you a call mate.' or 'See you later for a pint,' many of them may not meet up again. In those days the British Merchant Navy was under the auspices of the Board of Trade, and seafarers had coined the phrase that, they were only BOTC's or 'Board of Trade Travelling Companions.' It was just their way of dealing with a transient way of life, one which formed strong alliances and bonds of camaraderie whilst working together on the high seas. But which possibly evaporate quite quickly once they left and were waiting to sign on for a new voyage. This is not to say that these temporary friendships were shallow or false, and in many cases it didn't apply, especially those who settled with one shipping company. Those company men had every chance of sailing together again, but others, well, who knows what fate and coincidence had in store?

Sitting on the Liverpool bound train that afternoon Sparky was feeling very comfortable, and was looking forward to some leave. The summer was just around the corner, he might go off to spend a few days in Snowdonia... Looking at him from the seat opposite was a pretty young woman, probably in her early twenties. Each time he tried to hold eye contact with her she looked down at her hands, or out of the window at the blurred scenery flashing past at sixty or more miles per hour. She did look familiar though, then he realized and said, 'Excuse me, don't I know you, aren't you the receptionist at the Marconi office in Liverpool?' Her face lit with a big smile, 'Yes that's right, I thought it was you she said, but if you don't mind me saying so, you look a bit more prosperous than the last time we met, so I wasn't really sure. You've got a great tan.'They both laughed, and he said 'Thanks for the tip you gave me in your office, I got the job with Siemens, been with them just over six months now.' They agreed it was a small world, and she had been right, things did turn out okay. She said she had been down to Head Office in Chelmsford on a training course for a couple of days.

They talked for a bit and he bought them both a drink of tea and some sandwiches. The journey seemed to go quickly and before they knew it the train was pulling out of Runcorn, next stop Liverpool Lime Street. They walked down the platform together towards the barrier, and Sparky was plucking up the courage to ask her for a date, but as they exited through the gate, she looked up and waved at a dark haired man standing in the middle of the concourse. 'My husband,' she said softly, looking at him as if she knew he was about to ask her out. Sparky smiled,

'I didn't realize,' he said, 'no ring,' 'Er no,' she said fumbling in her hand bag, as she deftly placed the gold band on her third finger. Her husband greeted her with a big hug, whilst looking hard at Sparky over her shoulder. 'Good course then darling,' he said 'Yes, excellent thank you,' she replied rather thinly. Seizing the opportunity Sparky said 'Your wife kindly helped me find a job last year,' 'With one of our main competitors as well,' she said quickly, looking slightly embarrassed. 'Must rush,' said Mr Dark hair, 'your Dad's waiting round the corner in the car.' As they moved off, with him carrying her suitcase, she looked back over her shoulder, and although he couldn't swear to it, he was convinced she'd blown him a kiss.

He had a welcome homecoming, his dog Togo ran around smiling and wagging his tail. The family were pleased to see him and interested in his stories, especially the photographs he had taken during the trip. However, it wasn't long before he went to bed, it had been an eventful day. As he switched out his bedside lamp he caught a glimpse of a kiss being blown across the Lime Street Station concourse. Next morning he was up early, just in time to see his dad before he left for work in Liverpool. The sun was already warming the bench in the back garden, and it had the promise of a lovely spring day.

After breakfast he took his 'Viking, Ian Steele' road racing bike out of the garage and gave it a good clean, oiled the chain and checked the brakes. He was planning to cycle down to Mold and look up a some of his mates.

It was really nice to be getting some decent exercise, it was one thing about a seagoing life which he missed, there were no facilities on board ships in those days to cater for such activities. Passenger ships and large oil tankers however sometimes boasted full gymnasiums, and eventually ship owners would realize that a fit crew were an asset. But in the meantime people like Sparky, who had a passion about fitness, would have to make do with walks around the deck, press ups, and anything else which helped.

As he free-wheeled down the long hill of the A494 from Mynydd Isa towards Mold, the sun warmed his face, and he felt great. His best mate Barry was still in bed when he arrived at the house. Barry had recently started working as a trainee manager with John Summers steel works at Shotton, and was currently on the night shift. But his mum told him he was due up soon, so they sat in the back garden having a nice cup of tea and a good old gossip about Sparky's life at sea, he kept her entertained with considerably edited versions of his adventures. She was a lovely person, always bright and positive. In his early teens he had dated her daughter Carol, they went everywhere together. Carol's big passion was horses, and she worked for no pay at a local riding stable just outside Mold. Her reward was free riding lessons, and an insight into the Equestrian way of life.

Peter Jones the stables owner, was a good friend of the family, and had known her since she was born. She was the daughter, he and his wife never had. In fact they had no children of their own, and as a result they both spoiled her rotten. She was their little angel and blue eyed girl. Tragically when Carol was only ten years old Peter's wife Megan died of cancer. It was a huge shock to everyone, it was very sudden and after her death he was never quite the same again. He worked hard, throwing himself wholeheartedly into his business, expanding and improving the facilities, building extra stables and offering a service of providing full board and care for pony owners who had no land of their own. This went down really well, and the Moel Famau Riding Stables went from strength to strength.

Carol was a talented rider, and was never happier than when she was working at the stables. Peter had two ponies of his own, called Flash and Zara, and Carole took great care of them both. One day she asked Sparky if he would like to have a riding lesson, he was well up for that, and immediately saw himself charging across the American Prairies being chased by dozens Apache Indians. Carol soon brought him down to earth, but it wasn't long before he started to get the feel of it, realising that it wasn't as easy as she made it look.

His first experience of being allowed to canter across the fields, surprised and excited him. The power of the animal under his saddle was amazing. He could sense the massive strength flexing and pushing them forward, in particular he was in awe of the enormous strength of the horses neck. It took him all his time to control it, and although it was only a canter, their perceived speed over the ground terrified him. At the edge of the meadow he almost failed to bring the pony to a halt as it charged towards a dry stone wall, preparing to jump. Carol was close behind on Flash, shouting instructions, in between fits of laughter. When he finally came to a halt his heart was racing, and an adrenalin charge gave him a huge buzz. He jumped from the saddle, still holding the reins, and put his arm around Zara's neck. She blew through her nostrils, as if to say I bet I had you going there young man.

The village of Cilcain was in the northern shadow of the beautiful cone shaped hill known as Moel Famau, although only 1,821 feet above sea level, it dominates the surrounding countryside and with good visibility can be seen for many miles. It is the highest hill within the Clwydian Range, formerly the Flintshire Range, on the boundary between Denbighshire and Flintshire in North Wales. The hill, which also gives its name to the Moel Famau Country Park, has been classed as an Area of Outstanding Natural Beauty since 1985. and is surrounded by several well-preserved Iron-Age hill forts. Stunning pony trekking trails were just literally on their door step, and during the long warm summer school holidays the pair would often take off for the day, pretending they were crossing the great Savannah's of Africa or America. They were teenagers, and there was plenty of time to grow up later. Although in Sparky's case that took rather a long time. But life moves on, and eventually they went their separate ways, still staying the best of pals. Carol enrolled at Agricultural College, and he went off to travel the World in the merchant navy. Not long after Carol had started college, her mentor and friend Peter passed away one Saturday night in his sleep, natural causes was the verdict. He was sorely missed and many people attended his funeral. Much to everyone's surprise Peter left his whole estate to Carol, to be inherited on her 21st Birthday, at the time of his passing she was just 18 years old. The bequest was conditional to her completing, and passing her agricultural exams, which she did with flying colours.

The back kitchen door creaked as it opened and his mate Barry almost stumbled as he saw Sparky sitting with his mum. 'I thought I could hear your voice,' he said blearily stifling a yawn. 'You're looking very fit, must be all that sea air,' he continued as he sat down besides him on the garden bench. His mum got up asking Barry if he would like a cup of tea, 'Yes please Mam,' he drawled in his best Welsh accent. The two pals were soon into into catch up mode. Barry was very happy to be working at Shotton Steel, the business was thriving, and his trainee management position had good prospects for the future. Barry's dad also worked at the plant and had just been promoted to electrical manager in charge of maintenance and service. Barry already knew the story of Sparky's disastrous first trip, but his mam and dad were not acquainted with all the details. Lowering his voice Barry leaned over towards him and said 'Well, did you manage to keep out of trouble this time mate?' Sparky smiled and said 'I'll tell you all about it later, when do you finish this night shift lark then?' Barry stood up and stretched his arms in the air. 'Last night as it happens, don't have to do it again for another two weeks.' 'Right,' said Sparky, 'its the Red Lion tonight, and maybe go through to Chester on the train and check out the talent.' Barry was just about to reply when his mam came out with his cup of tea, so he just smiled and nodded.

The weather stayed fine for the next few days, and he enjoyed visiting more friends. He also spent quite a bit of time in Grandpa Nev's workshop, who quizzed him about the technical part of his job, saying that the future of electronics lay with the Transistor and semi conductors. They would revolutionise everything. Sparky new a bit about these devices, but they were in their very early stages as far as Marine Communications was concerned. Nev shoved his old trilby hat to the back of his head and said 'Come on then, let's go and have a cup of tea.' They went around the side of the workshop towards the house, and Sparky smiled as he had a sudden flash back moment. He remembered him and little Norman constructing their Para Mark 1, parachute, all those years ago. Then as they stepped through the doorway, grandma Emily shouted from the kitchen 'Take yer hat of Nev.' Nothing changes thought Sparky.

He decided to go walking in Snowdonia for a few days, staying at YHA hostels. He would catch a train from Chester to Bangor, and then a bus into Llanberis. He planned to walk the well worn trail alongside the Snowdon railway track to the summit, at 1,085 metres (3,560 feet)above sea level, Snowdon is the highest mountain in Wales. From the summit he would climb Crib y Ddysgl and then traverse along the spectacular Crib Goch ridge down to Pen-y-pass, where he planned to stay overnight at the YHA hostel.

The Crib Goch has arguably been called the finest ridge walk in Europe, and the route from Snowdon's majestic summit to the Pen y pass ,was in his opinion the most rewarding and exciting in North. He had completed the route a number of times, and would continue to do so for many years. The following day he would climb up from the back of the hostel to Glyder Fach, walk along the Glyders, down Bwlch Tryfan and up to the summit of Mount Tryfan itself, his most favourite of mountains.

After which he would descend to the Nant Francon pass, and spend a night at Idwal Cottage Youth Hostel. He was excited at the thought of being in the Welsh mountains again, it had been more than a year.

He was almost finished sorting out his rucksack, boots and waterproof clothing, when he heard a noise outside, he looked out of his bedroom window, and saw a red post office telegram service motorbike coming up the the drive. The rider steadied the bike on its stand and came up to the house, Sparky answered the door and signed for it. Mounting his machine the rider accelerated down the drive, spraying gravel behind him like a speedway ace. 'He's in a hurry,' thought Sparky to himself. The telegram was addressed to him,and basically it instructed him to join the mv Gosport in Seaham Harbour near Sunderland in two days time. He was also required to phone head office, and speak with the radio officer's admin manager, Mr Weatherall. His emotions were mixed, on the one hand he was looking forward to a few days in the mountains, but the prospect of joining his first ship was very exciting, if not a little daunting. But this is what he had signed up for, so he packed all the stuff back into his *Bukta* canvas rucksack, and put it into the bottom of his wardrobe. 'Don't worry, I'll be back,' he said, then went next door to use his grandmas phone.

Mr Weatherall was a very nice quietly spoken, no nonsense sort of a man, he cared for the people he managed. Always taking time to listen to what they had to say. Over the coming years Sparky came to like him very much. The mv Gosport was a coastal vessel owned by Stephenson Clarke's of Newcastle (The oldest registered shipping company in Great Britain, it was formed in 1730 in the reign of George the second, finally going into liquidation in 2012). She was a collier, designed primarily to carry coal for delivery to the county's power stations. Mr Weatherall gave him further details of his best train routes to Sunderland, and then suggested he get a taxi from the station to Seaham harbour. He further added that unfortunately the current radio officer would not be there to hand over the station, as he had broken his leg in a fall, and would have left the ship upon its arrival. 'Make sure you're in plenty of time,' he said, 'these ships work with the tides, and once cargo is loaded they are on their way.' Finally,, he told Sparky not to worry too much about this first solo appointment, he would soon get the hang of it, just remember what he had learned from his past six months.' He finished by assuring him that his unused shore leave would be carried forward.

He put the phone down and rushed in to see grammar Emily, who was sitting in the lounge reading a newspaper, he gave her a big hug and 'said I'm off to sea again Pop, using her family nickname. 'You really love it don't you?' she smiled. 'I certainly do, its wonderful, and all thanks to you for sorting things out with my dad.' 'Well I knew very well that you'd have left and done it anyway, but now you have a special job, and a future.' She hugged him back, then pushed him away playfully and told him to go and sort his out seagoing stuff.

The journey to Sunderland, via Newcastle went smoothly, but seemed to take forever. At least the scenery was beautiful, in between time he read his book, the Conquest of Everest, and occasionally dozed off with his head moving from side to side, in time with the rhythm of the train.

He had decided to wear his uniform, he was proud of it, and anyway he thought it was the correct thing to do. He may not have done so if he'd known was was coming when he finally boarded the ship. The taxi driver was very talkative, and spoke with an accent not unlike that of his Chief on the Nevis. Sparky found that he had quite a knack with different dialects, he seemed to be able to latch on and mimic them quickly, he particularly enjoyed listening to those of the English north-east coast. 'Are ye the ships pilot then hinny?' said the driver 'No, I'm not actually, why do you ask?' The driver looked at him through the rear view mirror and said 'Well me bonny lad, ah don't think ave tak'en a uniformed officer to a coal barge before.'

Sparky suddenly felt rather awkward, he looked himself up and down, nice clean white shirt, black tie, white cotton cover on his Merchant Navy cap, and new gold braid on his uniform sleeves signifying his rank as a radio officer, and with his nicely polished regulation black shoes he couldn't see anything wrong. The taxi arrived at the small village of Seaham, and drove through the main street turning left for the harbour and the sea. There was a steep road down to the harbour, then a right turn where the driver stopped the car. 'Its as far as I can tak yer' he said,' 'not allowed past this point like, that'll be three shillin and thruppence marr'a.'

Sparky looked out of the car window with a growing feeling of horror and embarrassment. At first sight it was a scene of complete chaos, on the far side of the dock were three ships up against the quay wall, towering above each one were huge gantry's with conveyor belts containing a never ending river of what was obviously coal. It spewed over the end of the conveyor in a solid black column, falling into the ships open hatches with ear splitting regularity. The whole scene was unfolding in a thick cloud of dense coal-dust, the dust was everywhere, on the ground, in the air, and was beginning to collect on the windscreen of the taxi. The mv Gosport was the last ship in line at the far end of the quay. He paid the driver, who thanked him, but did not get out of the cab to help him retrieve his sea bags from the boot.

Sparky stiffened his resolve, shouldered his kit bag, then picking up his relatively new brown leather holdall, which he'd recently purchased in San Francisco, he walked purposely towards his objective. He felt there was an air of physical hostility which was being specifically directed at him. Men were shouting orders, small trucks weaved in and out around the quay, orange lights flashing on top of the cabs, and blasting their hooters all the time. He dodged around bollards and wire hawsers, trying his best to look inconspicuous. He was convinced everyone was laughing at him, and by the time he reached the gangway of the Gosport he was sweating profusely. Staggering to the top of the gangway he dumped his bags on the deck. Suddenly a man appeared from nowhere, dressed in what might have been brown overalls, he was wearing a peaked officer style cap, the badge of which was falling apart, and kept flopping to one side. The man's face was covered in grime and black dust, the whites of his eyes seemed to accentuate the blackness of his face, he looked for all the world like someone out of the black and white minstrel show. Sparky opened his mouth to speak, but the man beat him to it. 'Replacement wireless man is it?' he said smiling, his teeth looking amazingly white. 'Follow me then,' he said as he turned round and walked towards the stern of the ship. He stepped over the weatherboard threshold of a door on the port side, and up a short flight of stairs. Sparky had brought his bags with him, and duly dumped them before following the minstrel up to the top and into a small office.

Suddenly Sparky was aware of how quiet it was compared to the activity on deck outside. There were two other men in the office, all three of them looked him up and down, a round faced bald headed man said, 'I'm the skipper David Greene, that's George the second mate,' he said pointing at the minstrel, 'and this young fellah is the company man,' 'Glad you could make it,' said the skipper, 'We were getting a bit worried. We sail in half an hour.' George will show you to yer cabin, dump yer kit, come back here with yer discharge book and we'll sign you on.'

The cabin and the interior of the ship was very nice, small but smart and very new looking. He put his bags down, took out his discharge book and went back to the office, signed the articles then went to sort himself out ready for sailing. He looked in his bathroom mirror, and simply burst out laughing, his cap cover was filthy, his face was filthy streaked with lines of dried sweat, his pristine white shirt and collar had turned mid grey, the rest of him was covered in coal dust. He stripped off, chucked everything on the deck and took a shower, changed into a clean set of clothes, navy blue pants and a sweater. He then went up onto the bridge deck and found the radio room, it was unlocked, when he entered he was pleased to see everything looked clean and tidy, there was an envelope addressed to him, propped up against the front of the main communications receiver. It was from the previous R O David Evans, it explained that he had broken his leg when he fell down some stairs in rough seas as they were passing Flamborough Head on their way to Seaham, he wished him luck, and hoped he would find everything in order.

Sparky had calmed down by now, he thought about his walk along the quayside from the taxi to the ship. He realised that he had over reacted to the scene which presented itself. He must have looked completely out of place, dressed in a smart new uniform, white topped hat a lovely clean shirt, a completely different world than the one he'd just left. He was now in a much more informal atmosphere. These ships were hard worked and running on tight schedules, so he put it all behind him and set about checking out his station. He read the daily radio log book, checked over the equipment, and the library of Admiralty Radio Signals. Everything seemed fine, Dave Evans was obviously a conscientious person. As Sparky was checking out his radio equipment, listening to the radio traffic, and test tuning his main transmitter, the Skipper put his head around the door and said 'Almost ready to sail now Sparky, everything OK?' 'Yes sir, thanks it's all fine.' he replied. 'Good,' said the Skipper, 'Once we get under-way and clear of the harbour, I'll give you an ETA for The Thames Pilot.' Then he turned and clattered down the stairs. Sparky didn't even know where they were going, but from what the Skipper had said it was almost certainly the River Thames and London. This was his introduction to life aboard a British coastal vessel.

The colliers (coal carrying ships) basically shuttled vast amounts of coal from the coalfields of England to feed power stations around the coasts of great Britain. The mv Gosport and similar ships had contracts to run between the North-east and the south coast feeding the never ending requirement to keep the nations power stations working.

As they cleared Seaham Harbour, and set a course south, the crew were just finishing off the hosing down the decks and steel hatch covers. Sparky stood on the bridge, keeping quietly to one side so that he could take in what was happening, and not be in anyone's way. The engine-room telegraph answered to the command of full ahead, and the the Skipper gave a course to steer for the helmsman. It was all carried out with a smooth, well practised efficiency, they'd done this many times before. Now that the coal dust had been washed into the North sea, the Gosport looked clean and shipshape. It was a calm, coolish evening as he stood and watched the Tyne and Weir coastline gradually fall into shadow. ' TR (traffic report) here for you Sparky,' said the Skipper waving a piece of paper in his hand. It was hard to understand why, but Sparky felt really excited about his introduction to the ships employed in the business of maritime 'home trade'.

The weather was not like that of the Caribbean or the Californian coast, the ships were small, they were designed and built like that so they could access the smaller ports and rivers of the UK and Continent. The Gosport was only a third of the gross tonnage of the Nevis, with a crew of 12. But they were restricted in their trading areas, there were internationally defined limits of where they could operate, this was partially dependent upon the qualifications of the ships Master. But Sparky really loved this new environment, it was more relaxed, and things such as wearing a full uniform were not necessary. They usually wore navy blue battle dress jacket and trousers, with epaulettes on the shoulders to identify a person's rank. However on some coasting vessels, slacks or jeans and a sweaters were often the norm. What he liked was the activity surrounding these type of ships, and the ports they visited. From Rotterdam to Glasgow, Ipswich to Dublin, Plymouth to Belfast and so on, with occasional treats to exotic places like Casablanca or Copenhagen. It would not take him long before he recognised ships as they were approaching each other in the north sea, or ploughing their way through the English Channel in a storm force eight gale. He soon learnt the funnel marking, and the types of vessels. General cargo, collier, gas carriers, north-sea or Irish sea ferry boats, cross channel ferries, oil tankers or timber ships from the Baltic. The coastal trade was booming, just like world trade in general. He loved it.

First of all he had to get to grips with life on board his new ship. The amount of radio traffic he had to handle was very small in comparison to what he had been used to these past six months. There were TR's or traffic reports, advising owners of the ETA at their destination. These were sent through a network of medium range coastal radio stations sited around the British Isles, from Lands End to John O' Groats. Their whole purpose was to handle short range radio traffic for all ships in UK territorial waters, but most importantly they would keep a vigilant watch on the maritime radio distress frequencies. These were 500 Khz for wireless telegraphy, and 2182 Khz for radio telephone traffic. A distress message on 500Khz would be transmitted as SOS (Save Our Souls), and all ships which carried a full time radio officer would be listening out on these frequencies during their watch-keeping hours. Outside of watch keeping times, automatic receivers on the ship would set off an alarm if an SOS message was sent by a vessel in distress.

The UK stations were fairly evenly distributed around the coast, giving them all excellent coverage. The south coast English Channel for instance was covered by North Foreland Radio, on the eastern tip of the heel of England, near Margate, then moving westwards would be Niton Radio on the Isle of

Wight, followed by Lands End Radio, on the tip of western England. Once around round Lands End and heading up the west coast, Ilracombe and Anglesey Radio were within range.

After Anglesey ship's could communicate with Portpatrick, and Oban Radio. Round the Northern tip of Scotland, East coast shipping could use Wick and Cullercoates, followed by Humber Radio. Thus completing complete coastal coverage, before arriving back within range of North Foreland. Altogether it was a very efficient system, passing hundred of messages a day, and with out any shadow of doubt, its existence was responsible for the saving of many lives over the period of its wonderful years of service. With the introduction of new communications technology, and changing regulations the last transmissions on the 500 Khz marine wireless telegraphy distress frequency ceased at midnight GMT on the 31st of December 1997, some thirty eight years after Sparky had first stepped foot aboard a British Merchant ship.

The following day the Gosport t entered the River Thames, and were heading for Deptford power station. The crew on these vessels were often a mix of seafarers resident in the south of the country, and those from the North-east. This meant that if they were sailing on colliers with long contracts to supply coal to places like Deptford and Battersea, then southerners would have the chance to see their families at one end, and the lads from the North-east when they arrived back at the other end, to load coal. This was not always the case, but it was a convenient arrangement, even though it was not an official one. As soon as they were alongside the berth, huge cranes commenced unloading the coal into large wagons, which would then take it away and tip it in the coal storage yards. This mountain of coal was in a state of continual replenishment, especially during the winter months when demand for electricity was at its peak.

Depending on the tides, and the speed at which the coal was discharged, they would be ready to sail north again within twenty-four hours. It was a hectic and relentless procedure. It had been an interesting and hectic few days for Sparky also, and he was satisfied with his performance. So he decided to stay on board that evening and take it easy. There were some letters to write, and plenty of little jobs to do in the radio room. Once their cargo was discharged, they moved off onto a lay-by berth to wait for the tide. The crew were all present and correct, and set about cleaning the ship in preparation for sailing at 0600 hours the following morning. Sparky was up at the crack of dawn, the ship was starting to come to life, and the hum of her generators provided a comforting feeling that all was well. He went up to the radio room and switched on the equipment in readiness for their north bound passage.

Outside an early morning mist was hanging over old Father Thames, as it swirled around the pontoons, and gently lapped against the side of the ship. It was summer time and there was an expectant feel that it was going to be a lovely warm day. Quietly and with very little fuss they slipped their mooring lines, and drifted with controlled efficiency into the middle of the river. The engine room telegraph rang out the orders from the bridge, as they navigated their way down the Thames passing Sheerness on their starboard side, before entering the North Sea on the way back to Seaham Harbour for another cargo of Black Gold.

PART 7

Life on the Grit

Cars on board
SOS
Sparky gets married.

———————◆———————

After just over a month on the Gosport, he signed off in the port of Sunderland, and went home on leave. It was mid summer and the weather was set fair, he sorted out his rucksack once again and carried out his previous plan to go walking in the mountains of Snowdonia. It looked like being a great trip, the long range forecast was for sunny and warm weather, and with nothing to trouble him, Sparky decided life was pretty good, and he was very pleased with himself.

The following day he took an early train from Chester to Bangor, then a bus from Bangor to Llanberis. He hitched a lift to the top of the Pen-Y-Pass, and after checking the map, and filling his water bottle he strode off on the long winding trail towards towards Lliwedd. The sparkling waters of Llyn Llydaw danced and dazzled him as he contoured round it's right hand side. The ascent to the top of Lliwedd was warm work, but the views were spectacular, and there were no other walkers to be seen. He stopped for a rest and a drink of water, whilst enjoying a slightly sticky Mars Bar. Before setting off for Snowdon's summit he took a few photographs, and after a strenuous hours walk, reached the top.

The Snowdon summit railway station snack bar was open for business, and lots of tourists were pouring off the narrow gauge railway, whilst it's wonderful little trains hissed steam, and belched black smoke out of their stacks. Occasionally they added to the atmosphere with a long pull on their shrieking whistles. Business was good, despite the rather high cost of beer and food, but then they were more than 3,000 feet above sea level. Sparky sat in the glorious sunshine looking westwards towards Anglesey and the Irish sea. Visibility was excellent, and he counted eight ships making passage north and south, he smiled as he looked down at them... wonder where I'll be sailing to next? he mused.

Finishing his beer and sandwiches, he set off to complete the Snowdon Horseshoe, taking the spectacular descent down the Crib Goch ridge.

It's not a place for the feint hearted, with sheer drops of a thousand feet either side of the dragons back style ridge, but he'd done it before. He was perfectly at home balancing with relaxed ease on the sharp edges of the ridges and pinnacles. It was exhilarating, he loved it and was soon making good progress. At the end of the ridge he dropped down to join the Pyg track, eventually reaching the Pen-Y-Pass car park, where he had started from six hours before. Sparky was tired, but very contented as he booked a bed for the night at the youth hostel.

Refreshed after a good night's sleep he woke early, at around six o'clock, to be greeted by another beautiful warm sunny day. He went outside the hostel and sat on a bench in front of the building. There was no traffic to spoil the moment, it was still and atmospheric. The huge mass of Snowdon dwarfed his southern horizon, whilst the rising sun began to burn off the mist on the ridges he had descended the previous day. He took a deep breath, filling his lungs with the fresh cool mountain air. He drew deeply on the exquisite feeling of that moment, this was the magic, the mystery and the emotion of being in the hills... he loved it with a passion, and he reflected that the vastness, and wildness of the sea, had a similar influence on him. Throughout the years to come, his affinity with these two elements never left him, they grew and were enhanced with time, they were stored forever inside his body and soul... they could never be taken away.

With a substantial breakfast inside him, he shouldered his pack and set off behind the hostel to climb northwards to Castell y Gwynt, and the summit of Glyder Fach. After this the trail wound steeply and precariously down loose scree and well worn paths to the col at the bottom of Tryfans Far South Peak, with fine views of Cwm Bochlwyd hundreds of feet down to the left. From here he climbed steeply up boulder strewn paths to the summit of his favourite mountain,Tryfan. The weather was still superb, the views all around were stunning, and with only two other people sitting at the top eating their sandwiches, it was almost perfect. Tryfan was the first real mountain Sparky had ever climbed at the tender age of twelve. It became his very special place, with many exciting days out, scaling it's impressive granite walls, arêtes, and chimneys on the north and east faces... *One day many years later, he would write a request that his ashes be released from the top of the mountain, on an easterly wind, with the hope that they would travel towards the Irish Sea. But that's a long way off yet.*

It had been a long day, and as he started to descend the north face ridge, he looked back at the monolithic granite columns of Adam and Eve, smiled, then gave them a cheeky wink. Tradition dictates that first time visitors to the summit of Tryfan were required to jump from one column to the next. There was a gap of around two metres between them, and the exposure was quite intimidating. Sparky had done this a number of times, but many people decline to take on the challenge. An hour later he reached the Nant Ffrancon pass and Idwall Cottage youth hostel, paid the warden for his accommodation,had a shower then made himself a meal.

Just as he was sitting down at the table, he looked up and spotted someone he knew from the Manchester University Climbing Club. 'What the heck are you doing here mate?' shouted Peter Vincent, 'Thought you were sailing around the world, and having girls in every port,' he added. 'Well I am really, but you need a rest now and again, so I came down here,' quipped Sparky. The two had climbed a lot together during his time at radio college, they always enjoyed each other's company, and laughed a lot.

Peter had left university, after gaining a degree in civil engineering, and was working for large construction company, specialising in the building of power stations. He was taking a few days leave before going overseas on his first major project. The two sat around catching up on each others adventures, it was great that they both had good and interesting jobs, but Pete thought Sparky's life of travel and exotic adventures sounded more fun than building power stations, 'But not as well paid,' smiled Sparky. They would have liked to have gone climbing the following day, but had no ropes or boots suitable or such antics. Instead they agreed to do some scrambling on Tryfan then finish off by going up the Bristly ridge and back down over the Glyders.

Next day the weather held fair and they enjoyed an energetic few hours before eventually descending down the impressive and sometimes atmospheric Devils Kitchen to Lyn Idwal. It had been a very enjoyable chance encounter with this old friend, and since Peter had a car, he offered to drop Sparky off in Chester on his way back to Manchester. They parted outside the railway station promising to keep in touch, adding that next time they met they would do some decent climbing together. It would be a while before that happened, but when it did, it would turn out to be a very dramatic and potentially life threatening experience. After a couple of days back home with his parents, he received instructions to join his next ship. This time is was a 2,500 ton coastal oil tanker called the Grit, owned by FT Everards of Greenhithe in Kent. The company owned dozens of ships of all sizes built for a wide range of trade. She was berthed in Avonmouth and he was to join her in two days time. Sparky had no means of knowing, but this appointment would be the start of one of the most enjoyable and hilarious times of his seafaring career. After an uneventful train journey he eventually arrived by taxi alongside the ship. The first thing which struck him was that the vessel hull was painted bright yellow, with white railings and wheelhouse.

Learning from his past experience, he was not wearing his uniform, but was never the less smartly dressed in grey slacks, a double breasted navy blue blazer, immaculate white shirt, merchant navy tie,and trendy black winkle picker Italian fashion shoes. He walked up the gangway and found his way round to the Captain's cabin. The door was open, and inside there were three men, and a rather attractive blond lady. They were all chatting loudly, with lots of laughter, and the room was full of swirling cigarette smoke. A distinguished man with a shock of swept back black hair, and beard, both flecked with streaks of grey, looked through the haze towards the doorway. 'Well bugger, me this dandy looking young fella could be our new brass pounder.' He said, in a broad west country accent with a sight lisp. Before Sparky could respond 'Black Beard' stood up and came towards him, 'I'm Charles Evans, master of this fine vessel, welcome aboard, the scruffy bloke in the corner is Eddie the Chief Engineer, the lovely lady is my wife Patricia, and the fat bloke over there is Douglas our local tame taxi driver'. Sparky was a bit taken aback by the relaxed way the captain had introduced himself and the others. 'Come in lad and have a drink, its my birthday,' slurred the Eddie. 'Er well thanks chief, happy birthday, but if you don't mind I'd like to dump my gear first.' The captain nodded and told him his cabin was up the stairs behind him, on the bridge deck.

The stairs were narrow and quite steep, so he used the bannister rail to pull himself up, whilst dragging his sea bag behind him. With just three steps to go he was suddenly confronted by the sight of a huge black German shepherd dog growling fiercely, its teeth bared, top lip curled and saliva dripping from its chops. The dog was moving downwards, the hair on its back bristling. Sparky was thrown slightly off balance as one of his winkle picker toed shoes became stuck in the corner of the step. He gripped the banister more firmly, letting go of his bag, which tumbled downwards and hit the deck with a thud. Man and beast faced each other, the dogs bloodshot eyes fixed on Sparky. Who then remembered his old grandpa Nev telling him never to look away or turn his back on an angry dog, but look it strait in the eyes and show no fear. The black beast was not impressed, and looked as if he was about to pounce. Sparky felt himself slipping backwards, when suddenly a female voice shouted, 'No Rex No... down now.'

The dog immediately backed off and lay with its belly on the deck, its ears folded down. 'I'm so very sorry Sparky,' said the captains wife, 'I had no idea he was on the bridge, he sometimes likes to curl up near Charlie's pilots chair in the corner of the wheelhouse, he's a big softy really.' Backing down the stairs to the deck, he picked up his bag and said, 'no problem Mrs Evans, I really like dogs.' At the same time he thought to himself, no point in getting on the wrong side of the captain's wife after only being on board for five minutes. He gave her a smile and went up to his cabin. As he passed the dog at the top of the stairs, it looked at him balefully and wagged it's tail. Mrs Evans had evidently been a police dog trainer, and Rex was retired into her care.

So began his introduction to life aboard the motor tanker Grit, with it's eccentric captain, and a motley collection of officers and crew. It would turn out to be the most enjoyable period of his seagoing career, lasting more the sixteen months.

The routine of daily was quite different to what he'd been used to on the bigger foreign going ships. They sailed UK coastal waters, including the Irish Republic and the continental ports of France, Holland, Germany and Denmark. They mainly carried fuel oil, and petroleum, which was pumped aboard from large refineries like Fawley on the Solent, and Milford Haven in Pembrokeshire. These new days at sea were full of interest and excitement for Sparky, he loved it, feeling at home very quickly. Their time between ports was usually days not weeks. With plenty of work, they were always on the go. He took an interest in navigation, plotting positions on the chart using the Decca Navigator, an amazing state of the art electronic marvel which continuously recorded the ships position using signals from shore based transmitters. During quiet times when they were in safe waters he was sometimes given the job of taking the helm, all under the supervision of the Duty Officer.

Late one evening they arrived at the Fawley Refinery to load a cargo of fuel oil. The Solent Pilot berthed astern of one the largest ships in the world at that time. It was a 200,000 ton Italian Super Tanker called the Michael Angelo. They had never seen anything quite like this so close before, it was simply enormous towering above them in the fading light. The next morning Charlie had gone ashore to report to the Fawley refinery dispatcher, as he was known. Here the ships captains received cargo details and various other documentation, as well as meeting up with the ship's Agent and making telephone calls to their respective owners. Immaculately dressed in his captains uniform,Charlie sat in the reception area awaiting his turn, the door opened and in walked the captain of the Michael Angelo. He as sat down alongside Charlie, then extended his hand and said 'Capitano Luigi Conte of a di Michael Angelo.' 'Captain Evans of the tanker Grit,' replied Charlie. The two men talked about this and that for a while, then Charlie told the Italian captain how impressed he and his crew were with the size of the Michael Angelo, and what an honour it must be to be captain of such an amazing vessel, adding that he thought Capitano Conte might also be impressed with the size of his ship. 'Si señor, how interesting, where are you berthed? I did not notice anything this morning when I came ashore.' Charlie gave a slightly cheeky smile and said, 'We are just astern of the Angelo.' The dispatcher was unable to avoid overhearing the conversation, and had to turn his face away, and struggled not to laugh out loud.

With their business concluded, they boarded one of the refinery Jeeps and the driver took them back to the berth alongside the Michael Angelo. When they got out of the Jeep, the Italian captain looked around him, and could see no sign of the Grit. The tide was now at its lowest ebb, and as a result the Grit was out of sight, not even the tops of her masts were visible. Charlie walked towards the concrete safety barrier and looked down towards his ship. 'There she is, the mighty tanker Grit.' Capitano Conte moved alongside Charlie, and looked over the edge. He burst out laughing, and put his hand on Charlie's shoulder, saying 'Mama mia you are right, I'm impressed, she would just fit nicely on our foredeck, we could use her as a lifeboat.'

Both Captains were smiling as they took the steep companionway up the side of the Angelo.

Before setting sail a few duty crew, including Sparky and the second mate Peter, were given a tour of the mighty super tanker by a very smartly dressed senior Cadet. Back on board the Grit, scouser Billy Bragg was telling the engineers that Angelo's engine room was so big it could accommodate both Liverpool Cathedrals, and still have room for Lime Street Station.

A few days later they were berthed alongside the Esso oil refinery in Carrickfergus, near Belfast Northern Ireland, discharging cargo of fuel oil. It was a beautiful warm spring day, and Charlie had been ashore to the agent's office, he looked very smart as he strolled casually back along the quayside toward the Grit. Dressed in his immaculate Khaki shirt and slacks, carrying an expensive leather briefcase, which he claimed had been presented to him by the First Sea Lord of The Admiralty, for services to submariners during the war. Third Mate Harry Johnston was on cargo duty, standing by the pump house door, checking pressure gauges and delivery rate. He wasn't Charlie's favourite person, they had never really got on well together, always at odds with each other. Harry was well qualified with foreign going First Mates ticket. He previously served on a number of large ocean going tankers, as chief officer. But for some reason he was now only Third Mate on a small home trade coastal tanker. A somewhat private man, he never talked much about his life at sea.

Just as Charlie put a foot on the Grits gangway, a loud bang followed by a high pitched whine broke the calm of the spring morning.

The flexible hose which was connected to the main discharge pump, had fractured, and a plume of thick black, smelly pressurised oil spewed upwards forming an arch as it headed towards the quayside. Sparky was on the bridge wing doing some maintenance on the emergency radio batteries. Hearing the noise he looked up with horror as the black stuff arched downwards and engulfed the ship's Captain. A number of crewmen were working out on deck, they all stood still, mesmerised by the sight of the unfolding disaster. Third mate Harry rushed over to the main cut off valve and turned the wheel furiously, desperately trying to shut off the flow of the thick, black oil. But it was too late, Charlie was completely covered from head to foot in dripping, refined Saudi Crude.

As the oil drained down his body, Charlie wiped his arm across his face, and as his eyes glared through the goo, he looked for all the world like a creature from another world. Third Mate Harry looked on in disbelief then, uttered the fatal words '*Oh death, where is they sting?*' Charlie dropped his now ruined brief case, lifted his arm, and pointing at Harry shouted 'Your fecking fired'. In the aftermath of the spillage the crew swung into action and began the messy business of mopping up the decks. Within minutes, the storage depot's emergency oil spill team also arrived on the scene, and began the tricky job of clearing things up using special foam detergents, and sucking it up with huge vacuum cleaners. By late afternoon things were almost back to normal. An examination of the flexible hose showed that it was almost new, and may have been faulty. It was sent ashore with the company's marine superintendent for examination by the manufacturer's. Charlie disposed of all his contaminated belongings, including his precious briefcase. A doctor was brought on board to check him over, declared him clear of any complications, and fit to go to sea. Harry was exonerated from any blame, apart from his rather unfortunate remark, but It was mutually agreed that he would be replaced in their next port of call.

Sparky's life on board the Grit continued to be enjoyable, there were plenty of opportunities to go ashore, and explore. It was like having a free tour of the British Isles, with the bonus of having three square meals a day, and a pay cheque at the end of the month, not a bad life at all, he often thought. One day when they were berthed at Cattedown Wharf Plymouth, undergoing some engine repairs, their indomitable captain pulled up alongside the ship driving a blue Austin Seven car. He parked carefully, locked it and strolled calmly up the gangplank. When they sat down to dinner later that evening, first mate Dave Brown quizzed the captain about his quayside transport. 'Well,' said Charlie, 'I've just been over to my cousin's house in Saltash, haven't seen him for ages. Turns out he's emigrating to Australia next week. Sold most of his belongings, but the Austin was still in the garage, he asked me if I'd like to buy it, so I offered him fifty quid, and he accepted.' 'Blimey that sounds like a good deal, what are you going to do with it?' said the mate.

Charlie looked at him and replied with a smile, 'I thought I'd bring it on board, and then we can all use it when we're in port.' There was a stunned silence before the chief engineer said, 'How the hell are we going to get it on board then Charlie?' 'Simple,' replied the captain, 'Peter's Dad has fixed up for one of the cargo cranes to lift it on board first thing in the morning before we sail.' Peter was the new third mate, and his dad was Captain Crane, the marine superintendent in charge of Cattedown Wharf, working for the Grits owners.

So began the bizarre story of the 'car on the wing of the ship's bridge.' The Grit sailed from Plymouth later the following morning, complete with a blue Austin Seven neatly stowed on the port side bridge wing. The weeks passed, and turned into months, they plied their cargo up and down the coast line and estuaries of Britain. They sailed to Germany, Holland and the west of Ireland. During all this time the little Austin never moved from its home on the bridge. Successive pilots would walk aboard to navigate the ship in and out of various ports. They would climb the stairs to the wheelhouse, then go out onto the wings of the bridge. Starboard side was fine, nothing unusual there, but when they crossed the deck and walked out to port they were confronted with sight of a gradually rusting and deteriorating small car. They were often visibly amazed. It was probable that they had never seen such a thing on any other ship, ever. Most of them would politely ask about it, but sometimes they ignored it all together, preferring to put it down to the eccentricities of an English sea captain.

The poor little Austin was now in a very sorry state, the constant exposure to the ravages of salt water spray, with the occasional battering by green seas during heavy storms, had reduced the car to a lump of blueish rust. The tyres were completely flat, adding that final look of ignominy to it's once jolly appearance. Even Charlie had to admit that it was time to commit the rusting body to the deep. They were returning from a trip to Foynes on the west coast of Ireland, severe North westerly gales in the Celtic sea stayed with them until they cleared Lizard light, and by the time they passed Portland Bill the sea state had moderated to a comfortable, long rolling swell. They were heading for the Solent via the Needles to load a cargo of fuel oil at Esso Fawley.

The sky was clear with a warming breeze, and Charlie had decided it was time to 'commit' the car to the deep. The bosun and some of the sailors had rigged a block and tackle, with some metal poles to form a derrick, and use this to lift the car above the bridge bulwark. The plan was to swing it out over the side, then drop it into the English Channel. Rope strop's were slung underneath the car, and when everything was secure the Charlie came out on the bridge. He instructed the helmsman to steer a steady course, and the hoisting began. Slowly the weight came on the tackle, things started to creak, and bit by bit the car lifted off the deck. There was a steady roll created by the sea swell, so that as the car lifted it began to swing in unison with the roll of the ship. Its travel being controlled by the sailors, but the higher it rose the more difficult it was. It had almost reached the height of the bulwark, but there was not quite enough room to clear the top. The poles were just not long enough.

The Bosun sent for some wooden beams he had stored in the fore peak, the sailors used these to lever the car onto the top of the mahogany handrail. Then, with two poles in place under the car, the Charlie gave the order to stand by and wait for the next big roll to port.

The atmosphere was tense, it was a critical manoeuvre, and potentially dangerous. The lifting gear was creaking, whilst the sailors stood ready for the instruction to lift the beams, and jettison their load. Unfortunately the Charlie misjudged the first roll, and as the sailors manfully lifted the beams the car became stuck on top of the handrail. As the vessel rolled back onto the starboard side there was a danger the car would slide back down onto the bridge, but luck was with them and it stayed put, balanced precariously on the mahogany rail. There was an eerie silence as they awaited for the Charlie's next order. A cooling breeze rippled over the bridge... 'Now,' he shouted... The sailors heaved upwards with their beams, and with help from the heel caused by the swell, the rusting blue body of the little Austin car, creaked, stuttered, then finally slid over the side of the ship. The Bosun pulled the cable release, and the little car finally detached itself from its tenuous links with the ship. A great cheer went up from all around as the hulk hit the waters of the English Channel with a spectacular splash. Everyone was on the port-side laughing, and shouting as the Grit continued on its course to pick up the Needles Pilot.

As Sparky kept his eye on the Austin, he realised that it had not sunk below the waves, but was still very much afloat, and assisted by the tide, was following in their stern wake. Meanwhile on the bridge the Captain was looking at the charts and plotting their position. Sparky interrupted him and said, 'Sorry Captain, but I think you should know, the car hasn't sunk yet, and could be considered a hazard to navigation.' Charlie went out on the bridge wing with his binoculars, took a long look, then went back into the chartroom, called Sparky and said 'Right then, send this message to Niton Radio.' (Niton, on the Isle of White, was their nearest coastal radio station). Sparky sat down with his transmitter tuned, and his hand poised over the morse key, he thought how bizarre this message was, but in truth it had to be sent, they had no way of knowing if the car had sunk or not. If it was still afloat then it could be a hazard to small boats. He tapped out GNI … Niton Radio's call sign, and was instructed to move up to a working channel. With a wry smile he sent the following message.

Attention all ships, hazard to navigation. Sighted at 1430 hrs. GMT today. Blue Austin Seven Car, approximately 4 miles due south of Anvil Point, Swanage English Channel. Car sailing due East at an estimated speed of 3 knots. Possible hazard to yachts and small fishing boats.

He waited for Niton to acknowledge receipt of his transmission, there was a short pause, then the operator asked him if he would transfer to VHF voice channel 12. Once contact was established, Niton asked him if he could explain exactly what it was they were reporting. Sparky told them to stand bi, then called the Captain. It was his responsibility to speak with Niton. Charlie was in his element, and proceeded to give a most convincing account of what they had seen as they passed Anvil Point, bound for Esso Fawley. Niton thanked him, and said, 'It was the first time they had ever heard of a car sailing in English Channel'... Charlie thanked them, and then added, 'By the way there was no driver on board.'

The ship/s busy schedule continued with a number of deliveries to Sunderland on the north-east coast. Russian or Polish fishing boats were often to be seen in the harbour, carrying out repairs or sheltering from bad weather. The sailors from these vessels would make themselves known by discreetly offering duty free cigarettes or real Russian Vodka at crazy prices to the crew of other ships. It was a risky business, but that didn't stop people taking advantage of such bargains, Sparky included. He was particularly interested in cameras and binoculars, so he cautiously developed a friendship with the bosun of a Polish trawler. He would go aboard and see what was on offer.

On one visit, after consuming far to many Vodkas, downed in typical Polish fashion by a toast of prost, the contents would be knocked back in one straight gulp, the glasses were then banged down on the table, where they were immediately refilled to overflowing. The bosun produced a kit bag from under his bunk, then emptied it on the table. Sparky's bloodshot eyes opened wide as he was confronted with a bounty of Russian made Leica cameras, Zeiss binoculars and Rolex watches. Even in his advanced state of alcoholic numbness he could tell these were very convincing copies. The bosun of course assured him that they were his own property, lamenting that he was forced into to selling them in order to support his poor ageing parents, and family back in Gdansk. Sparky staggered back on his heels, laughing uncontrollably, then fell backwards onto the side of the bunk. 'Look hear mate,' he slurred 'sorry about your family and all, but that's a load of bollocks.' The bosun also burst out laughing, then said, 'What the hell, you want to deal or not?'...

During their visits to Sunderland, Sparky met and fell in love with a lovely local girl called Mary. They spent as much time together as possible whilst he was in port. When he sailed away he kept in touch by writing letters and sending postcards. Eventually they would get married and move to Southampton. This was to herald the start of a new phase in his life, but for the time being he had no plans to give up his seagoing career.

It was a bitterly cold January morning as the Grit rolled her way through a heavy swell, half way across the Irish sea, on passage to Foynes,with another cargo of aviation fuel for Shannon airport. The visibility was poor, with a swirling mist, and the lookout on the bow stamped his feet and kept his gloved hands deep in his refer jacket pockets. *(At that time it was not unusual for ships to have no radar equipment, it was expensive, and would be some time, before shipowners were required to install them by law).* As the swirling mist parted momentarily, the look out called the bridge saying 'Yellow object five points off the port bow, range approximately half a mile.' Peter the third mate walked onto to the port-side bridge wing, focused his binoculars, straining hard to see anything through the wispy fog, then he spotted it, what looked like a marker buoy, painted with a series of yellows bands. At first he thought it was off a fishing boat, but it looked a bit big for that. He acknowledge the lookout's sighting, and decided to inform the captain, just in case. Charlie was already on his way up to the bridge, ever vigilant he'd been watching from his cabin's forward facing porthole. After a few moments of checking the bobbing rolling buoy, he ordered Peter to ring slow ahead on the engine room telegraph, and alter course towards it before the mist closed in again.

They approached carefully, drifting slowly alongside their target, making sure they didn't collide. The word had spread round the ship, bringing a number of people out of their nice warm mess-room to see what it was all about. Charlie was down on the well deck now with the bosun, some sailors and the first mate Dave. 'It's a Royal Navy gunnery practice buoy,' said the captain, with an air of unchallenged confidence. 'Lets have it on board Reg,' he said to the bosun, 'Secure it up nice and snug, we'll take it back to Fawley, and I'll get the Admiralty to come over and pick it up.' There was a stunned silence, as people looked at him and each other in disbelief 'Are you sure that's a good idea Charlie', said the first mate 'It might be dangerous, after all, we are loaded with nearly three thousand tons of high octane aviation fuel,' The captain smiled and said, 'Don't worry David, I've seen plenty of these in my time, it's harmless, and the Navy will delighted to get it back.'

Using their cargo pipeline gantry, they managed to hoist it aboard without too much difficulty. It was bigger than it first appeared,covered in slimy green moss. As it lay sideways on the deck, with the seawater draining off it, one of the sailors poked it with a boat hook... There was a unanimous intake of breath from everyone watching, and a couple of people instinctively moved away. The stunned silence was broken by a nervous laugh up on the main deck, then everyone joined in. 'Yer daft sod Jacko, yer could have blown us all the way to the Irish coast,' joked one of the deckhands.

Sparky was off watch, so he went down to have a closer look. There were no obvious markings, nothing to indicate what it was, or where it was manufactured. He moved closer and placed an ear next to a square metal box halfway up the buoy's latticed mast, but there was no sound at all. The top of mast was fitted with a 360 degree heavy duty perspex dome, inside he could just make out what looked like bevelled mirrors, supported on a spindle. There was a faint pulse of light, flashing dimly every ten seconds, it looked to him as though the battery power was failing fast. In true seaman like fashion, the bosun and his lads wrapped it in a heavy tarpaulin, then lashed it securely to some ring bolts on the well deck. The Second mate rang the engine room for full ahead, and they resumed their voyage to the River Shannon.

This was to be their last trip to Foynes for the time being, and Sparky was quite sorry not to be coming back. The trip up the Shannon was quite spectacular, to the north and south was a patchwork of lush green fields, dotted here and there with white farmhouses, hedgerows, and narrow lanes criss crossing one another. Sheep and cattle hardly looked up from their constant intake of succulent grass, as the ship's wake crashed over the river bank, gradually eroding it away.

The people ashore had always been friendly, welcoming them with cheerful greetings. The post office, general store, petrol station, gossip shop and well stocked bar were all under the one roof. The landlord Aidan Kelly and his family were always keen to see them, and no matter what time of day it was, he would always ask if they were, 'Partaking of the black stuff, and maybe a small measure of Jameson or Paddy.' His idea of a small measure was indeed a pleasure to behold.

They were not due to sail until late afternoon the following day, so a night ashore was on the cards. After dinner Sparky, the chief engineer, and third mate Peter decided to go to the post office and have a drink or two, leaving a few letters for home in the box for good measure. As they walked down the quayside a raw westerly wind from the Atlantic buffeted their duffel coats, and chilled them to the bone. A warm and cosy atmosphere greeted them in the bar. Some of their crew were already well ensconced in the corner by the dart board, and a game of cribbage was under way. 'My round' said the chief, Aidan the landlord was in fine mood, a bar full of local fishermen and a tanker crew, 'Grand then lads what's your pleasure'.

A grand evening it turned out to be as well, friendly rivalry between the fishermen and the Grit boys produced a close fought darts match, whilst at the pool table chief Eddie displayed the skills of a misplaced youth by thrashing all comers earning himself a fist full of Irish Punt into the bargain. His winnings went strait back behind the bar as drinks all round were served up by a very happy Landlord. Around midnight the fun broke up as fishermen and oilmen rolled out onto the cold street, which were now covered in two inches of snow. With their arms supporting each other they fell about laughing, and shouting ribald remarks at each other, as they went off to their respective bunks and beds.

Once again they were bound for Fawley, and the weather deteriorated as they headed south. The forecast was for a north westerly gale force eight, strengthening to nine was imminent. Sparky took the weather report onto the bridge, then went back into the radio room to complete his watch. The ships motion told the tale, things sliding back and forth, clacking noises as unseen objects collided. A rolling corkscrew action tested a man's balance, one hand for the ship one for yourself was the rule. He had to be careful not to voice his opinions at times like this, sailors were a superstitious lot. But truth was Sparky loved the drama, and the power of the sea, gales excited him and he liked to stand in the wheelhouse watching the ships bows part the ocean, then deposit tons of water along the foredeck before spraying great plumes of over the wheelhouse windows. As they rounded Valentia, steering an easterly course past Dursey point, Bantry Bay was visible on their port side. |Clearing Mizen Head signal station and Cloghane they left the Atlantic Ocean, and made passage across the Celtic sea.

By the time they closed on Lands End the sea state moderated. Two days later they were entering the Solent bound for Esso Fawley, and they were totally unprepared for the reception committee, which was already waiting for them on the quayside.

Clearly visible on the concrete roadway of the refinery was a blue Royal Navy Land rover, with four uniformed military policemen, and a naval officer watching their ship as it approached it's berth.

In the corner of the wheelhouse the VHF radio crackled into life, 'Dispatcher to Grit come in please,' said the voice. Charlie picked up the handset and acknowledge the call. 'Ah Captain Evans, a Royal Navy commander would like permission to board as soon as your secure fore and aft.' Charlie smiled knowingly, 'Permission granted dispatcher, thank you.' The he turned to the mate and said 'I told you David, the Navy want their toy back.' Two MPs remained at the bottom of their gangway, the other two accompanied the officer and were received by the first mate, who then took them to the captains cabin. Charlie was standing just inside the door way and extended his hand in greeting to the very smart looking commander. Once inside the door was closed, and the two MPs stood guard in the alleyway. There was a buzz of inquisitive excitement amongst the crew, wondering what it was all about. Time ticked on with nearly an hour passing before the door opened and the Commander emerged smiling, but looking slightly unsteady of his feet. 'Right then lads follow me,' he said, heading out onto the deck where he was met by the bosun and three sailors.

Down on the well deck they unlashed the striped Yellow buoy, and with some assistance from the refinery pipe lifting gear the buoy was landed on the jetty and loaded onto the back of a Royal Navy flat-bed truck, which had pulled alongside. Charlie appeared at head of the gangway and shook hands with the commander, who saluted and said 'Thank you Captain Evans, look forward to seeing you later.' As the the convey made its way down the jetty the first mate turned to the captain and said 'Come on then Charlie, what the hell was all that about?'... With a smile on his face and a twinkle in his eyes Charlie told him the following story.

Apparently the rather innocent yellow gunnery practice marker buoy, was nothing of the sort. It was in fact being used in a NATO submarine training exercise involving submarines from six different countries. They had been patrolling the Atlantic approaches to the Irish sea, their orders were to find and destroy the enemy. The Subs had been tracking and following a signal from a Royal Navy sonar radio buoy, the very one which the Grit had taken on board. The young Naval commander who had just left the ship was in fact a sub mariner based at HMS Dolphin Gosport, near Portsmouth. He had been aboard a Royal Navy sub during the exercise, acting as an observer. He explained to Charlie that things had been going well, most of the subs had located the target and were preparing to log their action confirming a successful kill, up to this point the target had been following a southerly tidal drift of three knots forty miles miles off the south coast of Ireland. Then suddenly at 1137 hours the buoy increased speed rapidly up to twelve knots, bound on a new course south west, around the bottom of the Republic of Ireland. He admitted that there was a considerable degree of consternation and bemusement in the control rooms of NATO's submarine fleet, various signals were sent to central command asking for verification, and status of the situation. Eventually an RN sub was instructed to close on target and deploy periscope depth for a visual report. Once the Grit had been sighted, and checked for its purpose and destination, new orders were issued to all Submarine Commanders instructing them to continue tracking at maximum range from the target until further orders...

Discreet communications had taken place at the highest level with the Irish government, who confirmed they had nothing to do with intercepting the buoy, and the likelihood of any subversive groups having such a capability was very remote. Instead of cancelling the exercise entirely it was modified, with one RN sub being assigned to monitor Grits progress, and eventual return to Fawley. After completing his very interesting story,the commander then cordially invited Grits Captain and whichever crew were off duty, to be their guests that evening in the officer mess at HMS Dolphin. It was a very entertaining night, and would be remembered for a long time by all those who were lucky enough to have been present. The drinks, food, and hospitality were superb. Although Grits actions were serious to some degree, never the less the humorous side of the incident was well appreciated by all concerned. It had also given Grits crew the rare opportunity to see the other side of seafaring life from a Royal Naval point of view.

The role of the ships radio officer was essentially created for the safety of life at sea. They were required to monitor the international radio distress frequency of 500Khz medium wave. All ships of all nationalities with a gross tonnage of 2,500 tons and over were required to to perform this duty. The working range on this frequency was in the region of two or three hundred miles, depending on the power of the transmitter being used. This effectively meant that in the busy shipping and trade routes of the Atlantic and Pacific oceans, these signals would generally stand a reasonable chance of being heard, and other ships could go to their assistance. In coastal waters with high maritime activity the airwaves were full of radio traffic, and due to the larger number of ships there

were more incidents of distress calls, especially in stormy
weather conditions.

Sparky had by now heard many of these messages, and on numbers of occasions had been involved in helping to co-ordinate the rescue. So it was that one October morning in the southern Celtic sea, with a very strong north easterly gale pushing hard on their starboard quarter, he received an XXX Urgency transmission from a ten thousand ton American grain freighter reporting a fire on board. The freighters position was approximately was 45 miles south west of their own, and captain Evans gave the order to change course and head for the causality. Sparky was now in constant communication with the vessels own radio officer, and gave them an ETA of 1230hrs GMT. The closest other ship gave it's ETA as 1400hrs GMT, and had altered course to assist. The casualty reported that the fire was spreading and they were having a problem containing it. Grain fires are notoriously difficult to fight, usually started by internal combustion, they could smoulder for hours then ignite suddenly with devastating consequences.

The weather conditions had moderated slightly, but the Grit was still rolling and pitching, the engines were on full power, and the Chief engineer was coaxing them to deliver as much speed as possible. Visibility began to deteriorate as a thick rolling mist obscured the horizon, the atmosphere on the bridge was tense as both the captain and second Mate paced back and forth, constantly checking the ships position.

Sparky was on full alert in the radio room, a number of other ships had responded providing their positions, and Lands End Radio had taken charge as controlling station. The distress and calling frequency of 500Khz was eerily silent, in UK and European waters it was normally very busy, but during the search and rescue procedure all ships were required to stop transmitting on this frequency unless, they were actively involved in the rescue. Sparky sat at his operating position, headphones close around his ears, he had two receivers tuned to the distress channel, just in case one of them failed. The transmitter was wound up to full power, and his morse Key lay close by his right hand. Occasional feint bursts of morse code interrupted the silence, possibly from ships on the extreme edge of their range, who may not have heard that a distress was taking place. It had been more than twenty minutes since the freighter had been in contact. 'Any news Sparky?' shouted the captain from the bridge, 'nothing sir,' he replied. It was hard to imagine what was going on just a few miles away from them. Fire at sea was the most feared and dreaded of maritime incidents, surrounded by water did not necessarily mean your salvation, fighting this demon was a terrifying prospect for all on board.

Suddenly, the staccato sound of the freighters transmitter resonated in his earphones, it was the fateful signal SOS. The fire was now out of control, and the captain had had issued orders to abandon ship. The Grit now had full sight of the stricken vessel, thick smoke was clearly visible at a range of eight miles. Charlie came into the radio room and told him they were closing, and expected to be on location in thirty minutes. Sparky immediately passed on the message, and received an abbreviated reply from the freighter, they confirmed they could see them, but the ships operator was now taking to his lifeboat station, he ended his transmission with the words God help us.

Sparky went on the bridge, and looked out of the wheelhouse windows, the casualty was now clearly visible, he stood transfixed alongside his Captain, Charlie, there was a moderate swell, and the wind had reduced to a light breeze... as they all concentrated on the unfolding drama, there was an eerie silence, a tension, a feeling of hopeful anticipation. Then, without any warning they saw a huge white cloud of smoke and steam gushing out of the ships funnel, and almost immediately the vessel sank beneath the waves. As the horror unfolded not a word was spoken on the bridge of the Grit, within a very few minutes the sea was empty, only the turmoil on the surface around the last site of the doomed vessel was left to tell the tale. It had completely disappeared. Debris began to appear, and all eyes looked for any sign of survivors, but there were none. Everyone was shocked, disbelief stunned all those who had seen it happen. Sparky in particular was devastated, only minutes before he had been in contact with them. They were taking to the lifeboats... there had been hope.

Charlie stayed searching the area for another two hours, Lands End Radio was advised of the situation, then with a feeling of helplessness they altered course and continued on their own journey. The consensus of opinion was that the intense heat in the hold became so fierce, that the bottom of the ship simply burst open allowing hundreds tons of sea water to flood in. There would have been little or no warning, nothing they could have done. Ships at that time were constructed with a single skin hull, no double bottoms. This meant that once a ships hull was compromised by being holed, it was only a matter of time before they sank. Later generations of ships were built to a much more demanding and safer standard.

In the last months of his time on the Grit, Sparky got married to Mary in Sunderland, and soon afterwards they moved to Southampton renting a house on the outskirts of the city, eventually they had a strong healthy son, and named him Stephen. Sparky continued with his life at sea serving on a number of other ships, including deep sea foreign going tankers and cargo ships. It was a good life and his young wife and son were occasionally allowed to accompany him for a few weeks, especially on continental trips to Europe. But gradually he found it harder each time he had to pack his sea-bags, and leave home for a few months. He missed his new found family life, and began to look for employment ashore.

A radio officer friend, known as Johnny The Greek, on account of his swarthy completion, and the fact that he had served on a number of Greek oil tankers, suggested Sparky might like to consider working on deep sea trawlers out of Hull or Grimsby. Trips were usually around three weeks in duration, the money wasn't great, but there was the possibility of extra money from the sale of cod liver oil, which the trawlers extracted on board from the livers of their catch. Johnny was currently working as an radio officer on an ocean going salvage tug owned by United Towing of Hull. He was in the Bay of Biscay returning from a towing job to Bilbao, on the north coast of Spain. They were due to dry dock in Hull within the next few days. He offered to meet up with Sparky and show him around the fish-docks scene, and introduce him to a few useful contacts. Sparky was due to go on leave in ten days time so he agreed to come up and have a look around.

Johnny was staying at the Stella Maris mission to seamen, and booked a room for Sparky. Over a few beers, he explained the responsibilities of a wireless operator on fishing boats. It was very different life from that of a merchant ship, involving many more working hours. Their job was constantly monitor weather reports, track the location of other fishing boats, and listening in to what they claimed to be catching. There were numbers of other duties, the most bizarre of which was the boiling of the cod livers, and extract pure cod liver oil. It was a smelly, messy job, involving the dragging of baskets of cod livers, cut out by the crew, to a boiler room, usually at the stern end of the boat, but in some of the older vessels it way up in the bow, under the forecastle head. As soon as they arrived back in port, the tanks of pure oil would be lifted ashore and sent to a fish dock laboratories for analysis, ascertain it's purity. If the job on board had been done properly, the resultant oil was sold onwards, its value governed by its purity. All the profit from this was then shared out between the wireless-man and the deckhands.

Neither the Skipper nor any of the other officers were entitled to a share, it was potentially a valuable bonus for those concerned.

Johnny made it abundantly clear that this was not a cushy number, the conditions on board most of these vessels were generally very poor. The waters of the Arctic circle were notoriously unpredictable and dangerous in the extreme. There was nothing easy about life aboard a distant water trawler, especially on sidewinders, so called because they shot their nets over the side of the boat, and hauled them back on board the same way. Potentially this was a highly dangerous procedure, with a heavy net full of fish, gale force winds and huge rolling seas, the possibility of the boat capsizing was always there. The majority of the Hull, Grimsby, and other UK fishing fleets at that time, operated in this way. Larger, safer and more productive Stern trawlers were already in use, and would eventually take their place.

It was a tough environment, with no room for shirkers. The Skippers word was sacrosanct even if he was wrong. The rewards could be very lucrative, or a complete financial loss. Every trip was a new enterprise with no guarantee of success, and the possibility of disaster was always waiting, ready to strike at any time.

Eventually Sparky did two trips to the Icelandic fishing grounds, and enjoyed the experience, despite the challenging conditions. He decided that it did not really solve his problem, the money was uncertain, and the only way to benefit from the short stay in port was to move from Southampton to Hull... On balance he thought his prospects were better served by staying in the south. He was of course completely unaware that a few yeas later he would return to Hull, as the manager in charge of one of the industries top marine communications companies, Redifon, who manufactured, installed, and serviced a first class range of communications and electronic fish locating equipment, as well as supplying the operators to man the stations.

PART 8

Sparky Gets a Shore Job

Family Man
Hard work and promotion

——————◆——————

During many trips his ship made to the Fawley petroleum refinery, he often went into Southampton, to collect radio spares, or stationary from the company's Southampton depot. He was employed by Siemens Ltd, they manufactured the marine radio stations, and supplied the radio officers to man the stations. During these visits he became friendly with the manager Jim Barriball, and they would often go for a beer after work at one of the local dockside pubs. One day when he was on leave, he accidentally met Jim in a pub near the docks. After catching up with company gossip, Jim asked him if he fancied a job ashore as a radio service engineer. The port of Southampton was expanding, with more and more vessels to look after, and Jim was looking for more staff. It was the opportunity Sparky was looking for, so after talking it over with Mary he contacted Jim to confirm that he would like to be considered for the position. Transferring from seagoing staff to shore establishment was quite a normal progression and was considered an asset to the company. However the process was time consuming, and Sparky continued to serve at sea for another four months before receiving a letter asking him to report to the companies head office in Woolwich London.

After an interview with the service manager Denis Norton, he was offered a position in Southampton. The job was conditional on him satisfactorily completing six weeks training at their Woolwich depot. Sparky was excited with the prospect of a new life ashore, but also very sad at the thought of leaving the sea. He would have to come to terms with the ways of landlubbers. It would take him almost a year to settle down, and there were a number of times when he was close to asking for his old job back. But gradually things became easier for him. He consoled himself with the thought that at least he was working on ships every day. It was interesting work, involving early morning starts, and late nights. Ships radio stations were required by law to be in full working condition, with a qualified officer on board, otherwise they were not allowed to sail. The shore staff were available on a twenty four hour seven day a week basis, including bank holidays and Christmas. This commitment gave Sparky a feeling of well being and pride, the work ethic was similar to his life at sea, and over the coming years this was to have a positive influence on his career.

During these early years ashore, he worked hard and never turned down the opportunity for overtime, Mary and he were saving up to buy a house of their own, so in addition to his regular job, he also set himself up with his first little business. The Eager Beaver TV and radio repair service. One of his friends at work offered him a small garden shed, and helped Sparky to install it in the back garden of his rented house. He fitted it out with benches and shelves, as well as a power cable and lights. He would often come home late from working on a ships radar, only to find a number of TV's waiting for him to fix. All the money was paid into a building society accountant, until eventually they had enough cash for the deposit on a new bungalow in the small village of Hedge End on the Portsmouth side of Southampton.

Life was good, with lots of work, so Sparky joined a mountaineering club and went back to climbing. The south coast was a lovely place to live in those days. The Solent, Isle of Wight, and the New Forest all within easy reach. He was settling down, and could see a future for himself and his family. Whenever he was not on call at weekends the family went camping.

On one such occasion they were on a site near Lymington, it was just after breakfast time when suddenly his boss Jim arrived. He came with bad news. Their company Siemens/AEI had been bought out by English Electric, who also owned Marconi Marine. It seemed that Jim's job servicing the Siemens engine-room equipment was to remain intact, but Sparky would have to transfer over to the Marconi depot in Southampton as a radio technician. Jim knew about his previous history with them, so he had had come down to tell him personally. It was certainly a blow, his nice rewarding life was in danger of being interrupted. It was assumed at this stage, that the local Marconi depot would not be aware of his past indiscretions, but it would not be long before his it caught up with him. It was doubtful that he would loose his job, but his chances of advancement with them didn't look good.

As so often happened in Sparky's life, things had a habit of working out for the best in the end, and in retrospect this change was to herald the start of a whole new set of adventures and experiences... but it would take a while. The change over would not to take place for another month, so he set about looking for another job. Within two weeks he had an interview and had been given a verbal offer of a job in Redifon Marine Communications Division, a rival of Macaroni's. His timing was perfect, Redifon were in the final stages of setting up a small service depot in Southampton. They assured him the job was his, and that a letter of appointment would be sent out to him within a few days.

A couple of months earlier Sparky had booked a Townsend-Thoresen from Southampton to Le Havre. The family planned to drive down through France and camp on the coast at Tarragona in Spain, south of Barcelona. A few days before they were due to leave, he received his official appointment to join Marconi Southampton on the Monday after he returned from his three weeks leave. But there was no sign of a letter from Redifon. He telephoned them to ask if everything was still OK. They assured him that by the time he came home the letter would be waiting for him. He wasn't too concerned, after all he had a job with Marconi, but he knew that wouldn't last long. They had been planning the trip for ages, with encouragement from his boss Jim, who had been there a number of times. Even so this was a huge undertaking, and they were all very excited. Young Stephen was an experienced camper by this time, and made sure he took all his favourite things, dinky cars, trucks, earthmoving diggers, mask, snorkel, and a small fishing rod with spinners. He was quite convinced that he would be able to catch the family dinner everyday, in fact he wasn't far wrong, except that most of the time it was either squid or jelly fish. In those days Townsend-Thoresen Ferries charged cars based on their length. Sparky's little 105E Ford Anglia was five inches too long for the cheapest tariff, so he unbolted the front and rear bumpers and planned to stow them on his roof rack for the trip across the channel, then fix them back on at the first available opportunity. This saved him quite a bit of money, as long as nobody spotted his cunning little plan. It was probably illegal to drive down the docks like that, but what the heck, they were off to have an adventure.

The poor little Anglia was loaded to it's maximum capacity, things were stuffed in every possible corner and space they could find, the back seat was left with just enough room for little Stephen to curl up and sleep, or sit up and play with his trucks, vroom vroom sounds accompanied them all the way from home to Tarragona, and back again. Loading the roof rack was a work of art, it contained the frame tent, poles (they were huge and heavy), camp chairs, folding table, large groundsheet, and initially a set of car bumpers. In those early days places like Halfords didn't exist, the art of safe roof racks was still being developed. The only one Sparky could afford, had rubber suckers on each stubby leg, and a pair of adjustable brackets which hooked onto the lip of the car roof. The car's suspension was down to it's lowest limits, and the body just cleared the tops of the tyres. At the ferry port he gave a sigh of relief when they finally boarded the ship without anyone challenging them about their load or the bumpers.

After a pleasant crossing with calm weather they docked in Le Havre, and followed all the other cars off the ship. This was the first time he had ever driven on the right hand side of the road, so with some degree of nervousness they cautiously navigated the local streets, guided by a prepared tick list of road signs and place names. Early on he made one mistake going the wrong way round a traffic island, there was a lot of shouting and honking of French horns. But they finally ended up on the correct route, heading south on the A28. Sparky had completely forgotten about his bumpers on the roof, and settled down to the drive ahead. Their plan was to stop after three hours, and hopefully find their first camp site, recommended by his boss Jim. The road was not particularly busy and they seemed to be doing very nicely. Then without any warning there was a grinding sound coming from the roof. The next thing Sparky saw was the sight of his fully loaded roof rack appearing in the rear view mirror. It crashed onto the road behind him, then slewed sideways toward the grass verge, where it tilted upwards and stopped. Fortunately there were no other cars, or pedestrians to be seen anywhere. He reversed towards their jettisoned possessions, dreading the thought of what he might find. Their holiday was in danger of ending before it had really begun.

Incredibly the whole rack and its contents was still strapped securely to the frame, one of the bumpers looked slightly bent, two of the rubber sucker feet and the fixing brackets were missing, and a bungee cord had snapped. There was a small lay-bye a few yards further back, so he manoeuvred into the space. Then he and Mary carried everything back to the car, meanwhile Stephen was contentedly emitting lots of vrrm's. A quick search soon found the brackets up the road, and the two missing feet were still stuck fast to the car roof. After half an hour Sparky had refitted and reloaded the rack, then fastened the bumpers back into place. With considerable relief they continued their journey south, arriving at Jim's camp-site a few hours later.

The remainder of the drive to the south was enjoyable, the countryside constantly changing as the weather became warmer. They had two more camps before crossing the boarder into Spain... One of them was superb, but the other was so awful, dirty and smelly that they left at five in the morning without paying! Later, as they left Perpignan behind them, it seemed as if payback time was keeping an eye on them. They were driving up a long and steep winding mountain pass, to the east of the Pyrenees All seemed to be going well, when the car suddenly came to an abrupt halt on a steep hair pin bend. Sparky managed to free-wheel back to a safer position on the side of the road, but as he lifted the car bonnet steam drifted up into the heat of the noonday sun. A full inspection of the engine compartment, water hoses, pipes and electrics gave no clue as to the problem. First Mary, then Sparky sat in the drivers seat and turned the ignition key, the starter motor whined and chattered but the engine refused to fire up. After twenty minutes he had exhausted everything he knew about 105E Anglia's, which was actually quite a lot, and included some tricks his grandpa Nev had taught him all those years ago.

Meanwhile Mary had been sitting in the shade of the car reading a book, which didn't impress Sparky at all, and Stephen was fast asleep, having given up on vroom vroom. 'You need to put a soaking wet rag around the carburettor fuel input line,' shouted Mary through the simmering haze of the alpine pass. 'How the bloody hell do you know?' retorted Sparky, 'because it says so here in the RAC handbook, in the section dealing with breakdowns in very hot weather.'... Of course, she was absolutely right, and five minutes later they were driving up the pass once more, with both of them laughing, as vroom vroom joined in from somewhere in the back. Their spirits were high as they cleared the Spanish Boarder, and headed in the general direction of Barcelona, they should make the Tarragona camp-site that evening. However the payback demon was still chasing them. With no warning at all the front wheels started to wobble, and Sparky struggled to keep control of the car. Eventually he stopped by a road side fruit seller. He checked all four wheels and could see nothing wrong, he thought it was a puncture, but everything was fine. Then he realized that the wheels were out of balance, they must have shed one or more of the lead weights which are used to keep them stable. This was one job he could do nothing about. They consulted the trusty RAC handbook looking for an authorised garage, the closest was in the suburbs of Gerona, around twenty miles away. It was now mid afternoon, and to make matters worse it was a Saturday, however not to be daunted by such trivial things they set off, driving slowly to prevent the wheels from wobbling off. By a stroke of pure luck, which in truth probably had more to do with Mary's ace navigating skills, they arrived at the garage. It was closed, the street was deserted, they were tired, hungry and slightly deflated. After driving around the block they found a small restaurant-bar, and decided to go for a meal.

When the waitress arrived to take their order she spoke to them in excellent English, seeing Sparky's look of surprise she looked towards his overloaded little Ford and nodded, he acknowledged her with smile. They sorted out some food and drinks, then when she returned he told her why they had ended up in the area. Anna, as she was called, listened carefully, then went back to the kitchen. Five minutes later a middle aged man came to their table, and introduced himself as Antonio Perez, owner of the garage, Anna the waitress, was his daughter in law. Sparky's luck had just cashed in, as Antonio offered to open up and sort out his wheels. Two hours later they drove off towards Tarragona, well fed and watered, with perfectly balanced steering, and a nice feeling about their first real encounter with local Spanish people.

Their camp-site was superb, spotlessly clean, well organised and only a few minutes from a beautiful beach. To top it all they had arrived at the start of the Tarragona wine festival, everywhere was alive and buzzing. They spent nearly two very happy weeks enjoying the sun, sea, and hospitality. They also met a young English couple, Marion and Jeff, who had come all the way down to Tarragona from Manchester on a Vespa scooter, complete with camping equipment. Eventually it was time to leave, and their plan was to go back via Paris to see the Eiffel Tower, Arc de Triomphe, and as many sights as they could manage in two days. Marion and Jeff were also heading for home, and had set off a couple of days before them. They agreed to meet up with them in Paris, at the Boise de Boulogne camp site in the heart of city.

They were sorry to be leaving Tarragona, it had been a great holiday, lots of sun, sea and sand, but Sparky had a living to make, and hopefully a new employer. Their drive north was uneventful and they arrived outside the camp site at around 10 pm on their second day. To their surprise and disappointment, the gates were closed, they would have to join the queue, sleep in the car and check in after 8 am. The site was huge, and very crowded, and more by luck than good management, they found their allocated space, put the tent up and had a nice big breakfast. It was a real jamboree atmosphere, surrounded by tents of all colours, shapes and sizes. As they were about to wash up the breakfast pots, a familiar voice shouted, 'Hey, there they are Jeff, just over by that wigwam.' Marion was first to greet them followed by Jeff who was pushing the scooter.

Their pleasant surprise soon turned to concern as they realized that their friends looked as if they had been in involved in an accident. Both had bandages on their hands, and Jeff looked as if he had come off worse, with plasters on his forehead and left ear. After the initial shock, Sparky was amazed that they had been able to reach Paris in the same time as them. While sitting down with a big mugs of tea, they spilled out the story of their somewhat dramatic journey. Evidently they had been cruising happily at 35 mph, along a lovely straight tree lined road, when all of a sudden their poor little overloaded Vespa engine packed up completely, and Jeff found himself struggling to control the machine. He was unable to change gear, and in the end they skidded sideways, mounted the grass verge and hit a tree, before being jettisoned back onto the hard gravel surface of the road.

They were both shocked and bloody when an American Army truck pulled up behind them, the driver and his companion came over immediately to offer assistance. They had seen the little drama unfold in front of them, the drivers mate was an army medic, and soon set about checking the two casualties. They were very lucky, things could have been a lot worse, their injuries were mainly superficial, grazes and bruises, but unpleasant none the less. He also gave them some pain killer tablets, with a pack of bandages and plasters. In his opinion there was no need to go to a hospital, but that choice was for them to make.

Meanwhile a couple of soldiers from the back of the truck had been checking out the damaged Vespa. With some pulling and banging they straitened out the bent body work, checked the wheels and steering, then with a bit more tinkering the little Vespa suddenly burst into life. Lots of smoke came out of the exhaust, but it soon cleared and the gallant little engine continued to tick over sweetly. A tall suntanned solider with fashionable crew cut hair, and a Texas accent, asked if they minded him taking their bike for a test ride. The pair smiled and nodded their consent. The big man mounted the saddle, kicked his steed into gear, then accelerated down the road they had just ridden up. To be fair, it was quite a comical sight, one big Texan astride an Italian pony, riding off into the distance, encouraged with a few whoops of 'ride em cowboy' shouts from his buddies. Upon his return Tex declared that all seemed to be well, adding, ' It's a tough litter critter you got here my friends, hope it gets you home okay.'

The Americans were also on their way to Paris, and kindly offered the two young Vespa owners a lift, which they very gratefully accepted. The tough little Vespa was hauled into the back of the truck, with Marion and Jeff riding up front with the medic and driver. It was a very kind gesture, and probably not strictly approved of by their military superiors, but this was the mid 1960's and one wonders if the same attitudes would exist today, some fifty or more years later. The two passengers were very well treated, and eventually dropped off close to the Bois de Boulogne Camp site. As a parting gesture the Americans gave them some of their special K rations and a couple of bottles of Coca Cola, before roaring off down the road.

After some breakfast with Sparky and family, they all decided to head off into Paris to see the sights. Now the little Ford Anglia was relieved of its heavy load there was enough room for all of them in the car. The next few hours were hectic and at times a bit scary, as they joined the never ending stream of cars rushing at break neck speed up and down the Champs-Elysée. They had no GPS or detailed road maps, just a tourist guide with scanty descriptions, and a few photo's to help them around the amazing city of Paris. But it was good fun, and they managed to visit Notre-Dame, the Bastille, the Louvre and the Palace of Versailles before arriving back at the camp site, exhausted but well satisfied with their achievement's. That night the dined at one of the restaurants close to the camp, and since they would be going their separate ways in the morning, they felt a bit sad, but they exchanged contact details and promised to keep in touch. They never did, but at least they had the memories.

The ferry from Calais to Dover was heaving with homeward bound Brits, and the drive back to Southampton seemed to take for ever. They were all pleased to be home, young Stephen slept most of the way, so they were spared the vrrm vrrm's. They unloaded the car, and headed off to bed, but not before Sparky checked his mail to see if Redifon had confirmed his appointment. To his disappointment there was no such letter. But at least he knew that on the Monday morning he could report to the Marconi depot, as agreed and start work.

He knew most of the engineers in Marconi Southampton, some of them actually lived quite close to him, so upon his arrival at the office, he was greeted with a few friendly faces. He was then given a few forms to complete and a tour around the depot before eventually being taken upstairs to meet the depot manager. It was all very cordial and he was duly impressed with workshops facilities and general layout. Half way through the morning the service manager gave him instructions to attend The mv Sand Piper, a small offshore sand dredger operating out of Poole harbour. It was fitted with Siemens radio equipment, and he had worked on her a few times in the past. A Marconi engineer was assigned to accompany him, so that he could learn more about the range of equipment they would now be responsible for.

Later in the day he managed to make a telephone call to the Redifon personnel department asking about the letter offering him a job. The young lady passed him through to the departmental manager who told him a letter had been sent two weeks ago. Sparky explained his situation, and was assured that another one would be sent out the following day. For the next few days, he was very busy working on numbers of service calls up and down the coast, from Weymouth in the west to Shoreham in the east. On the Thursday night when he arrived home from work, Mary handed him a letter which had the Redifon stamp on the back, he opened it eagerly, then looked at Mary and smiled, it was all OK, it confirmed his appointment, detailed his salary, which was more than he was currently earning, and asked him to confirm his acceptance and report to their Wandsworth head office the following Monday at 0900 hrs. He was absolutely delighted, it was just what he wanted, and he couldn't have been happier. Typical of the way life seemed to work out for Sparky, this new appointment was to be the start of an exciting, rewarding, roller-coaster period. There were good and bad times ahead, with adventures he could never have dreamed of as he signed his letter of resignation from the Marconi company.

The following day he went straight to the manager's office, and asked the secretary if he could see him. It was no problem, he went straight in and was invited to sit down. He handed his letter of resignation across the desk and sat back to wait for the reaction. The Marconi man took his glasses off and looked at Sparky.

'Well, I must say this comes as a quite a surprise,' he said, and putting his glasses back on he looked at the letter once again. Sparky had already realized that his position within the depot was probably reasonably secure for the time being, after all he knew all about the Siemens equipment, and was good at his job. The Manager put the letter down then continued.

'You know there is a great future for you within Marconi, your young, and could go far. The opportunities for advancement are considerable, eventually you could even be promoted in charge of one our worldwide service depots in places like West Africa, India, or the Far East.'

Sparky was surprised, and found it interesting, however at the back of his mind was his earlier period of employment with the company, and the fact that he had been sacked for missing his ship in the Panama Canal zone all those years ago. He knew that it would only be a matter of time before this was revealed. He thanked him for the advice, but confirmed that he would like to leave, and take his chances with Redifon Marine Communications.

That was it then, the necessary procedures were put into place, his wages were calculated, together with expenses due to him for lunch allowances and fuel used during his various service calls. At midday he walked out of the office after saying farewell to his colleagues, he had a weeks pay and more in his pocket, and the prospect of an exciting time ahead. As he jumped in his car to go home, he thought to himself, Life was pretty good.

He awoke at the crack of dawn on the following Monday, put his bag in the car and drove to Wandsworth and his new job. The next few days were hectic, completing all the forms required by the company, and meeting people in the departments. He was impressed with the friendly and enthusiastic way he was greeted, and began to feel at home very quickly. A training plan and initiation programme were sorted out, and his boss sat with him discussing what they would be looking for in the way of a suitable premises, for their new Southampton depot. He was told how much they had to spend, and what image they wished to present to the ship owners and agents in the port of Southampton. It soon dawned on him that he was not only being given a new job, but a new level of responsibility. Then when his bosses secretary gave him a box of smart company business cards, with his name and title of Southern Area Service Manager printed across the middle, he was in no doubt that his working life had just taken a new direction. The secretary explained that these were just to get him bye, until a permanent Southampton address was established.

He suddenly felt quite important, a swanky business card with his name on it, the die was cast and he was excited about his prospects. There was one thing Sparky had in abundance, and that was confidence in everything he did. He never considered failure as an option, even if he didn't know the answer or how to complete a particular task, he always began with the unchallengeable assumption that he would find a way, and succeed. As the years moved on he looked back over his life, and realized how much he had winged it. The trick was to take up the gauntlet, never say no, then just go out and make it happen.

After a spell at head office he was sent up to Hull for further technical training. Redifon Hull was the companies flag ship depot, and was located on the fish dock in the very heart of Hull's deep-sea fishing industry. It was fitted out with well equipped workshops and had a technical staff of fifteen engineers. They dominated the UK fishing fleets communication market in those days, providing 24 hour, seven day a week service to the trawlers both during their time in home port, as well as sending engineers to Norway, Iceland and Greenland if required. It was an amazing time for fishing, large trawlers were being built which could spend as much as two or three months away from home. The Hull fish-docks were buzzing with activity. Sparky absolutely loved every minute of his time there, after all it was the fishing boats of Fleetwood which had spurred his young spirit to run away to sea at the age of twelve.

Now, here he was up close and personnel with the vessels, the fishermen, the skippers and the owners of UK's highly successful fishing industry. There was drama and a romance surrounding everything connected with the fish-dock scene. It was a hard brutal life, dangerous in the extreme, with family histories stretching back generations. The cities of Hull and Grimsby were almost totally dependent on the lifeblood provided by fishing. Their sons challenged the freezing Arctic waters so the nation could enjoy their Fish and Chip suppers. Fishermen worked hard and played hard, a three week trip to Iceland and back for a cargo of prime cod and haddock could result in a top catch, which sold on the morning market for top money. But an unlucky trip could mean they only received a basic wage, just enough to get bye. The crew were paid a bonus each trip depending on the value of the fish landed on that day. Seventy-two hours after discharging their catch they would be off again, back to the frozen north. They continued to fish in the worst possible conditions imaginable. Out on deck for hours at a time in freezing temperatures and inhospitable seas, casting the trawl, or gutting the catch. By the nature of its harsh operating environment a defiant cavalier attitude often existed, which was spread across all levels of the industry, from the owners to the crew and their Skipper. Typically trawler owners would christen their vessels to reflect their attitudes. Names like Boyd Lines Arctic Freebooter, Arctic Warrior and Corsair, and there were many more similar examples. This was no place for the feint hearted or the shirkers, every man aboard was required to pull their weight. These were the last of the worlds great hunters. Sparky admired, and respected them, he was in his element. But he had no idea, that in the not too distant future, he would return to Hull, promoted to the position of General Manager in charge of Redifon's premier fishing Industry communications and electronics depot.

But in the meantime he would have to earn his stripes, and the Southampton office was to be the start of that process. In the absence of suitable premises his boss arranged for him to share a temporarily workshop with one of its associated companies Reddifusion, situated quite close to the city. Reddifusion were an innovative company who provided radio and television services to households, hotels and factories via underground and overhead cable systems. Customers could rent the service, which gave them an economic solution for home entertainment. The cost of buying domestic TV and radio's was quite considerable back in the 1960's. Reddifusion were highly successful for a number of years and provided excellent technical back up, with good after sales support.

Sparky shared a workshop with four other engineers, who were mainly employed in keeping their own companies equipment in good order. It was a friendly atmosphere and he enjoyed being in the company of other techies. Over the time he was there he gained more experience and knowledge about other communication and electronic systems. By sheer luck, working there also opened up his interest in climbing once again. One of the young engineers he worked along side, was called Mike, had a picture on the wall above his work station. It was a photograph showing climbers on a very hard and dramatic rock climb in the Cheddar Gorge Somerset. The climb was called Coronation Street, and It's first accent had featured in a live BBC outside broadcast one weekend, which followed the climbers during their epic and eventually successful attempt. At the time it was groundbreaking television, and so was the quality of the climbers and the route. Mike was inspired by the photograph, and admitted to Sparky that he would love to have a go at a rock climbing.

They hit it off almost right away, Mike was a talented engineer, he was interested in sport, played football and was very fit. They met socially outside work, which also introduced Sparky and his family to a wider network of people, It was just what they needed. Mike was also a keen photographer, as were quite a number of the other engineers. But he really wanted to have a go at climbing. So it wasn't long before Sparky had checked out the local scene, purchased a guide book, some new rock boots and a brand new rope. There were no mountains or large rock faces in the south coast region where they lived, but there were some excellent sea-cliff's near Swanage in Dorset, only an hours drive away from Southampton. It was early days in the development of coastal climbing, the situations were often spectacular, with steep and overhanging problems to solve, and the looseness of the rock and the ever present and restless sea introduced a completely new dimension for climbers to cope with and understand.

The Swanage cliffs, which lie to the west of Anvil point and beyond had already been visited in the early 1960's and a guide book was produced by members of the Southampton University Mountaineering Club. With its proximity to army camps in Dorset, the Royal Marine Commandos had also enjoyed the scene. Many routes had been pioneered, with grades from very difficult to hard very severe. The situation was dramatic, facing south across the wide expanse of the English Channel, its limestone cliffs varied in height from some fifty feet up to nearly 200 feet, in the areas known as Dancing ledge and Blackers Hole . The climbing areas had unusual and exotic names like Subluminal, Tilly Whim, The Promenade and Fisherman's ledge, and Cattle Troughs. Gaining access to these ledges to start the climbs, which were of course at sea level, involved some careful descents down steep cracks or slippery slabs. Further west, long, and hair raising free abseils were necessary.

This all added to the excitement and atmosphere of the place, and with its south facing aspect, even in the winter time it was often possible to climb in T shirts and shorts. Mike and Sparky were hooked, and after the first few tentative visits, they soon became confident at moving around enjoying the superb climbing. Mike was a natural, lithe and supple with strong arms, he revelled in his new found freedom, but in the early days was quite happy to be second man. It would take a bit more time before he was ready to take his share in the leading. It was a great playground, almost on their door step. Sparky was of course in his element, a regular climbing partner, a good job, and a stable happy home life. Eventually they would join the

Wessex Mountaineering club, where they spread their wings, travelling up to Snowdonia and the Lake District at weekends and holiday time. On these occasions families would often join them, and camping with wives and kids became part of the fun.

Back on the job Sparky was kept busy, and often worked long hours, including weekends when required. After a few months operating out of the Reddifusion depot he found a perfect location for his own companies operations. It was ideally situated in Queens Terrace, a well established commercial area not far from the docks. His boss came down from Wandsworth and was duly impressed, eventually they signed the agreement and moved in. There was quite a lot of work required to make it into a functional office, store room, workshop and showroom for the company products. Sparky was given a budget, and the responsibility to make sure the work was carried out properly. He was pleased to have been given the opportunity to prove himself, and set about making sure that everything went to plan. When it was all completed his boss told him he was well satisfied. The company hosted an open day, inviting customers to come and meet them and see their new facilities. Redifon Marine Southampton was now officially on the map, with a resident engineer and a respectable premises to operate from.

Over the coming months the work load grew steadily, and within a year Sparky asked for another engineer to help with the increasing amount of work. They had contracts with Red Funnel Steamers, who operated the ferry services from Southampton to the Isle of White. The Trinity House and Southampton Pilots, small tug boat companies, British rail, who had the ferry services from Portsmouth, Ryde, and Lymington, to the island. They also looked after a small family business called Williams Shipping, they operated a fleet of powerful well equipped sea going launches. They were used to ship stores and crew to various parts of Southampton Water and the Solent, or attend ships at anchor waiting for a berth, or carrying out repairs. It was a lucrative business, operating round the clock seven days a week. The VHF Ship to shore radio's were essential for the smooth operation of their fleet of fifteen well maintained and smart vessels. Sparky's job was to make sure the equipment was operating properly, if it went wrong they needed a rapid service response, day or night.

The equipment however was now getting old, and was certainly being put to the test. Breakdowns were becoming more frequent and Sparky had a hard time trying to accommodate them. He was very friendly with most of the skippers, and even the boss himself, Mr Williams seemed well disposed towards him. One day whilst he was fitting a new aerial on the launch Willbetty, the skipper took him to one side and quietly told him that Mr Williams had been visited by Marconi, who were trying to sell him their latest marine VHF. When he arrived back in his office he rang Wandsworth to ask for details and prices of Redifon's latest equipment. He was told it wasn't his responsibility, and that they would get the sales department to contact the customer in due course. Sparky was a bit put out, but accepted the situation and waited for someone to call him.

A few days later, down on the town quay, the Willbetty's skipper called him over again and told him that the Marconi man had taken Mr Williams out to lunch a couple of days before. Back in the office, Sparky called his boss and told him about the possible threat to the Williams contract. He argued the case for him to present the details and a quotation to Mr Williams, his boss said he would call him back later that morning. After a couple of hours he was contacted by the companies sales director, Bill Mordin. They spoke for quite a while, Sparky was a little bit overawed, Bill was a larger than life character, ex Royal Navy commander, and holder of the Merchant Navy's top qualification, an Extra Masters Certificate. He was well known for his aggressive sales philosophy, and was highly successful as a negotiator. Bill gave him the third degree, asking him why he thought it was so important for him to try and make the sale. Sparky argued that technically he understood the equipment very well, he also believed that the presence of a locally based man would go in their favour, far more so than a visit from a London based city slicker. Bill was amused, and seemed to admire Sparky's attitude and commitment. He agreed, to arrange for a demonstration model of their very latest VHF, together with technical specifications, and a full quotation to be sent to him within a couple of days.

Then Sparky delivered his killer punch, he suggested to Bill that the price should include the cost of a dedicated spare unit, which would be held at the depot, ready to be used on an exchange basis if a fault on board the vessel, could not be fixed within an acceptable time scale. Bill laughed and told Sparky he was a cheeky young bugger, but he'd see what he could do. The next day he received a call from Bill's secretary advising him that everything was going ahead, and that he was to make an appointment to see the customer, adding that he should speak directly to Bill, prior to his meeting. Sparky was delighted, he felt confident that he could pull it off, he immediately rang the Williams Shipping company office to arrange a visit.

His appointment was for the following Monday at 10.00hrs. which gave him plenty of time to prepare for what was to be a pivotal moment in his career, although at the time he had no idea how much this sales visit would affect his career, and future. The new equipment arrived complete with its paper work, and he spent all his spare time checking things out, and reading the proposal until he knew it off by heart. His plan was to actually take the equipment with him to the meeting. The quotation put forward by head office was excellent, it gave a schedule of when each of the Williams vessels existing contract would expire, with dates of delivery for the replacements, and finally it highlighted that the new contract would include a service spare unit exclusivity allocated for use on Williams Shipping vessels. The new equipment had more radio channels, more power and was attractively styled.

Over the weekend he sorted out his best suite, white shirt, and a Merchant Navy tie, he wanted to look really smart. Whilst he was sitting in the garden having a cup of tea and watching his growing son Stephen climb up their only apple tree. It suddenly occurred to him that although the Williams boats could communicate with other ships, and all the official port and harbour stations, including Niton Radio on the Isle of White, but they could not actually speak directly to their own office and workshops ashore. What they needed was radio base station of their own, fitted with a dedicated private channel.

This was all made possible by simply making an application for a licence to the Home Office radio regulatory division in London. Which in those days would almost certainly be granted. Then all that was required was to install a powerful antenna on the roof of their building, and the base station in a suitable location in the office. Redifon of course manufactured such equipment, it was very reliable, and quite easy to install. Sparky smiled, as Stephen shouted something like 'Batman,' and then jumped out of the tree onto the lawn. He was pleased he had stopped for a cup of tea, and could hardly wait for Monday morning to arrive. He'd spoken to Bill on the previous Friday, they went over the figures in the quote, and he listened whilst Bill gave him last minutes instructions and a few tips, finishing with the warning that he was not to loose to the order to those buggers in Marconi.

On the Monday morning at 0950hrs. Sparky was shown into the reception area at Williams shipping, to await his meeting with fate, and destiny. Mr Williams cheerfully called him into the office, and as he entered he was given an approving look. The nice white shirt set off the colours of his Merchant Navy tie, and Sparky felt completely relaxed as he sat down and began to discuss, and demonstrate the reason for his visit. Lots of questions were asked, and he answered them truthfully and with conviction. Half an hour later, and it seemed as though his customer was duly impressed. Mr Williams told Sparky that he would examine the contract in detail, and give him an answer before the end of the week. He could sense his time was nearly up, his customer had other things to do. But before he finally stood up to leave, Sparky gave him a clear and concise overview of his base station proposal. Mr Williams sat back in his chair, and told Sparky that he didn't think it was so easy to have communications with his vessels direct into their own offices. It would be a great asset to them, and he liked the whole idea. As he stood up from behind his desk, he told the now slightly sweating Sparky, to send him some costings for the new proposal as soon as possible, then they shook hands and he showed him to the door.

Sparky almost floated on air as he walked back to Queens Terrace, which was less the ten minutes away. He sat behind his desk and rang Bill Mordin. Bill seemed in good humour, but cautioned young Sparky about being too eager to count his chickens. However no matter what Bill said, or what the outcome would be, he was buzzing inside, the thrill of his first ever sales meeting face to face with a client was rushing through his veins, it was a powerful feeling. He felt really pleased with himself, he had given a comprehensive presentation, was honest, and hoped he had shown how much he would like to be awarded with the business. He wasn't quite sure why he felt that way, but he did, and it made him feel good. He told Bill about the VHF base station proposal, and asked him to arrange for a budgetary quote to be telexed to Mr Williams that morning. Bill agreed to have it done.

As Sparky sat in his office that afternoon,he suddenly remembered an incident which had occurred some years before when his was still working for Siemens AEI. He had been installing a new AEI Escort radar on the passenger ship, Windsor Castle, owned by the Union Castle line of Southampton. The installation had to be installed in just three days, so with the help of a head office engineer, John Rich, the pair worked very hard all day, and well into the night. After sorting out various set backs, they eventually completed the job, and carried out satisfactory testing in the very early hours of the morning. Later it was to be handed over to the ships Captain and officers by a head office salesman. They didn't go home that night, but slept on board, It had been a close run thing.

At 1100hrs that morning the Union Castle Marine Superintendent, together with the ships captain, and some of the officers, were due to be given a demonstration by the AEI head office salesman, who had successfully negotiated the contract. John Lewis was a tall slim, and smartly dressed man in his mid thirties, he had met with Sparky and John earlier, and had been fully briefed on the installation. He was very impressed with the work they had done, and complimented both of them on the quality of the installation, and the fact they had completed the job in such a short space of time. It was a state of the art equipment, so quite a feather in their respective caps. Sparkys boss Jim had also arrived on board earlier to make sure everything was working well, and it was. As the visitors arrived, and John began his introduction to the equipment, Jim suddenly said something to Sparky that he was never to forget, and which would eventually shape his whole attitude to his future career.

Jim said to him, 'Do you know what the two most insincere things are in the world?' Sparky looked puzzled and replied, 'No, I don't.' Jim looked across at John Lewis on the other side of the wheelhouse and said, 'The kiss of a prostitute, and the handshake of a salesman.' Sparky was quite shocked at hearing his boss make such a condemning statement, he didn't really know how to respond. He decided to just smile and say nothing.

Sparky was an engineer at the time, and had no idea that he would change his terms of employment in the future. But he did not agree with his boss's cutting remarks. He reasoned that if the salesman had not secured the contract, then he would not have been involved with installing it. Sparky held the view that to some degree, everyone was trying to sell something. It may be that they were trying to promote their talent at work, in the hope that their boss would reward them with promotion, or a salary increase. In many walks of life people often worked hard to sell their ideas about various issues, hoping that they may eventually persuade others to agree with them, and as a result, change their minds. It amounted to the same thing in the end...selling.

Of course the image of the dodgy car salesman who shook hands knowing full well that what he had just sold you was a heap of junk, was not lost on Sparky. He believed it didn't have to be that way. A salesperson need not be insincere, they could and should be proud to make a sale which pleased the customer, pleased the employer, and leave the customer with a feeling of confidence, knowing that they had made the right decision. This would almost certainly mean that they would be happy to deal with that salesperson, and their company again in the future. A naive opinion, maybe, but one Sparky would develop to his advantage and credit in the years to come.

PART 9

The Birth of a Salesman

Hovercraft
Promotion
Sparky buys his own house
South Coast Fishing Fleet

———————◆———————

hree days after his meeting, he took a phone call from Mr Williams advising him that they had decided to accept the Redifon replacement programme, and would also like to put the wheels in motion for the installation of a base station. He told Sparky that he was impressed with the prices, and the fact that a spare equipment would be on hand to facilitate quick turn round of service calls. Sparky was ecstatic and couldn't stop smiling for the rest of the day. Bill Mordin also appeared to be quite pleased. The die was cast now, and Sparky could see that a career in sales might suite him very much. But in the meantime he had a depot to run, communications equipment to repair and a family to think about. They were quite happy in their rented house in Sholing, but the prospect of buying his own home was a better solution. If he continued to work hard, put in as much overtime as he could, and repair lots of domestic TV sets, he was confident they would be able to save enough money for a deposit.

Redifon was doing very well, selling its range of equipment to ship owners large and small, and moving into new markets. One day head office called and told him he was to report to Columbine works on the Isle of White, and install a VHF radio on one a Hovercraft. He didn't really know much about Hovercraft. There had been reports in the press, and on TV about a craft that flew just a couple of feet above the sea, and could do the same over land. So was it a plane or a boat?

As instructed, the following day he caught the Red Funnel steamer to Cowes on the Isle of Wight, then took the chain ferry across the Medina to East Cowes, and reported to the yard manager at Saunders-Roe's Columbine works. The craft was being built and completed in the huge aircraft hanger, where Saunders-Roe had developed the famous Princess Flying Boat during the 1950s. They also developed and tested the first Hovercraft, the SRN1.

At the security gate they were expecting him, and the foreman George Harrison came over and took him into the hanger and through through a heavy set of screens. On the other side he was confronted with what looked to him like a large futuristic flying saucer, sitting on top of huge rubber skirt. The deck area was made of aluminium, and there was high sided cockpit at one end, which he assumed was the equivalent of a ships wheel house, and two large propellers at the other. Running along the length of the craft was was a saloon, with seating for a number of people. They climbed aboard via a set of steps which looked as if they'd been borrowed from British Airways Heathrow. It was all very fascinating.

There were people in white overalls clambering all over it, and strange sounds coming from the inside. George the foreman, guided him towards the cockpit, as they entered Sparky, stopped and looked around him. It was almost like being on the flight deck of a large Jet passenger liner. In front of him was a dashboard crammed with dials, switches, flashing lights with a myriad of gauges and meters. Two high-back pilot style seats, with what looked like joy-stick controls in front of them,dominated the centre of the cockpit space. Sparky had never seen anything like it before, on any ship he had ever been on. (With the exception of Royal Navy submarines). But was this a ship or a plane? George caught Sparkys look of surprise, and said, 'Fantastic looking stuff eh?' 'I'm impressed, and intrigued,' he replied.

They went through a hatch and descended a ladder into a very cramped area underneath the 'flight-deck'. Lying on the floor in a box was, a Redifon VHF radio. George pointed to a small shelf inside a recess, and said 'Well, we would like it installed in there, and the remote control unit up above in the cockpit please.' Now this was no problem for Sparky, but he was used to working in shipyards where the unions insisted on having lines of demarcation to protect their various trade members, and woe be-tied any one who stepped over those lines. 'If possible we would like the work completed today.' Added George. 'And don't worry about cutting, sawing, drilling and banging things around, we have all the tools and the people to help make it happen.' Sparky must have looked relived, as George added, 'You tell us what you want, and where it should all go, and we'll do the rest.' 'Sounds great to me,' replied Sparky, 'so lets get on with it.'

By mid afternoon the equipment was installed, the special antenna fitted on top of cockpit/wheelhouse and the controls mounted in the dashboard panel by the joy-stick position. The equipment had been modified by Redifon engineers, with special aeronautical style jack sockets, into which were fitted two sets of aeronautical headphones with boom microphones. This was new territory for Sparky, head office hadn't told him about this modification from the normal shipborne set up. But never one to be daunted, he continued as if he knew all about it, and completed the installation in accordance with the technical drawings provided. At this point they were joined on the flight-deck by a well built, dark haired man wearing immaculate white overalls, with epaulettes on the shoulders. He introduced himself as Peter Ward the Pilot, shook hands then said 'OK are we ready for testing?' Sparky looked sideways at George, then said, 'I need about half and hour to do my final checks, then we should be ready.'

Twenty minutes later he had completed his checks, but had not yet made a live transmission. Niton Radio and other maritime traffic could be heard on the receiver, so Sparky felt reasonably relaxed. Peter the Pilot together with another man in a blue boiler suite were busy flicking switches and watching dials. Sparky then realized that they were about to start up the engine. All none essential personnel were instructed to leave the deck area, and with the announcement that all was clear, the Pilot engaged the starter controls. There was short silence, then gradually the hanger was filled with the high pitched whine of a jet engine, which gradually increased in volume until it reached the point where conversation was difficult. Sparky was wearing one of the headsets, the Pilot wore the other. Intercom between the them was now possible. The craft was vibrating considerably, then suddenly it began to rise slowly off the floor of the hanger. Bizarrely it did not move one way or the other, but just remained hovering, the noise level by this time was quite considerable. Peter looked across at Sparky and said 'OK lets call somebody.'

Sparky was just about to press the transmit switch when he realized he didn't actually know what to call himself, he was used to saying things like, 'This is Tug so and so, or motor vessel whatever.' He switched to intercom and asked Peter, who replied with a smile 'This is Hovercraft SRN6.' Sparky seized the moment with relish, this was another first in his life, making a contact from the cockpit of this strange new mode of transport, it was the first of many he would make over the next couple of years. But for now all he needed was for this test to be successful. Everything worked fine, and Niton Radio gave him a five by five signal report. The captain was impressed, and made a couple of transmissions to other stations in the Solent. With everyone feeling happy at the outcome, Sparky asked George to sign his installation completion documents, then shook hands all round and headed back to catch the ferry home. He would return to install others in the future, but the memory of this one, was the sweetest.

The idea for the Hovercraft, although successfully developed by British mechanical engineer Sir Christopher Cockerell in the 1950's, has its origins dating back as far 1716. Swedish scientist Emanuel Swedenborg was experimenting with the concepts behind surface-effect vehicles, which could hover above the land or sea.

However the credit for making this a reality, and commercially viable, must go to Sir Christopher Cockerell. His group was the first to develop the use of an annular ring of air for maintaining the cushion, and eventually developed the all important air-retaining skirt which made it all possible. During the 1960's numbers of companies emerged as operators of passenger and car carrying Hovercraft. They pioneered services from Ramsgate and Dover to Calais, and across the Solent from South-sea to Ryde on the Isle of Wight. Over the next few years the Hovercraft principal was put to good use on a wide variety of craft, with many different applications. These included search and rescue operating across mud flats or swamplands. Military applications included large transports for beachhead landings, and in Vietnam the US army used them as fast patrol vehicles in the waters of the Mekong Delta. Private enthusiast built small ones in their garages or backyards, then used them for fishing and hunting trips. It was, in its time, a phenomenal worldwide success, and forty years later some of these craft are still operating.

Sparky's work continued to be varied and interesting, the Southampton depot was busy. Then one day he was summoned to head office to attend a sales and service conference, other depot managers and service engineers would also be there from around the country. He was looking forward to seeing some of the other people he had worked with over the past couple of years. The essence of the meeting was to outline the plans for the company's expansion into the UK's rapidly growing deep sea and offshore fishing market. Electronic fish finding technology had been developing at a phenomenal rate, world fishing was a huge and potentially lucrative business. UK and European companies had been developing a whole new range of equipment, from state of the art echo sounders capable of detecting different species of fish, at various levels under the vessels keel. New navigation equipment was being introduced, which would enhance the fisherman's ability to find good productive fishing grounds, and to return to them again. Radar, and radio communications equipment, which was essential to the safe operation of all ships at sea, was also undergoing a transformation. Technical advancement were making equipment easier to install, more reliable, and perform better. So, with their sights firmly set on the fishing industry, and no doubt influenced by Bill Mordin, they announced that Redifon had signed an exclusive distributorship with the Japanese Company Furuno, to sell and service it's full range of Fish finding electronics equipment and world renowned marine radar.

There was a definite buzz around the room as people began to appreciate what had just been disclosed. It was a huge change for Redifon to make. They were a manufacturing company, and had never before been a distributor or an agent for other peoples products. However, Furuno were a highly respected company, one of the best in Japan,with a wide range of superb marine electronics. They were already one of the leading suppliers to the far east and Asian maritime markets. Sparky was very excited, it all sounded great to him, new equipment to sell and service, in a market that was expanding. And he was working for a company who had made the decision to invest in products and infrastructure, with a commitment to go out and make it happen.

Once again he found himself in the right place at the right time. After the meeting closed he was asked to go and see divisional manager, Jim Turner. When he arrived at the office, Bill Mordin, and his own Service boss John Shepard, were also there. For a fleeting moment he thought he might be in some sort of trouble, but they all looked relaxed, and smiled at him as he entered. Jim explained that they were reorganising the structure of the Company's service depot's. The plan was to give the them more responsibility for sales, Sparky's Southampton depot would now look after an area stretching from Shoreham in the East, down to Landsend Cornwall, in the West, as well as South Wales and the Bristol channel ports. When Jim had finished, Bill Mordin looked at Sparky and said 'we want you to take charge, and make it happen, especially in the emerging South West fishing fleets.' Sparky was about to answer when Bill said, 'Well lad, how dose that sound to you then eh?'... As he drove home from the meeting that night his head was spinning, he'd just been promoted to an Area Manager, in charge of Sales and Service. He could hardly believe it, and couldn't wait to tell Mary, especially about the rise in salary.

This next phase in Sparky's life would help shape his future, it was a hectic, by the seat of your pants learning curve, and he was loving every single minute of it. He had an abundance of confidence, he never said no to a challenge. If he didn't know how to do something, he would do it anyway, and learn the lessons as he went. Fortunately for him, most of the time he pulled it off. The late 1960s and the 70s were made for people who went out to succeed, the economy of the whole world was booming. Sparky worked hard, and played hard. Despite his new found responsibilities, he was still Sparky, mischievous, adventurous, sometimes outrageous, and occasionally risqué. His family were well looked after, and were with him most of the time. The one thing he realized very early on was that he loved his job, he had enjoyed every single moment of being at sea, and now with this new direction,he could feel the excitement of the chase, the initial contact with the customer's, the opportunity to bid for their business. The presentation of his quotation, the anticipation of success, which, when it came gave him a buzz akin to an adrenaline rush, or if it was lost, a disappointment which was tempered with a desire to do better next time. He found it stimulating and fulfilling. The products he sold were technical in the their nature, but offered solutions which satisfied the customer, and often gave them considerable financial gain. He continued and developed in this environment for the remainder of his working life. It gave him many rewards and exciting experiences, but it was also fraught with disaster, however that was a long way off, and for now Sparky rode the crest of the waves, and loved it to pieces.

He revelled in the atmosphere, the drama, and the shear understatement of the dangers fishermen faced, every time they put to sea. And in turn they liked him, he was interested in what they did, and would take every opportunity he could, to go to sea with them. The offshore coastal fleets were mainly out fishing during the week, theirs was a hectic life. The only way to make the grade was to be there at weekends, waiting for them as they came in on a Thursday night or Friday mornings tide. The pub was his *Office, a* place to develop relationships, and get to know who the top skippers were, and more importantly who was making all the money.

The Furuno partnership was a great success, they provided excellent products, and superb support. However there was a degree of resistance by some fishermen, and trawler owners, to purchase equipment manufactured in the far east. Some of the prejudices were historical, based perhaps on experiences during World War 2, or maybe a misguided conception that it was unreliable and poorly made, this was far from the truth. The Japanese Fishing Industry was the largest in the world, after all, fish is their staple diet. They had developed their equipment over many decades, so the design and applications of their electronics was no exception. But Sparky and others were finding it difficult to convince the Skippers to invest in costly fish finding equipment they had never seen or used before. Realizing the problem, his head office and Furuno came up with a solution which offered the Skippers a try before you buy deal for one month free of charge. This was on the understanding that the Skippers or owners paid for the cost of installation.

The next phase was to find top high earning Skippers, and persuade them try it out. Fishermen were more likely to take notice if they could see that one of their own were increasing their earnings, as a result of installing the latest equipment. Some of the the West Country's top Skippers at the time were from the Pascoe family, based in Brixham and Plymouth. A trial was agreed for the installation of some Furuno equipment which was proving highly successful in many areas around the World. It basically allowed the Skipper to monitor the height of his net in the water, via a chart recorder and a visual display on a small screen. This was particularly suited to those boats who looked for fish which swam and fed above the sea bed, this was referred to as Mid Water or Pelagic Fishing. The most popular species found at these depths in the Northern hemisphere are typically oily fish, such Herring and Mackerel, and these were potentially lucrative money earners. Pelagic fishing takes place all over the world, involving fish generic to its geographic area. But all fishermen have the same problem, they need to know where their fishing net is in the water, relative to the fish they are trying to catch.

On the fishing grounds, Skippers would be continually scanning the water under their keels, using Sonar and Echo sounders which were designed to detect the presence of fish. This could show them that there was a large shoal ahead, astern or to one side of them. The skill and the trick was then to manoeuvrer their nets so they could scoop the fish into its mouth. Before the introduction of net sounders this could be a very hit and miss affair, often resulting in them only catching half or even less of the possible potential. This new Furuno Net Sounder was proving itself to be highly effective wherever it was used, and assuming the Skippers could see the fish, and that they knew how to operate the equipment, the chances of success were very high indeed. At the time there were numbers of other companies supplying a wide range of electronic equipment for both merchant ships and fishing boats, and some of it was excellent. Furuno however, were way up at the top of the league, and continued to be a force to be reckoned with for many years.

Sparky finally managed to persuade one of Plymouth's top skippers to participate in trials of the new net sounder, a date was agreed and a Japanese engineer from Furuno's Spanish office was assigned to attend sea trials and instruct the Skipper in how to operate the equipment. Sparky had been on a training course, he was no expert, but at least he understood the basics. It was the back end of March by the time everything was ready. The Japanese engineer made his way via train from London to Plymouth, arriving the night before the trials. Sparky met him at the station, he soon recognised him, and was very surprised to see that he was wearing thin light weight clothing, more suitable to the warm airs of Barcelona than the freezing cold wind blowing through the station that night. 'Good afternoon sir, I am engineer Shinohara from Furuno company,' he said in excellent English, Sparky returned the salutation, holding back on advising Shinohara that it was now evening, he didn't want to embarrass him.

In the hotel they met up with George a Hull based Redifon engineer who would be in charge of the installation, he had actually installed the same equipment on a Bridlington trawler earlier in the year. It was time to go and eat, and Sparky was concerned that their guest would not find anything to his liking on the hotel menu. To his and Georges considerable surprise, he asked for *Fish and Chips,* which was indeed available, and Mr Shinohara said he enjoyed it very much. They were due to be on board the trawler next morning at 0600 hrs., so an early night was had by all.

They awoke to find several inches of snow on the ground, and a temperature cold enough to match. The hotel were unable to offer a cooked breakfast at such an early hour, but did provide them with hot coffee and some bread rolls. Mr Shinohara was grateful for the coffee, but declined the cheese and tomatoes. The fish quay was alive with activity, boats preparing to leave, or loading their provisions and ice for the fish hold. A bitterly cold wind was blowing from the North-east, gusting at force three to four with snow showers, It was very cold. Both George and Sparky could still feel its keen edge through their heavy weather gear. It was obvious that their Japanese guest was already suffering as he stood along side Sparkys car, shivering in his cream coloured tropical suit. Sparky delved into the back of his car, and in his emergency box he found a old thick sweater, a warm duffle coat, some rather ancient weatherproof over-trousers and an old pair of waterproof wellies. He politely offered these to the very distressed looking engineer, who accepted them with thanks and a short bow. With Mr Shinohara now at least partially protected from the elements he and Sparky made their way to the boats wheelhouse where George was already setting up the equipment. The Skipper, a large man wearing bright orange waterproofs, and sporting a long black beard, with a gold earring in each ear, came up from the deck and was introduced to the Furuno representative, decked out in ill fitting and rather ancient looking gear. 'Welcome aboard my hansom, av e' cum far then?' he said whilst shaking hands. Mr Shinohara looked slightly overwhelmed, but he bowed and said 'Yokohama captain.' The skipper cast his eye over the rather shambolic attire of the Japanese engineer, then looked over at Sparky and said 'We'll we be off in a few minutes, it's a bit choppy in the sound, and the forecast is for it to blow up later in the morning. I'll run out as far as Penlee, and shoot the net on the way.'

The Skipper wasn't wrong, it was very choppy almost as soon as they were clear of the fish quay, and the cold wind was even more noticeable.

The trials were a great success, the Skipper soon understood the operation of the equipment, and was duly impressed, they were not out to catch fish that morning, but the prospect of using this new tool seemed to please him. A few weeks later the owners confirmed their acceptance of the equipment and placed an official order, their Skipper had evidently mastered his new net sounder, and had brought home some lucrative catches of prime fish.

This was the start of a very successful period for Redifon and Furuno, their partnership was working well, and sales were ramping up. Sparky was also enjoying a period of success, he was learning a lot about the fishing industry and the equipment he was selling. The Southampton depot was more than justifying it's existence, and Sparkys future was looking bright. However It came at a cost, there was a lot of travelling away from home, and many weekends spent in the various fishing ports developing his relationship with fishermen and owners. It was also important for him to develop the companies sales of their marine radio communications equipment. There were numbers of Shipowners in South Wales and the Bristol Channel area, and eventually Redifon agreed to open a service depot in Cardiff.

Over the coming years Sparky gained orders to supply main radio stations from new and existing shipowners in his area.

He was enjoying life and his new found direction. The company was also having considerable success, its many divisions were all expanding, and their share of the international markets was growing. It was an exciting time, the world economy was booming, technical innovation in the communications sector was forging ahead, and the company was keeping up with the demand created by new International regulations.

Sparky was enjoying an excellent social and family life in Southampton, it was a nice place to live and work, but a new phase was about to unfold, one which would allow him to benefit from the experience he had gained so far, and which would eventually introduce him to an exciting new market, where adventure was just around the corner. In 1969 at the age of 28 he was promoted to the companies Liverpool office as North West Area Manager, responsible for the sales of the companies marine communication equipment to Liverpool shipowners, and in addition he was to be in charge of Redifon's operations in support of the fishing industry in Fleetwood and Ireland. Ian, the previous Liverpool manager was the same age as Sparky, and they knew each other well, they had both joined Redifon at about the same time, Ian had worked out of the Wandsworth office for a while before being transferred to Liverpool. He was now leaving the company, taking up a position with one of their main competitors, IMRC of Croydon. They still kept in touch, meeting at exhibitions and conferences, eventually they would work together, but for the time being they were on opposite sides of the selling fence.

For Sparky, this was a huge step forward, all his hard work was paying dividends, he was very excited and happy with the move. His wife Mary, and his family were very proud of him. A few days before he was ready to leave Southampton, he happened to be down near the docks at lunch time, and decided to go for a beer and some sandwiches in the nearest pub. As he walked through the door, dressed in his best business suite, and carrying his solid leather brief case, he saw Jim his old boss from his days in Siemens AEI. When Jim spotted him, he came forward and shook his hand, 'Well, how nice to see you,' he said. 'What are you doing with yourself these days then?' Sparky smiled back and said 'I'm a salesman'...

The company were very supportive of their products, attending numbers of important Industry trade fairs and exhibitions at home and overseas. Sparky loved working at these shows, he was in his element meeting new people, demonstrating to them the various attributes of the equipment being exhibited. It was hard work, usually lasting four or five days, with little time to relax, but in the end there were new contacts to develop, new enquiries to progress, and new business to be fought over with their competitors. All this was the stuff of life to the now burgeoning, and still learning salesman, Sparky.

They sold their home in Southampton and moved to Liverpool, finding a suitable house in Burscough, close to Ormskirk, north of the city. It was an ideal location, providing easy access to his office, the M6 motorway network, and the fishing port of Fleetwood all within easy reach. Over the next two years Sparky consolidated his position within the company, looking after the traditional ship owning community of this great and historic port. Dealing with legendary companies such as Cunard, Blue Funnel, Bibby Line and others. Fleetwood was thriving as a fishing port, and there was no lack of business to be had. Every few weeks he would fly to Dublin, hire a car, then literally drive all round the coastline of Ireland north and south. Usually ending up some eight to ten days later back at Dublin airport with a brief case full of orders for Redifon and Furuno equipment. It was a crazy time, the European Union extended massive grants to the fishermen of the Irish Republic,and new boats were being churned out at an unbelievable rate, covering both the smaller inshore fleet, and large trawlers capable of fishing Atlantic waters, and further afield.

The style of doing business with the Irish fishermen, was similar to that which Sparky had been doing down on the south coast of England. Basically he got to know the top skippers, going on board their boats, talking to them, often meeting their families and getting them to trust him and his products. The pub or favourite bar was still the preferred office, and he was expected to be able to hold his own when the beer or whisky was flowing. The trick was to be able to remember what had taken place during some of the more aggressive drinking sessions. It was quite usual for Skippers to give him verbal orders to supply a new radio, or an item of fish finding equipment costing many hundreds or thousands of pounds during one of these sessions. It may have been discussed at length on board the boat beforehand, the price agreed, with delivery and installation, but the order would rarely be forthcoming in the sober atmosphere of the boats wheelhouse, or even the skippers cabin. They would usually say things like, 'Well that's all fine then eh lads, lets just go over to Murphy's bar and tink about it.' Then when the alcoholic haze was reaching its zenith they would put their arm over his shoulder, breathing fumes of almost pure Jameson or Guinness into his face and say 'I'll have one of dem tings then, alright?' It was also absolutely essential to be able to understand what people were actually saying, a strong Irish accent was sometimes difficult to decipher above all the noise and mayhem which often accompanied these occasions.

Almost all the fishermen were members of a local cooperative which handled all their stores, ice, water, new nets, engine spares and the like. It gave them buying power and a lot more.

Sparky new all the co-operatives managers, and had a system whereby he would advise them of any transactions which may have been concluded in the bar, or anywhere else for that matter. The manager would then confirm this with the Skipper, and if all was satisfactory, they would issue an official order to supply the items which had been agreed on their behalf.

With a bit of luck Sparky would receive the paper work before he moved on to his next fishing community, otherwise it would be telexed to his office. The system worked well most of the time, but occasionally the Skippers changed their minds, but forget to tell the Cooperative manager... it didn't happen very often. It was not unusual for Sparky to receive phone calls at home, late in the evening or over the weekend from Skippers enquiring about the whereabouts of their new equipment. Sometimes they would put one of their young children on the phone for a chat, its was all quite laid back and often hilarious.

Living in the North West of England, and being located in Liverpool, meant that he and his family could access the Lake District in the north, and Snowdonia in the south. The Yorkshire moors were also close and very accessible. They all loved the outdoors and took full advantage to visit these areas as much as possible. His dad was now living in Blackpool, managing one of his companies busiest and largest outlets, so family visits became more frequent.

With his work and family commitment Sparky had done no climbing since arriving back in Liverpool, but to keep fit he continued with his passion for running, going out two or three times a week or more if possible. Whenever he travelled away from home he always made sure he had his running kit with him. This habit stayed with him all through his working life, and on more than one occasion during an overseas business trip, he found himself in awkward and sometimes potentially risky situations, especially in the Middle East and Africa... but he was yet to enter the world of international travel, now he needed to concentrate on doing his current job properly.

PART 10

Sparky Moves to Hull

Disaster in the Arctic Circle
Omega Navigation
The Rise and Fall of The Fishing Industry
Sparky Leaves Redifon
A New World of Oil and Gas

———————— ♦ ————————

In the late summer of 1971 Sparky and his family were invited to stay the weekend with his boss Bill Mordin and his wife at their holiday cottage in Abercych, Dyfed South Wales. The invitation came out of the blue on a Thursday afternoon. He was intrigued, and ever so slightly concerned, but accepted without hesitation. Sparky and family travelled down the following morning, they had never visited the area before, and the cottage wasn't easy to find, but after making enquiries at a local pub they finally arrived to be greeted by Bill himself, who was in the middle of building a drystone wall at the top of the drive. He was wearing a pair of old Royal Navy overalls with his name and rank just visible above the breast pocket. It was a hot afternoon, and Bill was sweating under his battered old sun hat. He welcomed them with a big smile, and then shouted out to his wife, letting her know they had arrived. Pam came out with a tray of iced orange juice and some glasses. Closer examination of Bills retreat revealed extensive renovation work was underway, and it appeared that Bill was doing most of it himself. The cottage was on the side of a hill, and a small terrace had been cleared for garden chairs and an old wooden table. As they sat enjoying their cool orange drinks Bill told them about his plans for the restoration of the property. Sparky was fascinated to see his boss in such a different light, he was usually very smartly dressed and always carried himself with an air of authority. But here he was completely relaxed, and seemed to be revelling in the prospect of the hard work. It was late afternoon, but the sun was still bathing the terrace and house, in a pleasantly warm glow. Pam showed them to their rooms, which were very comfortable and cosy. Bill had said he was going for a shower, and suggested they all meet again in half an hour for a sundowner.

Their hostess was already there when they arrived, she asked them what they wanted to drink, and in particular what young Stephen would like. Bill soon arrived looking much cooler in a casual shirt and old khaki slacks. They sat around for a while talking about the local area, Sparky was anxious to know why he had been summoned, and it must have shown, because Bill suddenly took over the conversation, paused to light up one of his Havana cigars, looked at Sparky and said, 'There are a number of important changes about to take place in the company, we are growing at a very steady pace, the future is looking good, but we need to restructure things so that we can take advantage of the opportunities which are coming our way.' He topped his glass with tonic water and continued,' Jim Turner is to retire very soon, and the MD has asked me to take over the running of marine division, reporting directly to him. We need to expand our UK and overseas service capability, and Len Calvert, the current general manager, is to relinquish his position in Hull and move down to Wandsworth. Len's brief is to streamline our worldwide marine service organisation, making it ready for the next generation of equipment.' Sparky was tying to get his head around what Bill had been saying, and work out work out how on earth he fitted into any of this. Bill sat back in his chair, took a sip of his drink and said, 'I want you to go to Hull and take over Len's job as North East Area Manager.'

Sparky was just thirty years old, he had only been working ashore for a dogs watch in comparison with numbers of his colleagues, and here he was, deep in the Welsh Countryside being offered his dream job of managing the companies premier fishing industry operation in Hull. Not only that, but he would be taking over from Len, a man who was a legend in the marine communications of the north east fishing industry.

He glanced quickly across at Mary, who was fidgeting with a button on her skirt, she seemed as shocked as he was, Stephen had wandered over to Bills drystone wall and was busy pushing small rocks into various cracks. Pam stood up and said,'I'll go and prepare dinner then, will seven thirty be alright?' Mary offered to give a hand, it was gratefully accepted and they walked off towards the house. Bills cottage was in a very quiet and peaceful position on the side of a sheltered valley, the sun continued to warm them as Sparky stood up and moved over towards Bill, and said, 'Thank you sir, I accept.' They shook hands, and with a smile Bill said, 'I knew you wouldn't turn it down.'

His appointment was officially announced two weeks later, and Sparky travelled over to Hull for a meeting with Len and all the staff. In the intervening years since his last visit, the company had moved from the original premises in the old fish docks, to a new purpose built office and workshops in Wassand Street, which was still close to the docks. It probably wasn't as interesting as the old place, where you could see fishing boats right outside the front door, but it was never the less an extremely impressive facility. Smart glass doors opened into a reception area, an impressive wooden staircase led upstairs to offices and a small canteen. The stores and workshop were at the back of the building, with access to the car parking and a loading bay.

Upon his arrival Sparky was greeted by Gill Richardson who was in charge of admin and the companies wireless operators. They were hired out to the trawler owners to operate Redifon equipped stations. Gill was a very nice person who had worked there for many years, and had also served on trawlers as a wireless operator. Sparky was concerned that Gill may have felt put out at not being given Lens job, especially after all his years of service with the company. However he later confided that he was not upset by this, and pledged his full support. Most of the engineers had been there for some years, and Sparky remembered them from the days when he had been up for training. Everyone seemed relaxed about his arrival, he was no threat to their own situation, wishing him all the very best of success, they new that more orders went hand in hand with more service work, and better security of employment.

The final introduction was with Jo Ince, his secretary. Jo was a very talented and highly efficient young lady, and Sparky soon realized how much of an asset she would be. Her organizing skills were excellent, and she ran their office superbly. Her other claim to fame was that she had a great sense of humour, and had been at Leeds University with rock star Joe Cocker. Sparkys first day went really well, and he was confident that he would soon justify his appointment, even though he was still secretly reeling from the shock of his meeting with Bill Mordin in Wales. It did not take Sparky very long to immerse himself in his new roll. Len Calvert was very supportive and spent valuable time introducing him to all the major trawler owners in Hull and Grimsby. They visited their offices, and whenever possible would take them out to lunch. It soon became clear that there were definite protocols to be followed when dealing with these powerful individuals.

At that time there were still numbers of family owned companies who had been in the fishing industry for generations, and there was the emergence of the larger operators who had grown their fleets through acquisitions or mergers. Regardless of who they were there was a sense of tradition, history, and pride. This was predominately a male dominated industry, it was a hard ruthless business where profit was everything. But there were countless stories of tragedy at sea in the unforgiving waters of the Arctic, and as Sparky gradually became accepted by the owners he would sometimes be fortunate enough to have some of these stories related to him during his visits. They were often told with genuine emotion and drama, sitting in their offices surrounded by paintings or photographs of fleets past and present. He was always moved by these tragic tales, this wasn't fairy tale stuff, or historical melodrama, these were accounts, being narrated by men who had been directly involved. Radio communications and all the associated electronic equipment was a vital part of their everyday lives. He soon realized that the terrible loss of life and ships touched everyone in the community, regardless of which ever walk of life they came from. It would not be long before he was also involved in such a drama...

Sparky had arrived in Hull at a time of expansion and investment. Large new freezer trawlers were now joining the fleets of Grimsby and Hull. Whilst ashore, frozen seafood processing plants were being built by the owners and others, to package and market the catches. Names such as Birds Eye, Ross Group, Findus and others became household names throughout the UK and Europe. They didn't just deal in cod and haddock, they introduced new species of seafood to temp the public. Fish Fingers and Beans became almost synonymous with lunch or evening meals for kids, and adults. A massive revolution was taking place, traditional fish and chips was not on its own any more, and the Captain Birds Eye brand, became a regular TV hero...

Redifon were very successful at gaining orders for sophisticated main radio stations to be installed on new trawlers. One of these was to supply such a station on a large super trawler, originally built by Brooke Marine of Lowestoft for Ranger Fishing, and launched in December 1971 under the name Ranger Castor, later she was acquired by British United Trawlers of Hull and renamed the Gaul. The 66m long stern freezer factory ship was christened a *Super Trawler*, she was designed and built to withstand the most severe weather conditions, the equipment on board was of the best and latest in its field, and the Redifon radio station was no exception. The Gaul had a very powerful 1500 watt main transmitter, two main receivers and a duplicate set of battery operated transceivers working in the marine VHF band. Everything in the radio room fully met or exceed the safety requirements and regulations laid down for such vessels at that time by the DOTI (Department of Trade and Industry).

On the 22nd of January 1974 the Gaul set off from Hull bound for the fishing grounds of the Barents sea in the Arctic Circle, north of Norway.

From the 29th of January onwards she fished continuously without incident, making contact with other fishing vessels in the vicinity, and also made telephone calls to her home port of Hull a number of times. This was a statutory requirement from the owners, and was required by commercial fishing regulations. In the early hours of February the 8th weather conditions in the Barents Sea had deteriorated rapidly, and storm force 10 on the Beaufort scale were expected.

These conditions are classified as a whole gale, with wind speeds of 55 to 63 mph producing very high waves between 29 to 41 feet (9 to 125 metres). This creates waves with long overhanging crests; producing foam in large patches which is blown in dense white streaks along the direction of the wind; on the whole the surface of the sea takes on a white appearance; rolling of the sea becomes heavy; and visibility is badly affected.

The Gaul was coping with the conditions and had been in contact with another fishing vessel in the same area. They had also made a call to their Hull office at 1100hrs on the 8th of February, at no time time during this call did the skipper report that they were in any kind of trouble, this was to be her last known transmission. Initially, nothing was considered to be amiss, but over the weekend of the 9th and 10th of February concern began to mount when the Gaul failed to report, and was not responding to radio messages sent from their office. By the morning of 11th February an alert had been issued for all fishing vessels in the area to be on the look out for the *Gaul*, and the Royal Navy frigate, HMS *Mohawk,*began a search.

That morning Sparky was in his office by 0745, alerted by a report on BBC Radio Humberside that the Gaul was not responding to radio messages, and that a search was under way. Shortly after that, the owners called him and asked for details concerning the state of all the radio equipment on the ship, prior to her leaving Hull on the 22nd of January. He was able to advise them that all the gear had been thoroughly checked and tested prior to her departure, and the only fault reported had been a minor complaint about the ships entertainment equipment. The mood in the office that Monday morning was sombre, everyone was affected, Gill and the engineers knew the radio officer on board, as well as other officers and members of the crew. Over the next few days there was all sorts of conjecture and debate about what, if anything, may have happened. Sparky asked all the staff to be careful about what they said to anyone outside the company. The families of the crew would be going through a terrible time, hopes that the ship may be found sheltering in the lee of some island, were still a possibility. The suggestion that the radio equipment had become faulty was being put forward as a reason for the silence... But everyone in Redifon's Wassand street office knew that the likelihood of that being true was very very remote. There were numbers of people making bizarre and thoughtless claims that they had been in touch with members of the crew, and one woman rang Sparkys office and claimed that she had heard a Mayday call from the *Gaul* on Sunday night the 10th of February at around 2100hrs. He took down her details and passed them to the owners.

A massive search was undertaken involving the Royal Navy's aircraft carrier HMS Hermes, the Norwegian Navy and coast guard service. An RAF Nimrod, and Norwegian P-3 Orion maritime patrol aircraft were deployed, along with Sea King helicopters. But at 1600 hrs. on the 15th of February, seven days after her last radio contact, the search was called off no trace of the Gaul had been found.

Over the next few years there were numbers of theories and claims concerning the loss of the Gaul, these have all been well documented and are readily available via numbers of reliable sources. It was a terrible maritime tragedy, and affected the relatives and people from many sections of society.

Sparky and his family settled down into their life on Humberside, there was a good school for their son, they had a nice house quite close to the river Humber, in the village of Brough on the west side of Hull. New friendships were formed and their social life was most enjoyable. During his first summer in Hull the family had taken a camping holiday in North Wales. One day they visited Caernafon, a small pleasant town at the western entrance into the Menai Strait. It boasted an impressive looking castle, which stood guard over the harbour. As they wandered around site seeing and enjoying the warm summer weather, they passed an estate agents window displaying a wide range of properties for sale, from farms, new marina homes in port Dinorwic, and old Welsh cottages. One place caught Sparkys attention, it was basically a derelict property in Port Dinorwic, and the price sounded very reasonable. He went inside to ask for details, and the key, so that they could go and inspect it. The young lady gave him a single sheet of information, and said, 'you don't need a key, the doors fallen off.'

Fifteen minutes later they arrived at the cottage, which was high up on a small lane overlooking the harbour, with magnificent views across the straits to Anglesey. Not only was there no door, but the staircase leading up to the next floor was rotting away, and with just a few precarious looking steps to balance on Sparky gained access to the rooms above. Mary and Stephen struggled cautiously to the top. Sparky shouted out for them to be very careful, because most of the floor boards were missing. The upstairs front room was dark and damp, with plaster falling off the walls, and half the ceiling missing. It was totally wrecked. Then sparky stuck his head through the hole, which in better times had been a window and after a few seconds proclaimed,'I'm going to buy it'. The more sensible and cautious Mary looked horrified. 'You have to be joking, this place is a dump,' Sparky smiled and said 'I agree with you, but just have a look through this hole.' She balanced herself carefully over the rotting floor joists, and looked outside. 'That's amazing, just fantastic,' she said. 'That view alone is worth every single penny of what their asking,' Replied Sparky, lets go back to the agents and do a deal.' He paid the agent a deposit and confirmed that he would sort everything out when he arrived back at work the following Monday.

Eventually the deal was done, and Maes -Y- Mor, as it was called, became part of their lives for many years to come. He set about renovating the cottage, which was almost a rebuild. Managing to secure the services of local Port Dinorwic builder, Will Jones, without whom the work would have taken much longer, and probably been more expensive.

His job continued to bring good rewards as the company expanded it's activities in the fishing industry, and the smaller offshore fishermen took advantage of grants to build new boats. But more troubled times were gathering on UK fisherman's horizons... The first Cod War, as it was called by the British press started in 1958 when Iceland extended its fishing exclusion zone from 4 mile to 12 miles. British boats had been benefiting from the excellent fishing around the coast of Iceland for centuries, and there were disputes going as far back as the 14th century.

But the 1958 battle with the fishermen of the UK basically heralded the beginning of the end of their lucrative fishing off the coast of Iceland... and over the next eighteen years there were to be two more of these so called wars, the second started in September 1972 and went on until November 1973 with Iceland extending its fishing limits to 50 miles. The third and probably the most aggressive cod war started in November 1975 until June 1976 when the Icelandic Government imposed a 200 mile fishing exclusion zone around their coast. The full story of this period is worthy of a dedicated book, and there are many to choose from.

Leaving aside the issue of fish stock conservation, the political implications, territorial claims, and years later the European Common Fisheries Policy, all have a valid place in this drama, But it cannot be denied that the resultant effect of all these issues finally saw the end of the British Deep-sea fishing industry as it was at that time. The loss of access to these fisheries devastated many British fishing communities, such as Hull, Grimsby, and many Scottish ports. More than 1,500 fishermen and several thousand shore-based workers from these areas lost their jobs for ever. The UK government were powerless against the Icelandic strategy, and the final trump card held by Iceland was their ability to veto, if the wanted to, the safe passage of NATO submarines in Icelandic waters, this was a masterpiece of brinkmanship. It was a crucial issue at a time when the cold war between the NATO alliance and Russia was at it's height, they were troubled times and the threat of a nuclear war was at that time was a grave reality.

The halcyon days of fishing were coming to an end, and although the writing was on the wall, it would take some time before the true effects would be felt. Eventually Hull, Grimsby, and Fleetwood fish docks, and others, would bare witness to the true tragedy as they became the graveyards for their once proud trawler fleets. The stores, offices, repair yards and general infrastructure gradually fell into a state of decay.

But Sparky's and his company continued to move forward, He was enjoying his new found social life and had taken a keen interest in sailing. He made good friends with an ex radio officer called Dave Peacock, who was was a senior lecturer in the radar department of Hull technical college, they first met at one of the colleges open days. The two of them hit it off from the very start, their background, their sense of humour and their common interests, were all very similar, and Dave also had an interest in sailing . He kept his boat at the Brough sailing club, only ten minutes from Sparkys house. It wasn't long before Dave invited him and his family out for a sail. One Saturday morning they set off from Brough in Egret, Dave's 24 foot Ketch rigged wooden sloop. Sparky had some limited experience of sailing from his time at sea, usually during lifeboat practice, and occasionally when he lived in Southampton. Egret was a comfortable old boat, originally built for cruising the Norfolk Broads, with four berths, a small saloon and a nice deep cockpit. Dave's wife Sue, and their two boys Mark and Andrew were all competent sailors. It was a very pleasant day, cementing a relationship which lasted for many years. Over the remainder of that summer, Dave taught Sparky a lot about sailing, he was a natural instructor and Sparky a more than a willing pupil.

In March of the following year, Dave told Sparky about a very nice wooden sloop which was for sale by a Brough Sailing Club member. Sumarnic was a 25 foot carvel built mahogany sloop, with a deep keel and Stuart Turner two stroke auxiliary engine. She was in excellent condition, with a new aluminium mast and full compliment of good sails.

Below deck the galley and saloon were well fitted out, with two long settee berths, and two pilot berths under the cockpit. It was love a first sight, Dave knew the boat well, and went on board with Sparky to have a good look around. After a short consultation with Mary and Stephen, Sparky made his offer, and the owner accepted... His love of sailing was to last for quite some time, and over the years he had many a seagoing adventure to talk about, which most *Yachties* do over a few pints of beer in the club or the pub.

Typical of Sparky, the complete confidence he had in his own abilities, sometimes outweighed his actual ability to perform the task in hand.

He had owned Sumarnic for less than a month, and Dave had taken her out a couple of times with him on the Humber river for short evening sails. One weekend Sparkys friend Terry, an ex radio officer and boat owner, (or so he said), came to stay with the family for a few days. Sue and Dave were going away for short break, and had left the two boys with their grandmother. The weather forecast was good, with sunny dry spells and light winds. Perfect for taking Sumarnic out for a shake down cruise, thought Sparky.

His plan was to sail across to South Ferriby, about an hour away on the Lincolnshire side of the River Humber, where they could lock in from the Humber into the none tidal river Ancholme. The plan was to tie up for a couple of hours, have lunch in the near-bye Hope and Anchor, then sail back to Brough in time for tea. Stephen asked if Mark and Andy could come along as well, 'Why not,' said Sparky. He then phoned the boys grandmother to make sure it was okay with her. He promised to look after them, and suggested they could stay overnight, grandma was agreeable, she was well used to sailing antics of her family. Stephens face lit up at the news, he really liked the Peacock Boys, they were great fun. 'Thanks Dad, that's fantastic.' Sparky was blissfully unaware ,at that precise moment, how fantastic that would be...

An hour and a half later they cast off from their mooring at the club, and motored out into the creek towards the Humber. The tide was quite low, so he had no problem finding the channel. Once out in the brown swirling waters of the mighty Humber River, Sparky felt quite relaxed as he set a southerly course towards the lock gates at South Ferriby. He could see then clearly in his binoculars. The Boys quickly unfurled the mainsail and broke out the jib. With both sails set Sumarnic leaned slightly to port as a moderate westerly breeze filled the canvas. 'This is the life eh lads,' said Sparky to his eager crew. Terry shouted 'eye eye Cap'n,' in his best long John Silver accent, and they all had a good laugh. Mary came up from the galley clutching three mugs of tea and wearing the Tea Cosy as a hat. There was more frivolity and laughter as the Lincolnshire coast drew closer. With sun shinning down brightly on the land, and only a few clouds in the sky, it all looked very inviting, with Sumarnic making four and a half knots, and slicing easily through the slightly choppy waters of the Humber.

Sparky was on the helm, and had just taken a drink from his 'I'm The Boss' tea mug, when without any warning the boat suddenly came to an abrupt stop. The mast shuddered as the wind spilled out of the sails, Mark tumbled down into the cockpit from the deck, landing at Sparky's feet, unharmed, as Terry shouted, 'We've run aground.' Sparky immediately let go the Jib and Mainsail to take the pressure off the boat, which was being pushed slightly more over to port by the force of the wind. With the sails now flapping and slapping around freely, the two Peacock brothers set too and secured them both in a very seaman like manner. Sparky was impressed. As he looked at the water churning around his boats hull, It didn't take him long to realize that they were on a falling tide... The Humber was making its way down towards the North Sea at a rapid rate of knots, and before long, if they were lucky, they would be high and dry in the middle of the river between Yorkshire and Lincolnshire. If they were unlucky the boat may not remain upright, but might settle over on her port side.

'How stupid can I get?' thought Sparky, 'leaving the security of the Brough Haven on a falling tide'. In truth he had not even looked at the tide tables that morning. A costly and idiotic thing to do, but a hard taught lesson that he would never ever repeat in his sailing years still to come. All these thoughts rushed rapidly through his mind, he wanted to panic and shout *'What can we do about it?'* But his tea mug said he was the Boss, so he surveyed the situation carefully, asked if everyone was OK, and they were. Then went below to look at the chart, have a quick shudder, and a short silent scream. 'What did you say? Shouted Terry, 'Nothing,' he retorted. As the waters around them receded rapidly.

As he looked over the side he could see that they were not actually floating any more, but were resting upright on the boats nice long keel. On deck Mary and the boys were standing around watching the drama unfold. They seemed remarkably relaxed under the circumstances, or was it, he thought, because they had faith in him and his ability to get them out of this predicament. He nodded over to Terry indicating that he should come aft. Facing away from the deck, and looking back at Brough sailing club, he said 'What do you think then Terry, will she stay upright?' He was looking for some small pearl of seafaring wisdom from his long time friend, something which would make the sickening feeling in his guts go away, but Terry looked down at the brown diminishing waters and said 'I don't know mate, I've only ever dried out on a bilge keeler, or a flat bottomed boat, and they generally don't fall over.' They looked at each other and started to laugh, 'a lot of bloody use you are then,' said Sparky. Very soon after this they were high and dry, standing on top of a pristine sand bank, and apparently not falling over.

It was now just after eleven am, it would be many hours before they were floating once again. To emphasise the mood on board, grey clouds began to drift in from the west, and soon the warm comforting sun was hidden from view. A cool breeze whistled around the deck putting an end to outside activities, gradually everyone went below and sat or lay around. The boys soon settled down, chatting between themselves and playing games. Everyone was hungry, but the truth was they had brought hardly anything with them, expecting of course that by now they would be in South Ferriby enjoying the hospitality of the Hope and Anchor. A stock count uncovered three and a half bags of Salt n' Vinegar Crisps, a Mars-bar, one Yorkie, (the truck drivers friend), two sticks, of chewing gum and nearly a litre of drinking water. Mary unearthed two Tetley Teabags of questionable quality, and half a packet of dry Jacobs Cream crackers. She further reported that there was also half a kettle of water, just enough to make four hot drinks. 'Things could be worse,' said Sparky, 'Not much,' said a small voice from somewhere in the starboard side Pilot cot.

The hours went by slowly, as they do when your marooned on a sand bank in the middle of the River Humber, with a dwindling supply of stores, and an almost mutinous crew. But as late afternoon approached, and the light began to slowly fade, Sparky detected movement in the navigable channels. Ships were starting to come in on the flooding tide, heading for Hull docks. A bit later on he could see that their sand bank was getting smaller, salvation was here at last he thought. He watched the water rising getting further and further up the side of the boats hull. He advised everyone that the tide was on the make, but suggested they stay below for while. He asked Terry to come up on deck, and then told him of his growing concern. The water was rising further up the hull as the tide came in, but the boat was not moving off the bottom, she seemed to be stuck in the sand. Sparky turned the key, and pushed the engines starter button, the little Stuart Turner coughed, spluttered, and then died. 'Bloody two strokes.' he said under his breath. Pulling back the throttle he pushed the button again, this time the engine fired right away and settled down to a nice steady beat.

As calmly as he could he advised everyone to put on their life jackets together with all the clothes they had with them. 'It's almost dark now,' he said, 'We have to navigate back to Brough, so best if we all keep together.' Back in the cockpit, Terry was watching the rising water in fascinated silence. Sparky joined him and shone his torch down the side of the hull. The water was now literally inches away from deck level, the boat was not moving at all, and Sparky was really scared. But earlier, just in case, he had taken some distress flares out of their waterproof canister, and put them ready in the pockets of his waterproof jacket. The two friends looked at each other through the loom of his flash-light, there was only a couple of inches to go before water would start pouring into the cockpit. Sparky decided to get everyone out on deck... Then without any warning whatsoever, Sumarnic suddenly shot upwards, free from the sand and mud which had held her keel fast for so long, now the powerful buoyancy of her broad beamed hull sucked them out of trouble...The relief was palpable, they were free and ready to go home.

Although he felt elated, Sparky now had the problem of navigating in the dark back to the other side of the river, and try to pick up the perches which marked the channel leading to the sailing club. He had only ever done this three times before with Dave, and that was in broad daylight. This was now a completely different experience. He had studied the chart in detail during their day of inactivity, and knew he needed to sail North-east against the incoming tide, which would prevent them being pushed past the entrance to Brough by the strong incoming current. He gradually closed on the dark shoreline, straining his eyes to see a marker or a leading light. Terry was sweeping the foreshore with Sparkys powerful binoculars. At last they picked up a marker and turned to run with the tide. Somewhere in the gloom ahead was Brough sailing club, but Sparky was not sure he'd got it right, a feeling of apprehension eroded his confidence. This was no time to panic...'Steer for the flashing white light just fine on the starboard bow,' said a quiet young voice by his side in the darkened cockpit. 'Where?' said Sparky, 'I cant see where you mean,' he replied to young Mark Peacock. 'There now, straight ahead, right on the bow,' continued the teenage pilot. 'Got it,' confirmed Sparky.

He backed off the throttle, the tide was pushing them too quickly for his liking, and he now sensed the channel ahead, rather than saw it. Mark the pilot however, as he was to be known thereafter, calmly told Sparky which perches and markers to steer for, before he or Terry could even see them. As they approached their safe haven, the scudding clouds parted and revealed a beautiful full moon. It was now possible to make out the masts of the boats secure on their comfortable berths. Mark was absolutely spot on, and they entered the creek with fathoms beneath the keel. The force of the tidal rip was now diverted by the land, and the water in the creek was smooth and quiet as Sparky steered Sumarnic alongside the pontoon. The three boys jumped ashore, took the mooring lines, securing them safely. It had been more than thirteen hours since their departure that morning with its unscheduled visit to a sand bank.

It had been a long eventful day, and as they squared things away on the boat, Sparky praised them all for their patience. Adding an extra thanks to Mark for his piloting skills. They all went to Sparky's house, and Mary rustled up some food and drinks before they lay down to sleep. Sparky however could not settle, he took full responsibility for what had happened. It could have been worse, thank goodness it was sand and not rocks out there in the river, he thought. His complete and woeful lack of preparation, his blind confidence that everything would be OK were testimony to his lack of experience. However they had escaped unscathed, tired and hungry, but safe in the end. Over the years to come, Sparky never allowed himself to forget the lessons he learned that day. Eventually he would sell Sumarnic and gradually moved to a larger and more powerful 36 foot Clipper. He sailed the Irish sea and the west coast of Wales for a number of years, often taking solo trips to the Isle of Man and the east coast of Ireland. His seamanship and navigational skills improved with every trip, it was an interesting period in his life, but an expensive one. Later, menacing black clouds of fate would gather and his whole way of life was to eventually unravel... but that was in the future, for now he continued to prosper, worked hard, and moved into a new and exciting business environment.

Sparky and his family remained friends with the seagoing Peacock's for many years. Eventually Pilot Mark and his brother Andrew would buy themselves a Sabre 27 sail boat, with the help of their mum and dad they refitted it with heavy weather rigging. Then still in their teens, they set off from the Brough sailing club and crossed the Atlantic Ocean via the Caribbean to Newport Rhode Island, where they were given a rousing reception by members of its world renowned Yacht Club. The boys stayed for a while, then sold their boat to a local yachtsman before returning to Hull. Sue and Dave bought an ocean going sail boat and spent many months and years cruising the Mediterranean and the Greek Islands.

During his time in Hull Sparky's dad retired from his job in Blackpool due to ill health brought about by a heart attack, and moved to Northop Hall just over the border in North Wales. Sparky and his family visited them often, but his dad did not embrace retirement, he had always been a busy active person, the heart attack slowed him down, and eventually with his health failing he had another attack and died at the age of only 66 leaving behind his devoted wife Shelia, and their two children Diane and Ian.

Sitting at his desk one morning his direct line rang, it was Ian Urquhart the man whom he had replaced in Redifon's Liverpool depot a few years earlier. They had kept in touch, often meeting at exhibitions or conferences. Ian was one day younger than Sparky, being born on the 21st of June 1941. He was a Londoner by birth, and a bit of a wheeler dealer, a bit of a lad, always on the look out to make a few quid, as he would say. He was also smart, and an excellent salesman. Sparky admired him for his professionalism and his attention to detail, they were in fact great rivals, but that didn't stop them from being friends. After some small talk Ian came strait to the point, and offered him a job with IMRC of Croydon. Ian had been promoted to company Sales Manager, and his Job in Liverpool was vacant. He wanted Sparky to take over from him, yet again. The salary and conditions he was offering were excellent, the money being considerably higher than he was currently earning. But Sparky was very happy where he was, very comfortable doing a job he was proud of. He thanked Ian and said he would think about it, and call him later.

He rang Bill Mordin to tell him about the offer, and was instructed to go down to Wandsworth and discuss it further. Bill clearly didn't want to loose him, and tried to change his mind. The money was a huge incentive to Sparky, but Redifon were not prepared to match it... so in the end he accepted Ian's offer and resigned. He was very grateful for everything Redifon had done for him, especially Bill Mordin and Len Calvert, and he was genuinely sad to be leaving. But he was only in his thirties, he was ambitious and saw this as a new challenge, as usual he had the utmost confidence in his ability to succeed.

Sparky Joins IMRC
A Liverpool Docker
Offshore Oil and Gas
Goes to Pittsburgh to see his sister
The world of international sales

————◆————

His new place of work was perfect for him, the IMR depot was in the Hornby Dock, in a converted house which during Victorian times had been the lock masters residence, this was not unusual in those days. The building was well fitted out with good workshops, stores, and offices. Sparkys was upstairs and had view which literally looked out at the Lock system, he could sit at his desk and watch ships sail right passed his window. It was a pleasant and happy environment, there was lots of work, and the most famous shipowners in the country, and some would say the world, were only ten minutes away in the city. Companies such as Cunard, Blue Funnel, Ocean Fleets, Bibby Line, T J Harrison's, P and O and many others. Liverpool was steeped in maritime history, at its zenith it was the busiest port in the world, with the largest enclosed dock system stretching for miles along the banks of the mighty river Mersey. Across on the Cheshire side of the river Birkenhead docks were almost as impressive, with dry-docks, engineering firms, warehouses and the famous Camel Laird ship yard.

Its shipowners and merchants became wealthy beyond the understanding of the average working man. Fortunes were made and lost, but the city grew and prospered. Architecture to rival the nations capital provided a maritime skyline which even today, in the 21st century draws visitors from all over the world. The Liver Buildings, India Buildings, the Port of Liverpool Head Office still remain as testimony to its greatness. But to its shame much of that early money came from the disgrace of the slave trade, caverns and tunnels were built under the city so that its citizens would not be witness to the movement of its shocking human cargo. Abolition would eventually see the end of this despicable activity, and if any good can be found in the legacy of those years, then perhaps its in the rich culture of Liverpool's vibrant ethnic community.

Sparky and his family moved to Formby, a thriving and enjoyable place to live. It was only half an hour to his workplace, they were close to the beach, a good school and a new circle of friends. There followed a number of very good years, they prospered and life was excellent. Sparky was running and climbing as much as his busy job allowed, and his son was growing up into a strong and intelligent young man. The Offshore Oil Industry was booming, and communications equipment was in great demand. His company was owned indirectly by American giant ITT, which also brought with it access to some of their European acquisitions, mainly in the Scandinavian countries of Denmark and Sweden. This broad range of high quality manufacturers was a great asset to IMRC, allowing them to offer a wide selection of solutions. It was perfect for the new world Sparky now found himself in. He had been promoted to Sales Manager Offshore Oil and Gas. A fancy title no doubt, but in those heady days, most people had fancy business cards, they were a persons contact list, email had not even been thought about at that time. In reality Sparky was responsible for the companies north sea communications Sales. It was a demanding job, lots of trips to his birth city Aberdeen, meeting Texan Oil Men, and learning about what it meant to deal with Americans. In those early days of North Sea Oil development, the American oil industry played a vital roll in exploration, drilling, production and servicing the vast potential which was available off the coast of Scotland and the North East of England.

Newly formed British companies grew in size and strength during this amazing chapter in UK's history, helped by the huge experience of their American cousins. It was a crazy environment, and Sparky loved it. Deadlines had to be met, if you wanted to succeed you needed to perform. Equipment that was not reliable meant downtime, and this was to be avoided at all costs. Downtime meant loss of earnings to the companies operating in the hostile waters of the North Sea. It should be remembered that this was the 1970s and 80s. The revolution in wireless communications was not quite ready for the oil industry. The mobile phone and the satellite communication were just around the corner, but in the meantime the sale of long range rig to shore communications systems was rampant. It was not unusual for Sparky to receive a call late on a Friday afternoon requesting the delivery of one or more of his transmitter or receivers to be helicoptered offshore the following day, or within forty eight hours.

Service company's covering everything from food supplies, to specialized welding teams, with hot shot technicians available to be sent offshore 24/7 and much more. Aberdeen became a boom town, the flagging fortunes of its fishermen now found themselves working on huge offshore supply ships, the pay was good, and the conditions far less arduous than the hours spent gutting fish in a force eight gale. They knew the local waters, they were skilled seamen and were in great demand. Sparky was fascinated by the whole scene, the Aberdeen was vibrant, and there was a feeling of excitement. There was a good living to be made by anyone willing to work hard, and Cowboy Boots became a popular item of footwear.

His new job involved more overseas travel, and he made regular visits to Europe, usually with potential clients or existing customers who wanted to inspect some new equipment, or one of the companies manufacturing facilities. This type of travelling suited him very well, and would stand him in good stead over the coming years. In the spring of 1976 the company sent him to Houston Texas, where he was to attend the annual OTC, Offshore Technology Conference, the largest and most important event of its type in the world. His brief was to attend the ITT Marine exhibition stand, or Booth as the Americans called it, and to introduce himself to as many of the UK based American company's as he could. When the conference was finished he was to spend a few days visiting the offices of some of his current American customers.

The conference and exhibition was held in the recently opened (1975) Houston Astrodome, the worlds first multi purpose domed sports stadium, and home to the Houston Astros, a major league baseball team. It was a simply a breathtaking structure, often referred to as the eighth wonder of the world. When the playing surface of the baseball field wore out, they introduced an artificial grass known as Astro Turf, the first of its kind in the world. During the conference,the floor of the stadium was fitted out with Red, White, and Blue deep pile carpet. Thousands of people attended the show, and yet every morning when Sparky arrived for duty on the ITT stand, the carpets were all cleaned and in pristine condition. A remarkable achievement for such a huge surface area. The number of exhibits covering every aspect of the oil related business was staggering, the oil company's occupied their booths which were enormous, four of five times bigger than anything Sparky had ever seen before.

Back home in the UK he had supplied communications and entertainment systems to Penrod Drilling, an American company who had commissioned the construction of three new drilling rigs at the Scott Lithgoe ship yard on the river Clyde, Glasgow. The American in charge of supervising the contract was a Texan called Mark Guines. With two of the rigs competed on time, and all Sparkys equipment working well, Mark suggested that he visit the *Penrod Booth*, whilst he was at the OTC, and that he should introduce himself to the vice president of the company. On the second morning of the conference, Sparky went onto the Penrod Booth and asked for the VP, he was told by a very pretty Penrod hostess that the VP was currently in a meeting, she asked for his business card, and suggested he come back in half an hour. When he stepped back onto the Booth twenty minutes later, the pretty young hotess spotted him and motioned him to follow her to the VIP hospitality suite. She took him inside, and announced him to a very distinguished, tall, silver haired and immaculately dressed gentleman, who came over and shook his hand. 'Mark has told me all about you young man,' he drawled in real Texas fashion. 'He says your equipment works just fine, and that you gave him a great price on the whole deal, Penrod appreciate that, so thank you kindly.' Sparky was flabbergasted, the sheer fact that Mark had actually spoken to his VP and mentioned his name was awesome...

During the coming days of his visit he was to discover that it was not impossible to meet with the VP's and CEO's of these huge organisations, you simply had to ask, and if it was possible, then it would happen. They all seemed keen to listen to what he had to offer, often asking pertinent questions instead of just paying lip service. The meeting would usually end with the executive saying that he would pass on Sparkys business card to the operations department and that they would be in touch with him in due course... and most of them did. He wondered how easy it would be to secure an appointment with the CEO of British Petroleum when he was back to the UK.

Sparky had travelled out to Houston with his friend Terry, who had been with him on the Humber sand bank escapade.

He now worked for an offshore radio communications systems supplier called EAE Plessey. They specialized in putting together complete, fully functional radio stations installed in Port a-Cabins. They contained everything required for offshore comms, even down to the swivel chairs the operators sat on. All that was needed when they were lifted onto the rigs by helicopter, was to connect the power and the antennas. The customers could either purchase them, or more usually rent them. It it appeared that Terry had persuaded his boss to send him to the OTC, but Sparky could never quite work out what he was doing. Anyway it didn't matter, they were best friends and it was great to have his company.

Sparky had already telephoned his sister Eileen in Pittsburgh to tell her he was in the US, and that he was intending to fly home via New York, calling on route to visit them. She was ecstatic, and couldn't stops crying. It had been seventeen years since he had waved her goodbye as she sailed off on the SS Corinthia from Liverpool's famous pier head. Now she had two teenage children, and he was their uncle, that really thrilled him, and he of course was now married with a wife and son.

With their business commitments completed, Terry and Sparky decided to hire a car and drive to Dallas then take a flight to Pittsburgh via New York. They visited the Alamo, and the Rock Island Line, It was nice to relax after a hectic ten days of exhibition and customer visits.

The flight to New York was uneventful, and as their domestic onward flight to Pittsburgh was not for another five hours, they took a helicopter ride into New York which landed them on top of the Pam-am building. They had both travelled on helicopters before, to the North Sea oil rigs and other places. But this flight was really special with its amazing landing on top of one of New York's Iconic Skyscrapers. Down at street level they spilled out of the Pan-am building into the hustle and bustle of breakfast time New Yorkers. They just went with the flow, following the surging humanity as it darted in all directions heading towards their places of work, or maybe going home after the night shift. As they walked over a pedestrian crossing, a lady in front of them accidentally dropped a bill fold full of money, and carried on unaware of what had happened. The cash spilled out onto the road, then to their amazement a gentleman picked up the wallet and the money, chasing after the unsuspecting owner. He caught up with her and smiling politely, handed it over to her, before rushing onwards to work, or somewhere. The two friends were very impressed, their first time on New York's streets and they had witnessed a simple act of kindness and honesty. They both remembered the incident for many years afterwards. There was not much time to spare before the flight back to the airport, and the onward connection to Sparky's sister. They took in as much of the city as they could, and treated themselves to a huge 'New Yorkers' breakfast at one of the many excellent food outlets, it was hectic but great fun, and both vowed to return as soon as possible.

During the approach to Pittsburgh Airport Sparky was very quiet, it had been seventeen years since he had seen his sister, and his emotions were running riot, his heart was pounding, and he was finding it difficult not to cry. It seemed to take for ever for their bags to appear on the carousel...Then at last he was walking into the arrivals hall, scanning the crowd in font of him, desperate to find her. But Eileen was already rushing towards him, shouting his name as she pushed her way through the throng of people...and then they were locked in an unbreakable embrace, crying, stuttering, laughing and so very very happy. It was exquisite and, he never forgot that moment.

Terry rode up front in the BMW with Sparky's Brother-in-law Jim, a big powerful man with a passion for European cars, sailing ships and Whiskey. He was a founder member of the famous nationwide U.S. parcel service UPS. He had a zest for life, worked hard and played hard. In the back Eileen and Sparky nattered on about family, England, and her most favourite place in the world Blackpool. When they finally arrived at 941 Angelo Drive, it was as though Sparky had already been there. His sister had kept him well supplied over the years with photographs of their house, his niece and nephew, (Tracy and Michael), and Jim's cars.

It was a fine American style house, roomy, attractive and well built, certainly in a league not yet seen back in the United Kingdom at that time, unless you had a lot of money. Yet it was just a typical home in middle class America. Once inside the house Sparky soon became acquainted with Tracy and Michael, both teenagers seemed delighted at meeting their English Uncle... it was all very relaxed and comfortable. He had bought presents for everyone, a Texan leather cowboy belt with his name engraved on the back for Michael, perfume for Tracy and Eileen, and a large bottle of Tennessee '*Suppin*' whisky for Jim. That evening they enjoyed a fine family meal and sat talking for hours around an impressive old European oval table, given to Eileen by Jim's German parents. The wine, beer, and spirits flowed in copious quantities, whilst they all told funny and entertaining stories. The kids were delighted to be allowed to stay up, and may have managed to consume a few crafty glasses of alcohol disguised as Coca Cola, they certainly became more vocal, until it was time for them to go to bed.

It was well into the wee small hours of the morning when everyone eventually admitted defeat and crashed out. Sparky awoke some hours later, he was still fully dressed, with a banging in his head which sounded like a Jack-hammer in a coal mine. Eileen was curled up on the floor by Sparkys bed snoring peacefully, without a care in the world. Terry could be heard mumbling something which sounded like 'Oh Hell were in trouble now'. This because his alarm when he saw that the bottle of Tennessee '*Suppin*' whiskey they bought for Jim, had left a deep circular stain in the centre of the antique Bavarian table. Big Jim was oblivious of all that was going on around him, completely naked, he snored his way peacefully back and forth in his suspended hammock chair.

Regrettably, two days later Sparky and Terry boarded their flight to New York, then onward bound for England, but not before Jim and Eileen had taken them round Pittsburgh and its outlying beauty spots. It had been a fantastic reunion, and heralded the start of many visits by Eileen, Jim and the children to England over the coming years, and everyone one of those visits included a trip to her spiritual home, Blackpool.

Back home after trip to the USA the business continued to thrive, it was not just the offshore work which kept him busy, he also had a number of shipping companies to look after. The Nigerian National Shipping Line had its main UK offices in Liverpool, and their ships were regular visitors to the port. It was quite a large fleet, and at least half of them were supplied with IMRC radio stations and radio qfficers. Sparky dealt directly with the company's Marine Superintendent, a man by the name of Captain Tunde Jonah. He had served his apprenticeship as a cadet on NNSL ships, and was the first Nigerian to gain a Masters Ticket from a British nautical college. Jonah was a larger than life character, with a wicked sense of humour and a large capacity for enjoying himself. One of his more amazing skills was to be able to remember any telephone number he was ever given, he claimed that his uncle, who was a witch doctor in Kano State had passed this magic on to him when he was a very small child. He and Sparky got on well together, and Tunde nicknamed him the White Monkey when he heard that Sparky was a climber... it was all good natured, and no malice was intended. Tunde would sometimes visit Sparky at his home in Formby, arriving in an old Roll Royce, driven by his long suffering wife Ann, and a back seat full of kids. It gave Sparkys neighbours something to talk about as the kids screeched up and down in his back garden shouting in a mix of scouse and Yoruba.

One day Tunde called him into the office, he closed the door and quietly informed him that NNSL were in the market for nineteen new, state of the art cargo ships, it wasn't yet official, but he said it would certainly happen. The designs had all been approved and they would probably place orders with successful ship builders in the next few weeks. Tunde was concerned that a German company had been written in to the communications and entertainment specification, he was uncomfortable with that because his current fleet was a mixture of IMRC and Marconi. It was valid point, and although there was no technical problem with the German equipment, it would be quite a departure from the current way of operating their ships. All spares, personnel, service depots, in the UK and West Africa, were well established with the current mix of radio stations and officers. The next step would be to wait for the Shipowners decision as to where the ships would be built. Some six weeks later it was announced that NNSL had signed contracts to build nine new vessels at the Brodgogradiliste shipyard Split, in what was then known as Yugoslavia. The remaining ten ships would be built at the Hyundai Shipyard in South Korea.

After due consideration the German radio specification was replaced in favour of Sparky's company IMRC, but it would still need to be negotiated with the respective shipyards individually. Their bids to supply the ships would have included a price already provided by others, any change would mean that the cost of replacement equipment would have to be similar or less, if it were more then the shipowner would have to pay the difference. Regardless of the advantage IMRC seemed to have by being specified, it was obvious that this very large contract would be fought over very fiercely by numbers of world wide suppliers. A decision was made that Sparky should make plans to visit the two yards as soon as possible, and come back with the orders. This would be the first real International business trip he had made, and was the prelude for things to come.

The first yard to be visited was Brodgogradiliste, he travelled out with another of his company's salesman, a high flyer called Rod Dolling. Rod already had a contract underway with the Split yard, and another under negotiation. Quite rightly the MD had decided that Rod would be of considerable help, able to introduce Sparky to the right people and generally show him the Yugoslav ropes, as it were. On the first day Rod introduced him to a shipyard employee called Francovic, he was a senior manager in the Electrical specification and planning office. Francovic spoke excellent English, was a very amiable man with a great sense of humour and fun. What followed over the next five days was to be a baptism of fire for Sparky. During this time he experienced the truth about what was required to secure this type of business, it was hard and frustrating work. Every day at six thirty in the morning he was required to attend the offices of Boris Petric, the shipyards general manager, who allegedly spoke no English. All conversations were therefore conducted via Francovic. Boris was a huge bear of a man, a shock of swept back black hair seemed to accentuate his stern features, and Sparky found him rather intimidating. The first meeting lasted just over an hour, Francovic presented Sparkys quotation for the supply of his equipment to Boris, who quickly became quite agitated. His booming bear voice was raised on several occasions, during which time they were all served with numerous small cups of thick black coffee,and shot glasses containing neat vodka. Every time this refreshment arrived the vodka was downed in one swift action.

When they finally left the meeting, Sparky was feeling the after effects of his full on Yugoslav breakfast, but Francovic seemed to be completely unaffected. 'I don't know how you do it,' he slurred.' His Yugoslavian interpreter smiled back and said, 'Well my friend, that's because me and Boris were drinking water, not vodka.' Back at the hotel Francovic explained that they were not the only company bidding for this business, but were the most expensive. He explained that over the next few days Boris would see four more radio company's, and by the end of the week a contract would be awarded. Sparky had been given instructions from his MD concerning the discount he was authorised to offer, and if he reached a crisis point, and may be in danger of not securing the order, he was to call him, at any time day or night. The next four days were acted out in a similar way to day one, only now each time they sat down to drink their coffee and Vodka, the dialogue was all about the price. It appeared to Sparky that the shipyard were not really interested in the unique selling points offered by the various vendors, they were probably correct in assuming that all suppliers were of high quality, and conformed to all the international regulations. It was the price that mattered.

During these visits they also met their competitors, either as they were going in or when leaving the meetings with Boris. Francovic seemed to be well acquainted with Boris, and Sparky guessed there were forces at play which were not within his remit to know. All that mattered too him was whether or not they were making progress, and Francovic assured him they were close... On the fifth day their appointment time had been changed to eleven o'clock, so they went to a café near the yard, as they watched the world go buy, and drank cups of strong black coffee, but no Vodka. They entered the shipyard ten minutes early and were just parking the car when they saw the German radio suppliers Yugoslavian agent leaving the building, he didn't look very happy, but acknowledge Francovic with a nod, and apparently suggested they meet afterwards in a bar for a drink.

As they entered Boris's office, Sparky was feeling very nervous, but managed to appear relaxed and confident. They sat in the now familiar seats around a large coffee table, this time Boris came over to join them, instead of taking a tactical position being his huge desk. The coffee and Vodka arrived, carried in on a large silver tray by a rather nervous looking young lady. When she left the room, Francovic and Boris exchanged a few few words, then Boris looked over at Sparky and said in perfect English, 'I am pleased to advise you that our contacts department are to issue the order for supply of radio equipment in your favour. It should be with us in a few minutes.' He then lifted his shot glass and to Sparkys surprise he said,'Cheers.' as he knocked back his vodka. Sparky stood up and extended his hand towards Boris, and said 'On behalf of my company I thank you very much Mr Petric, it has been a pleasure doing business with you.' The huge bear towered above him and began to laugh,' You English have such excellent manners.' then sitting back down he said,' It's one of the things I remember most during my time at Oxford.'

The contracts manager eventually arrived with the paper work, and Sparky was asked to check the agreed pricing schedule and sign confirmation of its receipt... Ten minutes later they were in Francovic's car heading towards a bar, and a rendezvous with their competitors. Sparky was slightly numb, but ecstatic, and could hardly stop smiling. Francovic said,' By the way, this time we drink no water, only good Vodka.' When they reached the bar his college Rod was also there, talking somewhat intimately with a very attractive woman who turned out to be the sales director of their French competitor. They evidently knew each other quite well, and had crossed swords on numbers of contracts before this one. There was also another Englishman, who was introduced to Sparky as Frank, from UK Radar Manufacturers Kelvin Hughes. He had already received his order for the NNSL ships on a previous visit, and was at the yard now bidding for some new Yugoslavian coast guard vessels, which was the other reason Rod was there.

Sparky was fascinated and excited at being involved with this type of selling. His job gave him a big buzz, especially when orders were the end result, but this was different, not so clear cut as the sales back home. In this environment you needed to have allies, people like Francovic, they would play a vital role in the outcome of any business, but they had to be right for the job, there were plenty who made claims to have the inside track, who said they knew the top brass, or that they were cousins of the President, or even the King, if you were in Saudi Arabia. This may sometimes,have been true. The trick was to have the real fixers on your side, but it wasn't always possible to know who they were. Sparky would eventually become quite adept at developing the right relationships, but it was not always easy. On some occasions he found that it was not unusual to have people ran with the hare and the hounds, or have a foot in both camps so to speak.

However all this was in the future, for now a celebration was in order and the rest of the day was spent eating, drinking, smiling and generally having a good time,after all it was Friday... In between bars and restaurants Sparky found a telephone and made a call to head office. The MD was delighted and called Ian to come and share the good news, ' See you in the office on Monday then,' said the MD, 'Right, great,' confirmed Sparky. Back at their hotel he booked a flight, leaving Sunday afternoon from Split to Zargreb, then onward to London Heathrow.

Over dinner that night Rod suggested they have some R and R on the small Island of Hvar, less than a couple of hours drive south of Spilt. One of his best customers in Yugoslavia owned a small villa located near a sandy bay on the south western side of the island. The owner would not be able to join them, but advised his housekeeper to expect them. It was a wonderful opportunity not to be missed, and Frank the Radar man was also happy to join them. The drive down the coast the following morning was spectacular, with the sun sparkling on the Adriatic sea to their right and towering mountains to the left. They took the ferry from Drvenik to the beautiful harbour and terminal of Sucuraj, and less than an hour later they arrived at the villa, It should be remembered that this was 1977, and although tourism was a growing business, places like Hvar were still relatively unknown and unspoilt at that time.

The housekeeper who lived locally, was a pleasant lady in her mid fifties with very little understanding of English. However she had made up their rooms, provided them with some bread, cheese, and a couple of bottles of local wine. The Villa was very nicely appointed, spacious rooms, and a large veranda overlooking the sea. Rod explained that his customer's family had owned the house for many generations, and he was a very successful businessman, with a number of company's throughout Yugoslavia. Sparky wondered how much such a show of capitalism was looked upon by the communist elite.

The weekend was most enjoyable, they walked along the beach, did a bit of swimming and visited the local village shops... on the Saturday evening they enjoyed a meal in a local quayside cafe, it was very nice and very cheap.

They were relaxed, if not a bit unsteady after enjoying a couple of bottles of the local red wine and a rather palatable glass of brandy each. When they arrived back at the villa Sparky brought his short wave radio out onto the veranda, and searched the wavebands for some rock and roll stations. Meanwhile Rod had found the keys to the wine cellar, and produced some more red wine and a few bottles of the local beer. 'It looks as if things might get a bit hectic' thought Sparky. Tuning round the dial of his radio he pulled in a very strong signal from a station known as AFM (American Forces Network). It was the US governments entertainment station for it's armed forces, and was broadcast twenty four hours a day, all over the world. It also doubled up as a highly effective propaganda machine... in the years after World War 2 it was a very popular station with a great choice of rock and roll, jazz, and the latest hit tunes of the day. This was just what the trio wanted, especially since the station was playing Elvis Presley. After a few songs the DJ made an announcement which stopped the three friends in their tracks. He basically reminded the listeners that they were tuned to AFN Germany, then followed this with the news that The King was dead, Elvis Presley had passed away at Graceland, and as a tribute AFN would be playing nothing else but Presley's music for the rest of the night. It was August the 16th 1977, Elvis was 42, and Sparky had just turned turned 36, only six years younger than the King of rock and roll. All three were shocked by the news...but instead of dampening their spirits, it had the opposite effect. With every tune the station played, the trio sang and danced along with the music. Rod was the star of the show, performing a fantastic impersonation of the swivel hipped Elvis,and using a small kitchen pan scrubber as a microphone, he jumped up onto the large kitchen table and sang his heart out. Sparky found an old carpet beater and played the air guitarist. Frank who seemed more intoxicated than the other two, had set up a few pots and pans from the kitchen cupboard, and with a couple of wooden spoons he beat out the rhythm. It wasn't long before their antics attracted the attention of the neighbours, who came round to see what all the noise was about. Then the whole place started to rock, the music was none stop, the wine flowed like like a never ending fountain, as more people joined in the fun. It was a great night, which went on until the first of the dawn light was just starting to appear behind the mountains to the east.

The three of them were in a pretty bad way, the ravages of too much wine, brandy, and local hospitality, not to mention endless rock and roll, took its toll... but it was a night they would all remember for a very long time. Very much worse for wear, they left the island on the midday ferry to Drvenik. It was imperative that Sparky caught, the afternoon flight from Split to Zargreb and the onwards to London. He had to be in head office the following morning to see his managing director. Rod did a sterling job of getting them to the airport in time, despite his massive hang over. He and Frank were staying on for a few more days business, they had an important meeting with the the Yugoslav coast guard.

Despite the after effects of the previous night, Sparky was very happy, he was on the way home, and had a very valuable purchase order in his brief case. Upon arrival at Zargreb airport, the check in desk advised that there was a delay of two hours for the London flight... Sparky wasn't feeling so good, the previous nights antics were catching up with him, and to make matters worse the airport was very busy and oppressively hot. If there was any air-conditioning then it certainly wasn't working.

He was sweating profusely, and felt really awful. He decided to go to the bathroom, strip off his clothes, and use some paper towels to dry himself off. A few moments later he was standing in the cubicle naked, apart from his underpants, and was feeling much better, there was plenty of time before his flight, so there was not need to rush. Suddenly the cubicle door was pushed open wide, and standing outside was a cleaning lady, complete with mop and bucket. She took one look a Sparky, screamed at him, then rushed out of the bathroom shouting all the time. Sparky was convinced she had gone to find the airport police.

He couldn't afford to be delayed, or worse still arrested, so he hurriedly put his clothes back on, then cautiously left the bathroom and mixed in with the crowds of people milling around in the main concourse, keeping an eye out for the cleaning lady. But she was nowhere to be seen, however he was very relieved when his flight was called, and they eventually took off for London.

At head office the following day he was warmly greeted by his managing director, and the company finance director. The purchase order was carefully examined, the terms of supply and payment were acceptable, congratulations were extended all round, and after being treated to a very nice lunch by his boss, he caught the train back home to Liverpool.

The remaining ten ship order with the Hyundai Shipbuilders was negotiated in a completely different style than with Brodgogradiliste. It was not necessary to visit Korea, Hyundai had opened an office in London, and invited all interested vendors to come and discuss their quotations directly with dedicated teams of specialist. The London office had full authority to place contracts without recourse to Korea. The idea was to provide a speedy assessment of the various bids so that orders could be placed quickly. It also became apparent that Hyundai were keeping to the original specification, and were not looking to seek alternative radio manufacturers, they just wanted the best deal for the best price. As a result only three meetings were required and the order was placed within ten days of their first discussion. IMRC had now secured all 19 ships radio stations, radio officers and traffic accounts, together with comprehensive entertainment and internal public address systems on all ships. It was a massive order, everyone was highly delighted, and Sparky was on top of the world.

PART 11

Bad Karma

Sparkys mum passes away
From riches, almost to rags
Fighting back from the abyss
The First Iraqi Gulf War

———————◆———————

L iving in Formby was most enjoyable and his family were happy there, they made lots of new friends, and life was very comfortable... but the dark clouds of change were not very far away now, and no one could have predicted how much they were to alter everything he had worked for. In the meanwhile Sparky continued to build his customer base, working hard to become a top rate salesman, and get results.

The company's office in Liverpool's Hornby dock was a great place to be situated, there was always lots of activity, this was a booming period of world trade, and Liverpool was getting its fair share. There were union disputes and stoppages, which were costly to both dockers and the owners, but they were not as often as they had been a few years earlier.

In there own offices Sparky and his staff had a friendly and productive relationship, scouse humour was never far away, they couldn't help it, sometimes making a wise crack with just one or two words. Sandra, who looked after the companies radio officer admin, ran the office, and helped Sparky with his typing, also made great cups of tea. She was often hilarious without realizing what she had said, almost every morning when she arrived she would have some comment or joke to make about her journey into work.' But none of them were prepared for what happened one day...

It was beautiful sunny day in June, and all the staff had gone out for lunch. Sparky was in his office upstairs working on some reports, when a voice shouted out.

'Er allo, anybody there like?'

He went out on to the landing, and looked down the stairs to the front door. Standing at the bottom was a Liverpool docker, complete with a cargo hook over his shoulder, wearing a cloth-cap on the back of his head, a canvas jacket, and trousers tied at the knees with string.

'Can I help you?' He asked the docker. 'Er dunno mate, do you work 'er like?' and before Sparky could reply he said 'I a'vent been in this place since the end of the war, it was great then mate, used to be the old Dock-masters House, like you know.' 'Yes I know it was,' said Sparky.'Er are yous the boss ere then mate?' Sparky confirmed that he was indeed the boss. The docker then walked a bit closer to the bottom of the stairs, transferred the hook to his other shoulder and said 'Eh that must be great that lad, how many staff yer got ere then like?' 'Ten all together,' said Sparky.

'They all gone out then like, left you to man the ship eh, leaving you all on yer own, whilst they slope off to the ale house for a few swift half's eh, well suppose you get more money than them anyway, eh?'

Once again Sparky was about to speak when Mr Docker shifted the hook back to the other shoulder, looked up the stairs and said 'ave youse got an Austin Maxi Princess car?' and before Sparky could utter a word, he continued, 'don't like em much m'self like, gor-a Ford Anglia last year, great little car that mate, often take me missus, and our little scallies to North Wales for a day out, goes like little sow'in machine like, ye know?'

By now Sparky was getting a little impatient, and was just about to say something, when the docker said 'Is yer Maxi a blue one mate?' ' YES' Sparky shouted down to him.'

'And it's got ally wheels and a roof rack?'

'YES it has' retorted the increasingly agitated Sparky.

'Aww great them roof racks arn't they, eh? get loads a stuff on top o them cant yu', a'vent got one m'self like, cant afford it.'

'So that's yer Austin Maxi car, just out side then eh, with ally wheels and a roof rack?'

'YES, it bloody well is' snorted Sparky.

'It's yours then, like yer know, yours?'

'NO' Sparky almost screamed 'its a company car, why?'

'Well mate, *IT'S ON FIRE.*' he said, as he rushed out of the door.

Sparky ran down the stair's three at a time, and launched myself into the blinding sunshine, sure enough the car was well and truly ablaze with smoke and flames pouring out from under the bonnet.

'Lets push it in the lock then mate, that ll soon put it out,' smiled Captain Hook. 'Don't you even lay a finger on that bloody car,' said Sparky rushing back inside the office for a fire extinguisher.

Ten minutes later, he was on the phone to his MD in London telling him all about it, but he was stopped in mid sentence by his boss, who said;

'You know, you never did like that car did you?'

It was true of course, he never did like the car, and with the fire now under control, he could see that it was basically a total wreck. Back inside he put the kettle on and made a cup of tea, and as he thought about the docker and what had just happened he couldn't help but laugh to himself. 'Scoucers eh, you just cant beat em.'

Although everything was ticking over just fine, Sparky was about to enter a period in his life which was to change him and his personal circumstances dramatically. It would last for some time, and there were occasions when he thought it would never end... But before all this happened he continued to enjoy himself both a work and play. He joined a local sailing club, was running on a regular basis, and climbing as often as possible. His family were happily settled into Formby life, Stephens High School was very good, and he worked hard at his studies, never needing to be prompted by his parents.

One evening completely out of the blue whilst Sparky was down at the sailing club, his son Stephen arrived to give him the news that Sparky's mum was in hospital with a severe stroke. Sparky had been drinking so Stephen drove him immediately to the hospital in Blackpool. Apparently his mum had collapsed on the kitchen floor, by her husband Reg when he came home from work. It was touch and go for a number of days, but eventually she appeared to recover slightly, she had lost the use of her left arm, and had facial paralysis, which the doctors said may return to normal.

After a week the Doctors allowed her to go home, but six days later his mum was back in hospital with another massive stroke. Sparky was at her bedside within an hour of being told, she was not conscious and appeared to be asleep, breathing very slowly. He knew she would not recover, and was utterly devastated, his mum was only in her early sixties, and it seemed so wrong that she should be passing away at such an early time of life. He stayed with her until the end, it was around four in the morning when the doctor confirmed she had died. Sparky was besides himself with grief, he loved his mum more than anyone could have ever known. She was his friend, his soul mate, they were a kindred spirit. She loved him and was so proud of him, and everything he did.

His sister Eileen came over from Pittsburgh for the funeral, she was also devastated, they had been very close, almost like sisters. Their mum was cremated and in due course Sparky would take her ashes out into the Irish sea on his boat, and scatter them to the winds... She would have liked that.

After a few months in the sailing club he became friendly with a man we will call, Jack, for reasons which will become clear later in this narrative, it would not be prudent to use his real name. Jack was a charismatic man, who had all the trappings of a successful life. He owned an upmarket car, wore a Rolex watch and sailed the biggest yacht in the club. He was in his late thirties, always well dressed, and fancied himself with the ladies. Sparky would have probably caught Jack's attention at an early stage, after all he was also a successful young man in his own right, lived in a nice area, had travelled the world, kept people amused at the club bar with stories of a sailors life, and he too wore an expensive Rolex watch.

Having sailed with Jack a few times, and been invited to his house parties, Sparky was already impressed by the man's life style. One day he visited Jack's impressive offices in the city, and then out for lunch in one of the better local restaurants. After a couple of drinks Jack told Sparky that he was looking for a business partner to help him develop a new area of operation. He could see that Sparky's knowledge and experience in communications was impressive, he could also see that times were changing and that opportunities to expand into this exciting new arena were just around the corner. Jack wanted to be in on the ground floor. Basically he was offering Sparky an opportunity to head up a newly formed division of his company. All the infra structure was in place, offices, staff, capital investment and a business plan, the only thing missing was someone to drive it forward. He wanted Sparky to join him as a director of this new division, servicing and supplying the thriving offshore oil and gas industry, and the growing market for marine electronics equipment for yachts and small boats. He asked him to go away and think about it.

Sparky was flattered at being considered for such a position, the offer included attractive benefits, and an increased salary, which would be reviewed on a regular basis. He talked it over with his wife Mary, she was pleased for him, but was not enthusiastic about the prospect of leaving an already established company, where he was well regarded. She did not trust Jack and suggested Sparky should think very carefully before making up his mind... A woman's intuition can be a powerful thing, and if Sparky had taken heed of what she had said, all their lives may have been better off for it. However he chose to dismiss her misgivings, and after a few more meetings with Jack, he resigned from IMRC and started his new life as a company director. It would be a while before he realized what a terrible decision he had made, but the die was cast, and so he launched himself wholeheartedly into this new challenge, determined to make it succeed, failure was not an option. Later he would reflect on how naive he had been, dazzled by the prospect of riches and status.

PART 12

Sparky Leaves IMRC

Joins Jacks Emporium
And Disaster Strikes

———◆———

The first few months in his new position were exciting, he actually booked orders in the first few days, and within a few weeks he was beginning to pay his way. His list of contacts was considerable, and in the early days he was busy on the phone spreading the word that he was now working with a new and ambitious company. As the business grew, they acquired dealerships with major communications and electronic suppliers, Sparky had a good reputation,he was trusted and they all wished him the best of success. Within eighteen months his division had expanded, employing another sales person, a service engineer, and extra office staff.

It was hard work, and on the surface they appeared to be very successful. Jack was responsible for the overall administration and finances of the company, and encouraged Sparky to embrace his expansionist plans, telling him not to worry about that side of the business. 'Keep driving the sales forward,' he'd say with a smile. So Sparky did just that.

The full story of the companies downfall, and Sparky's subsequent downward spiral are best left out of this narrative, but the effect on Sparky, his family and his health were to be considerable. It all began one morning in the Autumn of 1982. He had just retuned from a ten day sales visit to west Africa, during which time he had secured an order to supply a twenty-five of sets of satellite navigation equipment, to a large shipping company. As he arrived back into his office, Jack asked him to join him and the Company Accountant. With little ceremony they informed him that during his absence, Sparky's company, a separate division of Jack's main operations, had gone bust. The official receiver was already in the building, winding up their affairs. He was asked to hand over his company car keys and further advised that his employment had been terminated by the receiver. He was to vacate his office immediately, after removing any personnel effects...

This devastating news was not completely unexpected, Sparky knew they were having financial problems for some time, but his own naïvety and complete lack of commercial acumen now weighed heavily on his shoulders. He should have asked questions, taken advice from independent people, asked to see the company accounts and had them checked. He did none of these things, he had trusted that Jack would sort it out. Sparky was in a state of complete shock. He sat in Jack's office and looked around him, he could not comprehend what he was being told. He felt sick, angry, affronted and gutted. There was no magic cure, this was it, he was out on his ear, he didn't even have the means of getting back home. As he stood up to walk out of the office, the accountant was aimlessly shuffling bits of paper, unable to look Sparky in the eye. Jack however sat behind his expensive leather topped desk and gave him a sickening superior smirk, rather than a smile, but didn't even say a word.

He gathered a few personnel items from his office and left the building. His mind and emotions were in turmoil as he walked dejectedly towards the railway station. At home he told his wife what had happened, it was tearful encounter. The finality of it all would just not sink in, the disgraceful way he was treated, the look on Jack's face, it was horrible and he wasn't coping very well. Mary was sympathetic and supportive, and may have even felt slightly vindicated, she had told Sparky on more than one occasion that she did not trust Jack at all, but he had always dismissed her remarks as groundless. Her feminine intuition had proved to be right.

When Sparky woke up the following morning he was to enter a new phase in his life, one in which he had no experience. If he thought the day before had been bad, it was nothing to what would unfold over the coming weeks and months. Bad Karma was rampant and having a field day. After breakfast he walked over to his bank in the village and asked for a current account statement. As the bank assistant passed it across the counter, Sparky detected a slightly sorrowful look in her eyes, surely she hasn't heard about my current circumstances he thought. Moving over to far side of the bank he unfolded the statement, then gazed at the figures not quite understanding what they meant. Seven hundred and sixty pounds overdrawn, it read, printed in red ink, he was dumbfounded.

This was in the days when Bank Managers were real people, trained to look after their customers, talk to them face to face and help them with any problems. So as Sparky sat in the managers office with a customary cup of tea, his friendly manager confirmed without doubt that the figures were correct. It was apparent that he had not actually received any salary or expenses from his employer for the past five weeks. In the 1980s, seven hundred and sixty pounds was a lot of money. But he had been an excellent customer, never going into overdraft all the time he had banked with them. The manger was very understanding, especially when Sparky explained what had happened the day before, he agreed to give him a couple of weeks to sort it out, but in the meantime he would not be able to make any withdrawals, even for a few pounds. So he literally had no money, and no job. He signed on at the nearest dole office in Southport, filled in all sorts of forms, and was told they would come to his house and means test him. He would not be eligible for any advance payout for at least three weeks. They were now, absolutely broke. The clerk at the employment desk advised that him they had no jobs available for company directors in the communications sector. Sparky said he would be willing to take anything at all, including digging holes in roads...

This set the scene for what was to come over the next few months. It transpired that Sparky was the only person to loose his job back at Jack's emporium. All his employees had been transferred over to a new communications company, which Jack had discreetly set up whilst Sparky was away in Africa. It was completely separate from Sparky's company and took no responsibilities for any of its problems. Within a few days he received correspondence from Jack's Solicitors informing him that under the terms of his previous position as a company director, he would be held responsible for the repayment of any shortfall which would undoubtedly occur when the official receiver had completed his task of winding up his company affairs. Amongst all the gloom surrounding him, a ray of hope and sunshine arrived from his old friend Johnny The Greek. Johnny had married a girl from Southport some years before, and left the Merchant Navy to open a Telex and Office Bureau in Liverpool. It was based in the famous Liver Buildings, and when Jonny heard about Sparky's desperate plight he contacted him and offered the free use of a desk and phone, in his office, until his fortunes changed. It was an extremely generous act of kindness, and gave Sparky a sense of hope and purpose, he was having a difficult time living off the money he received from the social security or dole as it was then known... And job prospects were almost none existent.

The day finally arrived when the appointed receiver had completed his work, and a creditors meeting was convened at their Water Street offices in Liverpool. Sparky walked over from his temporary refuge in the Liver Buildings with a heavy heart, and a fair amount of apprehension. He had only ever read about such things, and had no real idea of what to expect. However he knew, he would come face to face with various suppliers who had placed such faith in him, in the early days when he started out on his new venture. He had know some of these people for a long time, and he was feeling very uncomfortable. When he entered the room it was already full, maybe some twenty or so people stood around talking in groups. On the far side of the rather austere room, he saw Jack complete with his tame lawyer.

Sparky looked around at everyone else, and decided to brace himself for a hard time, he stiffened his resolve and mustered as much confidence as feeling of desperation would allow. A distinguished looking man in a smart pinstripe suite, and sporting a regimental tie, called everyone to be seated. He thanked them for attending, and then proceeded to read out the winding up report. Quite a lot of what he said was lost on Sparky, his resolve had weakened and he felt detached from what was happening. There were a number of gasps of dismay from the assembled creditors, and Sparky felt they were all looking at him with accusatory scowls. His spirit began to sink and he wished he could escape to a friendly place, with warm sunshine and a nice cool beer.

The distinguished gentleman rounded off his presentation with a summary of the Company's debts list of the creditors... Then suddenly it was over, people were standing up, some were leaving the room. Jack was nowhere to be seen, and Sparky seemed rooted to the spot, unable to decide what to do, he had never felt so alone and desolate in his whole life. Then walking towards him was one of the major creditors, a man Sparky knew quite well, and who he liked very much indeed. He was a distinguished looking man in his sixties, with grey swept back hair, and wearing his company tie. They were one of the most famous marine manufacturing companies in the country, with a history going back to the days of sailing ships. For the purpose of this narrative we'll call him John. He came close up to Sparky, and then unexpectedly extended his hand out and placed it on Sparky's shoulder, 'Its a bad business old boy,' he said quietly and before Sparky could respond he added, 'I want you to know that myself and some of the others in this room, do not hold you personally responsible, for what has happened.' For a moment Sparky was speechless, then he recovered and said, 'Thanks John, I'm so sorry for the way things have turned out, and I'm very grateful for what you have said.'... The room was now almost empty but as Sparky walked towards the door, two more creditors approached him, they were suppliers of marine instrumentation, radar, and general electronics, for commercial ships and yachts. Their company, BPI, was well run and profitable, with a diverse range of activities. He knew both men, one of them, Bob, went back to his days in the fishing industry. They both re-iterated what John had said previously, but then added something which Sparky could hardly believe.'We would like to talk with you in about an hours time, if that's okay, is there anywhere we could meet?' Sparky explained where his temporary office was located, and gave them the phone number...

Back in his bolt hole office Sparky sat alone at his desk, Johnny had gone out to a meeting leaving the young telex operator in charge. She brought him a cup of tea, then closed the door quietly as she left. Sparky read through his copy of the receivers report, it was a depressing document, the company owed thousands of pounds to various suppliers, including the tax man. But the most shocking revelation was the amount they owed to the bank, this was nearly two hundred thousand pounds, and unless his eyes were deceiving him, he was responsible for repaying most of it. This time he really felt sick, panic came over him and he wanted to run out of the building, and keep on running until he was exhausted. But he knew he couldn't do that. A knock at his office door brought him back to reality, it opened and his two colleagues from the meeting came in and shook hands with him. More tea, and some chocolate biscuits later saw Sparky smiling. He had been offered a full time sales job with BPI, selling their range of services and products into the marine industry on a nation wide basis. They offered an acceptable salary, with car and the usual expenses for travel etc. Sparky accepted, he was delighted, especially since they wanted him to start on the following Monday. He was to report to their Basingstoke office and would stay for three days. They asked if Johnny would be happy to rent the spare office to them for Sparky to use as his base and office. He was almost certain it would be okay, so they agreed to call him the following morning and sort it out. With handshakes all round they left to catch their train from Lime Street station...

At home that evening Sparky and his wife went to the local Italian Bistro for a slap up meal, accompanied by far too much Chianti. Good Karma was showing just a tiny part of its spirit, but for the time being Sparky was more than grateful for even the smallest sign that things could get better. However there was still the spectre of the Bank loan which had to be resolved. The final chapters of this sorry saga gradually unfolded over the forthcoming months. Sparky met with the bank, and they were most understanding of his personal circumstances. After some discussion a monthly payment, which Sparky could afford, was agreed, it seemed like a small amount considering the size of the debt. He was afraid they would insist on him selling his house, but that was not even mentioned.

Every month he personally took the money into the bank, and paid it in over the counter. He could have made a standing order, but it felt right to Sparky that he made that gesture, even though he was still devastated by the events of the past months, and felt he had been very unfairly treated by the liquidator. Then one day when he went to make his payment the cashier asked if he could come through to see the Manager. Inside the office he met the same three people who had been at his previous meeting. One of them smiled at him and said, 'We have some good news, as a result of further investigation the bank has decided to discharge you from your liability with regard to the outstanding loan, and we will issue an official letter to that effect today.' Sparky was staggered, it was the last thing he had expected. The bank official then said 'It is the opinion of our investigators that you were personally not to blame, nor were you directly involved in the securing of this loan, the bank will pursue your ex business partner in the recovery of this money, and I can assure you we will succeed.' He walked out into the spring sunshine, stunned at the turn of events, he wasn't sure whether to laugh or cry so instead he headed for the nearest pub and had a couple of beers.

As a postscript to this sorry chapter in his life, Sparky subsequently learned that allegedly, there were a number of irregularities within Jack's Emporium. These involved none payment of Value Added Tax, income tax evasion, none payment of national insurance, and money being transferred into offshore accounts. He was still gutted by everything that had happened, and withdrew into himself, not wishing to discuss the matter at the time. He just wanted to recover from the whole débâcle, and put his life back on track. Jack could go to Hell for all he cared...

Sparky was now forty one years old, and the traumatic events of those closing months, the loss of his mum, his downward spiral from a previously secure and affluent life, to near bankruptcy, all took a heavy toll on him. For a while his confidence was badly affected, and he struggled to cope with what he considered to be a failure on his part, he blamed himself for the predicament they were in. Although he put on a brave face, behind it all things were far from easy. They had been forced to sell their much loved holiday cottage in North Wales, and his 32 foot sail boat Osarian, in order pay off some of their debts and reduce outgoings. He began to drink heavily, and the relationship between him and his wife became very strained. They would eventually end up being separated.

One morning he went outside to empty some household rubbish in to the dustbin, when he lifted the lid he was shocked to see a number of empty Vodka bottles close to the top. He asked Mary where they had all come from, and she told him they were what he had consumed during the past few days. He was visibly shocked, he found it hard to believe, but it was true... his drinking was out of hand, and was a serious problem. He was truly ashamed of himself, he walked out of the house and round the corner to his doctors surgery. He asked to see a someone right away, and when the receptionist said he would have to make an appointment, he lost control, broke down, and began to cry. He was taken to an empty office and given a cup of coffee. His Doctor soon arrived and sat with him for quite a while. Sparky explained everything that had happened to him over the past twelve months, culminating in the discovery of the empty Vodka bottles... His GP was just fantastic and gave him tremendous support, he told him that he was suffering from deep depression, hardly surprising considering what had happened. Sparky immediately gave up drinking, and with the help of some excellent medication, and a superb doctor he pulled himself together, and eventually started running again. It was time to fight his way back, start earning money and put the past behind him. The new job was perfect, it brought him into a market he new well, his old customer base were all aware of what had happened in Jack's Emporium, they seemed pleased to see him again. Within a couple of months he had pulled himself round, stopped his medication and was fighting fit again.

Authors Note

Once he became established and was paying his way in life again, Sparky took a back packing trip to Nepal in the Himalayas, with a long time climbing friend Paul Deketalaire. They completed the Annapurna circuit in a three week trek, Sparky returned home and Paul stayed for a few more weeks. Over the next three decades Sparky would return to Nepal a number of times.

He was captivated by its people, the culture, the Buddhist faith, and of course the wonderland Himalayan mountains. In the year 2000 he took part in the Everest Marathon, which ran from Gorak Shap to Namche Bazaar, a full marathon distance.

During his time with BPI the mobile phone revolution arrived in the UK, the year was 1985, and Cellnet as it was then known, set up its first network of cell sites in the city of London. BPI were quick to see the huge potential and eventually formed a company geared up to sell the phones and provide a service. But It was early days, and the coverage was only available over a few square miles in the City itself.

When Cellnet merged with BT, the network rapidly spread throughout the UK at phenomenal speed. The market was growing faster than anyone had predicted. In the early days equipment was extremely expensive, in some cases an in-car mobile phone could cost nearly two thousand pounds, and the call charges were very high. But none of this seemed to deter sales, it was a communication's revolution, everybody wanted to be connected. Now more than thirty years later, it's hard to imagine what an impact the mobile phone had on everyday life. It could be argued that it's arrival at that time helped to stimulate the UK economy in many different ways. From large corporations to self employed people, the *mobile* gave them immediate access to a huge customer base. Self employed trades people such as electricians, plumbers, and many others could be contacted at almost any time, often resulting in them being able to secure additional work on an almost daily basis. The mobile communication's revolution continued, and all these years later is still evolving.

In those early days, the main players, BT and Cellnet, together with mobile phone manufactures needed to spread the word. Undoubtedly, at that time the American giant Motorola were the biggest supplier of mobiles and hardware in the United Kingdom. They were already well established in their US home market. Cellphones, using a similar Cellular System philosophy was already proving to be a huge success. Motorola therefore were initially able to capitalize on their ability to have stocks of equipment in the UK just waiting for the eager Brits to part with their cash. Competition was not far behind, with Scandinavian company's such a Ericsson, Nokia and others increasing their production output to cater for the huge potential available in the UK.

A joint venture with BT, Cellnet and Motorola was formed to launch a VIP publicity event in London. The idea was to charter a large Thames Passenger Cruiser, load it with food, drinks and hospitality, then sail off up the river Thames one evening. Once under way the VIPs would be given a presentation explaining how the system worked, and how the UK coverage would roll out and expand across the whole nation. The climax of the presentation was a closely guarded secret, and would prove to be an impressive, successful, and memorable experience for all those on board.

BT planned to have world famous British Yachtsman Chay Blyth make a Cellnet Mobile Telephone call from the saloon of the Thames Cruiser direct to the captain of the equally famous Cunard liner QE2 which on the night of the cruise would be docked 3000 miles away alongside in New York. The assembled guests would see Chay Blyth dial up the QE2 using a Motorola 8000X hand held cell phone The 8000X was forever to be known as, 'The Brick' mainly due to the fact that it was about the size, and weight of a typical household brick but fitted with a keypad and an aerial. It was emphasized that this equipment was not a long range HF transceiver using radio frequencies. It was a hand-held Telephone which would connect into the transatlantic telephone lines via the cellular network in London, which in turn connected into the BT land line telephone system, and then automatically route the call to the transatlantic sub sea cable distribution centre at Porthcurno in Cornwall. This information was only known to a few people, as BT wanted it to be a special event, with an interesting surprise element to it.

It is important to tell the Mobile phone story, because hopefully there may be younger people reading this book who were not even born when this event took place, and who like the majority of the people in the world today simply take for granted that they can communicate almost anywhere on earth, instantaneously on a handheld device, which can fit in the palm of the hand.

BPI saw an opportunity to help BT/Cellnet set up the necessary approvals required to make the call to the captain of the QE2, it needed people in Cunard shipping company to facilitate it ,smooth the way if you will, so that it all went off without a hitch, and BPI had a trump card... Sparky was asked by his boss if he could use his contacts in the Cunard Shipping Company to make this happen. He new all the people in the Cunard, radio departmental, senior technicians, radio Superintendents, and the radio officer personnel manager, they had know each other for years. It was a short walk from his office to the Cunard building. Over a cup of coffee, he sat down with Angus, and Bill , explained the outline of the plan, with dates and times of the proposed event. There was a lot of interest by Cunard in the potential to provide cellular mobile terminals on their passenger ships. It was early days of course, but there were exciting possibilities.

He left the request in their very capable hands and went back to do some work. Two days later Cunard gave the green light and the detailed plan started to take shape.

Whichever way you want to look at it, this telephone call, from the saloon of a smallish Thames Cruise boat sailing down the river Thames, to the captain of the QE2, probably the worlds most famous ship in service at that time, berthed thousand of miles away in New York was a significant piece of communication history. It was a commercially sponsored call, made over existing telephone networks from one ship to another. It may *not rank as highly as the epic achievements of Giovanni Macaroni's first transatlantic 2000 mile radio transmission from Cornwall England to Newfoundland on the 12th of December 1901*, but for the people who took part in it at the time, it was a very special moment. Sparky for one would never forget it. With the river cruise under way, the sixty or so guests, who were almost exclusively potential distributors, were able to ask questions of the BT staff about how the system worked, projected cost of calls, and the hardware itself.

At the prearranged time, Chay Blythe made an announcement on the ships public address system, requesting that everyone congregate in the main saloon, where a small stage had been erected. Chay then officially introduced himself, gave an entertaining little speech, and made the surprise announcement that he was about to telephone his friend, the captain of the QE2, which was currently berthed alongside the quay in New York, and he would do this using the Motorola Hand-held Cell Phone. There was an excited buzz of conversation as people began to realize what Chay was telling them. He then dialled the number, and the ringing tone was heard over the speaker system. After a few seconds, the phone was answered, and a voice said, 'Hello this is the QE2, Captain Hutchsen speaking.' Apparently Cunard had not told him anything about the arrangements, only that he should be in his cabin at 1600 hours New York time that afternoon, ready to receive a very important call.

The resulting conversation was crystal clear, no feedback, no static, no fading, it was perfect. Chay immediately responded with greetings and salutations, explaining that they were phoning from a cruise boat on the Thames. The two men talked for a few minutes, the captain said he was impressed by the quality of the call, and wished all concerned the very best of luck and success with this new venture. When Chay disconnected the line, the applause was spontaneous, it heralded a completely new era in telephone communications. A senior director of BT then told everyone that a number of Motorola phones would be made available for them to make free calls to any where in the world. It was the *marketing cherry* on top of the evenings cake. As Sparky circulated among the guests, he overheard people taking excitedly on their free mobile telephone connection. They were impressed with what they had seen and learned about this new business, they couldn't wait to set up their distributor agreements, start earning some money... and as they say, 'The rest is history.'

Sparky continued working with BPI, he was getting his life back together again. They sold their house in Formby and moved across the Mersey to a nice town house in Prenton on the Wirral. Their son Stephen had graduated from Formby High with excellent A level results. After taking a gap year working in Scotland for the National Trust, he enrolled in Glasgow's Strathclyde University, where he obtained a BA

Honours degree in Business Administration and Marketing. It was a proud moment for his parents, he was a credit to both of them, never having to be pushed into his studies, he was a naturally gifted student, and all round sportsman, a determined confident young man. Even at this early stage of his life Stephen was no stranger to adventure, he actively sought out pastimes and pursuits which involved considerable degrees of risk, and potential danger. He was a qualified Diver and took part in a number of wreck diving expeditions, where treasure hunting may have been undertaken, under the pretext of historical research. He obtained an explosive licence and became a salvage diver, nearly blowing himself up on more than one occasion. It would seem that he had inherited some of his dads earlier more carefree genetic tendencies, *Son of Sparky he most certainly was.*

During this period Sparky's friend Johnny the Greek, introduced him to a Liverpool based communications manufacturing company, called Micro-coms. They had originally made their name designing and marketing an innovative range of amateur radio equipment,and were just beginning to enter the more professional commercial side of communications. With a change in UK licence regulations there were opportunities to supply point to point radio transceivers operating in the 1.5 GHz band. The typical customers were water authorities, electricity and gas suppliers. Many of the applications were used for the transmission of data, or telemetry. The company had a talented staff of engineers, many of whom were radio hams, they were inventive with their designs, often able to provide solutions at very competitive commercial prices. Sparky liked what he saw, and was comfortable with the people he met. It was in a way, taking him back to his earlier routes of working with manufacturers and designers. He was unaware at the time, that this introduction would eventually change his life yet again, and see him embroiled in a drama which almost saw him jailed, and almost certainly were responsible for him being caught up in events, which would see him and others dashing for their freedom across the desert to Jordan... But that was in the future, in the meantime he was still busy working hard to recover from the events of his unfortunate experiences as a company director, and his fall from grace.

In 1985 BPI sent Sparky to work in Athens, he was based at the company's office opposite the Zeas Marina on the South side of the main commercial port of Piraeus. His brief was to work with their Greek Manager, Costa Manias. At that time there were numbers of large luxury yachts based in Greece, many of them belonged to wealthy Greek Shipowners. Communications was important to them, it was essential that they were kept informed about the financial markets, and their own network of offices around the world. The introduction of satellite communications for ships at sea, meant that they could keep in touch from anywhere, at any time. BPI wanted to be in that market, as well as all the associated electronics, radars, and navigation equipment which was now available. It was a lucrative business to be in, and was a perfect place for Sparky to work. His bosses also charged him with developing a closer relationship with the many Greek shipowners based in Athens and surrounding area.

It was a wonderful time for Sparky, he had known Costa for some a number of years, they were old friends from Sparkys previous days with Redifon. The company rented a small apartment for him in Glyfada, not far from the International Airport. It was a pleasant area, close to the beach, excellent for his early morning runs, before the sun mad heat of summer dazzled the eyes, and wilted the spirit. He fell in love with Athens, and the people, they was easy going, friendly and happy, their relaxed attitude was a pleasure to be around. He soon picked a few useful Greek words, and bought himself a set of Greek Koboloi, or worry beads. They became quite a habit for some time, he thought they were cool, and actually enjoyed the tactile experience of counting the beads. He continued to use them for a number of years, eventually he stopped, but it was fun at the time.

After being there for a week or so he decided to visit the Athens Mountaineering Club, or to give it its correct title Hellenic Federation of Mountaineering. He easily found their HQ in Milioni Street Kolanaki. As he walked up the stairs he was impressed by the collection of photographs lining the walls. They showed pictures of beautiful mountain peaks, many of them covered in snow. He cautiously entered a room full of people, all speaking Greek, laughing and smoking whilst they examined a number of maps on a table. Then someone looked up and saw him, Sparky pre-empted the man's reaction by saying, ' Good evening, is this the Athens Mountaineering Club?' there was a slight pause in the conversation around the map table, then the man said, 'Yes of course, what can I do for you?' 'I'm interested in mountaineering, and would like to go climbing whilst I'm here in Greece,' replied Sparky. From that moment on the evening just became better and better. A number of people came over to talk with him, asking what mountains he had climbed, and where was he from. It wasn't long before he was readily accepted in their company, they were all eager to hear about climbing in the UK.

One young man in particular seemed very keen to talk with him, he was called Demerits Sotriakis, a slight wiry young man, around five feet three inches tall, wearing a pair of dark rimmed spectacles, and a grubby tee shirt emblazoned with a faded print of mount Olympus. His deeply tanned face and sinuous arms, together with his scratched and bruised knuckles, immediately told Sparky that this man was a rock climber, he was just what he was looking for. Gradually the meeting started to disband as people left to go home, but not before Sparky had been invited to join then at the weekend for some walking in the Mount Parnitha National Park North of Athens. A mini bus would take them on the Friday morning from outside the clubs meeting rooms. Sparky kindly accepted their offer.

A couple of hours later Sparky was sitting outside in the warm Athens evening, drinking wine and talking climbing with Demerits and a few other members of the Athens club, who were all very interested in rock climbing. This was the start of friendships which lasted many years, and would result in them all meeting up at various times, both in Greece and back in the UK. Sparky's club, the Liverpool MC, visited Greece on at least four separate occasions. The Greeks reciprocated by climbing with them in North Wales, the Lake District, and an epic winter adventure on the north face of Scotland's Ben Nevis, the story of this near fatal encounter will be told later in the another chapter. The mountain ranges of Greece are spread over a huge area, they contain beautiful and exciting trails, high summits, snowy winters and scorching summers. The membership of the Hellenic Federation of Mountaineering boasts a proud history of alpine achievements, with literally hundreds of active groups using the hills all year round.

One day Sparky received a message that his long time friend Terry Hoyle would be in Athens for a couple of days, on his way home from the Middle East. He collected him at the Airport and booked him into a hotel overlooking the Zeas Marina. The following morning they had an enjoyable breakfast overlooking the marina. It was a beautiful warm clear day, and was memorable because from where they were seated they could see the Yacht Nabila, owned by the notorious International Arms dealer, and Saudi Arabian Billionaire, Adnan Koshoggi. Sparky was scheduled to visit the Nabila in a couple of days time to discuss the prospect of supplying a new marine satellite communications terminal, for the exclusive use of Koshoggi himself. She was an impressive sight, and at the time was one of the biggest yachts in the world. They spent the rest of the morning reminiscing about previous trips and people. Sparky then asked him why he had stopped off in Athens, surely it wasn't just to have a natter about old times. 'It's Gold,' said Terry, 'What the heck dose that mean Terry,' Sparky replied. Terry sat back in his chair, and looking slightly embarrassed he said, 'I'm acting as an intermediate broker for a gold dealer in Saudi, who wants me to meet a Greek gentleman this after noon at fifteen hundred hours, to discuss some mutually interesting business.' Sparky burst out laughing, but Terry looked serious... 'It's all above board mate, honest,' he said. Later that day Sparky took Terry to a five star hotel in Athens, he parked the car, and then waited in a coffee bar whilst Terry visited the Greek gentleman. Over an hour, and three strong Greek coffees later, Terry walked across the street and sat down beside him. 'Well?' said Sparky, 'are you going to be rich or what?' Terry smiled, stroked his chin slowly and said,'Maybe, maybe not, if I am, I'll give you a few bob.'... Sparky laughed and said, 'that would be very nice indeed.' Then he took his old mate to the airport, waved him goodbye, and went back to his office. Two days later he went down to see the captain of the Nabila, and although he was expected, and had a letter of authority the armed guards on the quayside would not let him on board until approval had been confirmed by the captain himself. He was then escorted to the upper decks by a sailor armed with, what Sparky guessed was, a Kalashnikov automatic rifle. On the way up, at each of the four deck levels, other Kalashnikov toting sailors were patrolling their patch, looking sharp and attentive. 'Sorry about that,' said the British captain, 'it's alright,' said Sparky.

Two days later he received a telex confirmation for an order to supply the new Satcom terminal. At forty thousand pounds plus installation costs, it had been a nice days work. The equipment was required to be fitted ten days later, and shipped out from Heathrow to Athens on one of Koshoggi's own private Jets.

But all good things come to an end, and although Sparky would have loved to live in Greece, the news which greeted them four days after he had received the Nabila order, would kill the whole prospect stone dead. In the office that morning Costa told him that as of that day, the Greek Government, in its infinite wisdom, had just imposed an new tax of fifty percent on the importing of all marine electronic equipment into the country. This rather strange and badly thought out action by the Greek Government, outraged the majority of the wealthy yacht owners. Many of them had been based in Greece for some time, providing work and revenue to the economy, now they were being penalized every time they wanted to purchase electronics equipment from overseas suppliers. Their response was to slip their mooring and sail off to a more convivial maritime host. Many went to Kusadasi in Turkey, others to France and Spain. BPI decided to close down their operations in Greece, and Sparky came back home. The fabulously wealthy Adnan Koshoggi cancelled his BPI order for a Satcom terminal and left for the Caribbean, where he no doubt purchased one direct from the USA.

Sparky was disappointed about leaving Greece, but grateful for the time he had spent there. It had actually done him the world of good, his confidence had returned, his bank balance was looking healthier, he'd had a lot of fun in the mountains, met lots of great people and was generally feeling pretty good about the future. He was happy with BPI, and would always be eternally grateful for the opportunity and trust they had placed in him, especially considering the events which lead up to it all. Even so, he often wondered how his future was going to pan out. Promotion and advancement seemed unlikely, there were no obvious avenues open to him. So he kept his eyes and ears open, just in case there was anything out there for him.

Over the months since his return from Greece he had developed a closer relationship with Micro-coms, he sometime played Squash with their MD Richard, and found him to be an interesting, humorous and extremely cleaver man. Richard was a highly talented engineer, had an honours degree in physics, and spoke a number of languages fluently. His knowledge on all things to do with radio communications was quite awesome. He was tall, dark haired and possessed a natural charm which he used to good effect in meetings, and general conversation. This charm also endeared him to the ladies, who often found themselves quite captivated by him.

As a company they were doing very well, but their dominance in the amateur radio market was under threat from the Japanese, who were offering excellent products which directly affected the Micro-coms traditional customer base. Richard saw that his company's future lay in the professional arena. He knew the existing radio communications regulations were undergoing a huge change for the better. There was an exciting time ahead, especially for an innovative company like his. The factory was already manufacturing Microwave Point to Point Links, the work force was stable and hard working. The only thing they seemed to lack was a properly structured, professional sales and marketing team. They were of course making sales, but it wasn't progressive and dynamic, to some degree they were still living off their name and reputation left over, from the halcyon days of good old amateur radio rallies. With his plans for the future still being formed Richard knew he needed to make some changes.

Sparky was not unaware of what was happening. One day, he took the plunge, and approached Richard directly, and simply asked him for a job as their Sales Manager. It was a controversial request, there was considerable opposition from within the management team. It wasn't personal against Sparky, they just thought they were doing alright as they were. But Richard knew they weren't. The process took some weeks, and a number of meetings before Richard finally offered Sparky the job, at the same salary and conditions he was already receiving with BPI. He was delighted and excited, this was the start of a very different challenge, but he was more than confident that he would justify Richards faith in him. BPI accepted his resignation in good spirit, they parted good friends, and wished him the very best of success.

PART 13

Sparky Joins MM

Almost goes to jail
Escape from Saddam Hussain
Sparky Moves to Derbyshire

————◆————

O ver the coming months Sparky settled into his new job, making friends within the company, engaging with the engineering department, getting to understand the products, and working hard with the factory management team, as well as the people on the production line. He soon realised that there were some staff issues, a few petty resentments from staff who thought they could do his job, and a few older die hard attitudes who were unhappy with the new direction the company was taking. But he did have an excellent team to help him with his marketing plans. Richard had assigned a young lady called Vanda to act as his pa and general assistant. She was a highly intelligent,very efficient person. She was smart, attractive, and dedicated to the idea of making it work. They got on famously, he respected her position and complemented her on her skills. Vanda would become an essential part of the team, and everyone in the factory seemed happy for her. So far however he hadn't made much headway in selling their products, and unusually for him, he had not taken any decent orders. But all that was all about to change...

It was the mid 1980s, the story of Sparky's involvement with Micro-coms, and the events which eventually unfolded over the next few years have now reached a pivotal point in this narrative. The company changed entirely from the one he joined as Sales Manager, therefore the author feels it necessary to explain some of the background to the eventual outcome before continuing with the main theme. There is no doubt, that the transformation of Micro-coms from its original beginnings as a manufacturer of amateur radio equipment, to a company who pioneered the development of cost effective video transmissions systems operating in the 22ghz radio spectrum, and lately in the milimetric spectrum of 60ghz, was nothing short of incredible. They should have developed and expanded even further, and should have become financially wealthy, maybe even a publicly listed company on the Stock Exchange. But there were issues within the organisation which inhibited that success. There were many and varied reasons why this wonderful little company failed to make it to the really big time. But the author feels that it is not within the spirit of Sparkys own story to dwell on those issues, and in any case to tell that story would take many more words than would be appropriate to the main theme of this book. As a parting comment, and for the record, Sparky was delighted to have been involved during those times, he was immensely proud of what they all achieved, and in retrospect, considers it to have been one of the most amazing times of his of his already, amazing journey through life.

It wasn't long before Sparky realised that out of all the company's products, the one that excited him the most was a microwave link which was able to transmit live images using a standard camera. The frequency band being used at that time was around 1.5 GHz, this was not a band available to the general public, therefore licences would not be granted in the UK. However things would change dramatically in the not to distant future, as International agreements were reached concerning the re-organisation of the worldwide radio frequency spectrum. The UK Police were already interested in this area, and it was possible for them to legally use equipment operating in the band 1.5 to 2.5 GHz. Richard was keen to support Sparky's plans and move the company into new area of operation. It was also clear that the main market would lie in security, an industry which was relatively new to both of them, but one which had the potential for tremendous growth.

Sparky now embarked on a series of security related exhibitions within the UK and overseas. These varied from high security venues involving police and military, to the more traditional general events organised to showcase all aspects of security. These covered everything from from CCTV cameras, access control system, domestic and commercial intruder alarms equipment, man guarding companies and much more. There were numbers of events in the UK each year, but without a doubt the largest and most prestigious was The International Fire and Safety Equipment Conference, or IFSEC for short. The first few of these took place at the Olympia exhibition hall in London, but due to its rapid expansion it was moved to the NEC in Birmingham, where it still meets to this day.

Sparky's first security exhibition was at Olympia, where they set up their stand, or booth if your an American, using the display modules and equipment from the factory demo room. It was an expensive undertaking, and they couldn't afford a prime position on the ground floor, but had to be content with setting up on the gallery upstairs. They took with them some working equipment, which transmitted live video signals across their own stand. As previously mentioned, this was the early 1980s, and this technology was not readily available from within the private manufacturing sector. It was an instant hit, their little stand was besieged with all manner of people, some of whom wanted to place orders immediately. But of course they had to be told that this was not yet legally usable in the UK, some said that didn't bother them, Sparky however cautioned them, and said they would have to wait a bit longer.

The overseas visitors, of which there were dozens, had different regulations and were very keen to have Sparky follow up their enquiries after the show had finished. It opened up the possibility of real business in the short term, and was the start of a completely new set of adventures for the now, forty year old Sparky. More than one of these adventures were to take him on exciting and challenging trips overseas, where he would meet all manner of people, good, bad and downright evil. Over the next year exposure to the market through publicity, and exhibitions raised the company's profile, enquiries flooded in and the phones were hot. Richard,had his eye on the future, he was an expert at understanding the complex business of rules and regulations connected with the overall future of radio transmission systems, both in the UK and overseas. At the same time he authorised the development of new and innovative products, as well as supporting Sparky and his sales team. In truth it could be argued that they were probably operating by *the seat of their pants*, but they had utmost faith in their abilities, and confidence in the future. With the benefit of hind-site, it is clear that they were running too fast, with slim resource's and insufficient financial control... but so were lots of emerging UK companies at that time.

One Friday afternoon when most people had left the office for the weekend, Sparky was still at his desk, putting the finishing touches to an overseas quotation for the protection of a large water treatment facility in the middle east. It was a beautiful late June evening, and he had plans to go climbing in the Lake District, so when he answered his phone, he half expected it to be one of his climbing pals checking on the time they had planned to leave. But after saying, 'Micro-coms, can I help you?' he was surprised to hear the somewhat dulcet tones of a rather well spoken Englishman, *lets call him Arthur,* who said,'good afternoon old chap, to whom do I have the pleasure of speaking?' Sparky introduced himself, then sat back as Arthur began to explain who he was, and who he represented. He claimed he was a retired Royal Naval Commander, now working as a security consultant to various heads of state, mainly in the Middle East and North Africa. He was also operating a large British company which manufactured a range of heavy duty, serious riot control and civil disobedience vehicles. These were designed to quell most civilian riot situations, they were able to withstand attack by fire, grenades and heavy calibre machine guns. They were fitted with high pressure water canons which could spray rioters with bright green die, which took seventy two hours to ware off. A rather flabbergasted Sparky tried to take all this in, *'is this man for real?,'* he thought, then Arthur concluded by telling him that the vehicles were however banned from being used in the UK and Europe.

'Well that's very interesting, but why have you called us,?' replied Sparky, 'I need some of your kit installing in six vehicles, one of which would act as the command and control centre, the others would be the front line riot controllers,' said Arthur. Sparky looked at his watch, it was nearly six pm, and he wanted to go climbing, but he was intrigued to say the least. Before he could say anything else, Arthur said, 'Look old chap, I know what your thinking, but I assure you the money is no problem, my client wants to sort this out as a matter of urgency, and I would like to visit your factory on Monday to discuss it in more detail.'

After a great weekends climbing Sparky was feeling on top form, so he decided to go in early to prepare for the arrival of the man with the dulcet tones, and the heavy duty anti personnel trucks. As he approached the factory he noticed a silver Rolls Royce, gleaming in the morning sun, sitting boldly in his own allocated parking spot. Outside the Rolls stood a slim distinguished looking man, casually dressed, but smart, and a very attractive lady. This must be Arthur, his royal naval commander concluded Sparky, and so it was, complete with his lovely wife. Evidently they had been visiting friends in Chester over the weekend. During the next hour Arthur explained his business in more detail, and its current requirement for video transmission systems. This particular customer, was in the Middle East, and although they had no problems with civil unrest at the moment, the rulers had decided to order Arthur's crowd control solutions just in case. The completed system, including trucks, electronics and full complement of service spares was to be delivered within a two month period. It would all be shipped out using the customers own Hercules, heavy transport planes, to a high security airfield where it would be stored out of sight in a huge air-conditioned hanger.

Sparky sat back in his chair fascinated with what Arthur was telling him, and not all together convinced that all this was for real. 'Why come to us for this equipment?' he asked, 'There are other suppliers, the USA for example.' Arthur leaned forward in his seat, and looking very serious he said, ' because old chap, the client wants to buy British, the whole package includes training and maintenance, which will be carried out by a specialised team of elite individuals, if you get my meaning?'...

Despite his own and Richards scepticism about the whole thing, they eventually received an order to supply six of their systems, complete with spare transmitter/receivers, and special low profile antennas which they subcontracted to a genius antenna designer they knew called Henry. Arthur was quite right, there was no problem with the money, the commercial banking arrangements were excellent. The equipment was manufactured and available for delivery two weeks before the actual contract date. Arthur sent two of his *elite individuals* to oversea the factory testing, and everyone was impressed with the their level of communications expertise and knowledge of Microwave technology.

Although the UK market was potentially huge, regulations and licensing were initially inhibiting security companies from legally installing this type of equipment. The license issue was soon to change however, and Richard had already anticipated this by investing in new equipment development which would put his company in the forefront of this cutting edge technology. In the meantime Sparky found himself servicing enquiries from companies all over the world, the next IFSEC exhibition was to move from Olympia to the new National Exhibition Centre near Birmingham. It was a big step up for the company, the cost was higher than the first one they attended in Earls Court London, but they realized that this would be an opportunity they could not afford to miss. It was to cover all aspects of Fire and Security, with a large international attendance. Many people thought that taking it away from London would prove to be detrimental, arguing that overseas visitors enjoyed the prospect of spending time in the capital as well as attending the exhibition. In the event this did not happen, the IFSEC organisers excelled themselves, it was extremely well marketed and advertised. The venue was impressive with large airy exhibition halls, superbly set up and administered. All the facilities were excellent, from transportation links, car parking, restaurants and numbers of high level conferences on a wide range of subjects. This was the real start of Sparky's involvement in security, and he would spend the next twenty-five years of his working life honing his skills, gaining experience and becoming highly successful and respected both in the UK and Internationally. He enjoyed the challenge and variety of projects which presented themselves in what was a rapidly developing technology. Most customers were looking to solve problems, often it may be as simple as how they could transit their video signal from one side of a river, or busy motorway, to the other side, without having to install or rent expensive and vulnerable cables or fibre optics. Point to point microwave provided a viable solution, and the market was growing. It's worth remembering that at that time the Internet was in its infancy, digital technology hadn't yet arrived, and security in all its aspects, from domestic intruder alarms, to town and city entre CCTV systems were just gearing themselves up for what would become a multi billion pound market. And all that was before the arrival of International Terrorism... Sparky was frequently travelling overseas, his department was expanding, he employed more salespeople to service the UK market, and put in place an admin department to interface with customers, and make sure payment was received and equipment dispatched on time.

One day he was contacted by a Jordanian, we'll call him Jadir. He worked as a broker for a number of Middle East clients, sourcing communications and electronic manufacturing companies in the UK, who were interested in exporting their products. Jadir lived in London, he spoke excellent English, and seemed to be well versed in Micro-coms range of equipment. At first he ordered small quantities of the companies existing range, items such as their weather-sat receivers which took signals from Darmstadt in Germany, decoded them and then using a standard printer, produced weather maps. These were the early days of satellite weather forecasting, it was not as sophisticated as it would eventually become, but it was part of the worldwide, growing requirement to have more detailed information available 24 hours a day. This unit from Micro-coms was inexpensive and worked very well.

After a few weeks, Jadir said he would like to visit the factory and discuss some of his other projects. The innocent meeting which took place, was to be the start of a long relationship, it would unwittingly propel Sparky and his company into a world of intrigue and potential danger, resulting in their eventual breakup. But all this was a long way off, there were no signs to warn them, and they were more than satisfied with customers who placed orders and paid for them immediately. Jadir arrived at the factory on time, pulling up outside in a new BMW six series. He was of medium height, a handsome impeccably dressed man with an air of sophistication about him, Sparky thought he looked more like a classical orchestral conductor than a businessman. As it turned out, he was a very accomplished musician, playing the violin and wide range of Arabic stringed instruments.

The meeting went really well, Richard joined them and was soon at ease in his company. Jadir outlined a number of projects, all of them in the Middle East. These ranged from monitoring CCTV cameras on Hydroelectric schemes, traffic control in large cities, and a hospital project in Baghdad Iraq. He explained that there was already a purchase order approved to supply a system for the new state of the art, Saddam Hussain Hospital. The requirement was to transmit live video signals from the operating theatre of the teaching hospital to five smaller outlying hospitals, and the University. Thus allowing doctors and students to observe and learn without having to travel across the overcrowded city roads. This was the perfect job for Micro-coms, so Richard asked Jadir why he had come them, and not the Americans or the French. Jadir explained that American based equipment was expensive, and there was reluctance to export it into Iraq. The French were in the frame, and had no such problems exporting to Iraq. So it was between the two of them, Jadir then handed them the full specification with terms and conditions of supply, the technical requirements proved to be no problem, and the commercial conditions were more than acceptable. Two months and a number of visits to London later the contract was placed with Micro-coms... It was the first of the hooks which were to draw Sparky and MM, into doing business with Iraq. They were not alone, many other British companies, large and small were finding it easy to trade with Iraq. The regime appeared to be encouraging such trade, and with their oil rich reserves money was not the problem. Iraqi business men were eager to move into this financially rewarding area, and the UK had diplomatic and commercial links going back many decades. At that time Saddam Hussain was largely tolerated despite reports of human rights atrocities. His vast oil reserves were coveted by the west, they didn't want to loose access to it... and of course his invasion of Kuwait was still a long way down the line.

Sparky began regular sales visits to Baghdad, these were facilitated in the main by Jadir who set up meetings for him prior to his departure. In the earlier visits he was always met at the airport by an Iraqi businessman called Khalid, he was well connected with other professional Iraqi's, all of whom were setting up to trade with the West. Khalid had lived in England for more than twenty years, and owned a farm in Sussex. He was a genial and friendly man, and they get on very well together. He was investing money setting up a business agency, he had purchased offices and employed a number of staff. His contacts seemed impressive, and never ending.

On Sparky's early trips he met up with people whom he assumed were civilians, and who had requirements for microwave transmission systems. It did not escape his notice however that the meetings were often attended by Iraqi Army officers, they rarely spoke to him directly, but asked questions via the supposed civilians. Not everyone spoke English, although he was sure they could if they chose to.

During the many trips he made to Baghdad his hotel of choice was the Ishtar Sheraton, it was close to the city centre, and the river Tigris. His days were usually taken up with meetings, but evenings were often free. Sparky felt reasonably safe walking around after sunset. The bazaars and streets within a mile or so of the hotel were busy with families enjoying the cool of the day. He was never bothered by any unwanted attention from street traders, restaurant owners or beggars, and no one ever challenged him about his camera. To the untrained eye Baghdad was a very liberal city. Unlike most of the Middle East alcohol was served in the hotel Bars, and Woman worked as receptionists, and waitresses. The most striking aspects of any trip around Baghdad at that time was the constant presence of huge posters showing their leader, Saddam Hussain. They started soon after leaving the airport, and were to be seen on nearly all road junctions and roundabouts. They presented him in a variety of poses, often benign and smiling down at everyone, others with children, and many exhibiting his warrior image, dressed in Army uniform holding an automatic weapon or a pistol.

Sparky enjoyed it for what it was, the Mosque's were everywhere and some of them were very beautiful, especially the Grand Blue Mosque opposite his hotel. Although he took little notice at first, he realised that he was always allocated the same room every he came, with same view from his sixth floor room of the Blue Mosque. One evening Khalid came to meet him in his room to discuss yet another project. As he entered he put his finger across his mouth, and shook his head. The meaning was clear, don't say anything which may be even slightly controversial. They talked for ten minutes, then Khalid suggested they go out to eat. Once in his car, Khalid told him that he should be careful what he said when using the hotel telephone for calls to his UK office, and under no circumstances should he entertain woman in his room. The whole of the sixth floor, and probably others, was bugged and monitored by Saddam's secret police. Sparky wasn't surprised, he had already spotted numbers of concealed cameras located in all the public areas bars and lounges.

Never the less his business in Iraq was paying dividends, the order for the Hospital project was close to being placed, and he was asked to have a final meeting with the Baghdad engineers to clarify some points before the order could be processed. He arrived at the Ishtar Sheraton the evening before the meeting, having flown from Cairo where he had been giving a presentation of his company's capabilities to the Egyptian Military. Once inside his now very familiar room, he had to rush for the toilet. He had obviously picked up a nasty bout of the dreaded gastroenteritis, or the squits, or Montezumers-revenge, take your pick, they were all the same in the end. He began to feel quite bad, and his visits to the toilet were becoming more frequent. He normally travelled with a supply of Imodium tablets, but on this occasion had omitted to do so. With his very important meeting only a number of hours away, he called reception and asked for the house doctor to attend him.

When he eventually arrived, Sparky was already in a poor state of health. The Doctor was a charming man, very smartly dressed, sporting a solid gold Rolex watch, an expensive looking shirt, and almost certainly wearing English hand made brown Oxford Brogue leather shoes. After a brief discussion about his symptoms he confirmed what Sparky already knew, and wrote out a prescription, adding as he did so, that it was not wise to buy these over the counter at drug stores, since they were often fake, and generally did no good at all. Relieved to have a solution in his hand, he asked the Doctor how much he owed him. 'Fifty US Dollars, cash,' was his charming reply. Sparky was a bit shocked, it sounded like a rip off, but he had no choice, so he saw the doctor out, and rushed back to the toilet for another debilitating session of uncontrollable bowel activity. After a shower and change of clothes he went down to Hotel reception and asked a very attractive female desk clerk if she could arrange for someone to collect the prescription from the pharmacy and deliver it to his room as urgently as possible. She advised him that she would send one of the bell boys out immediately. As Sparky walked cautiously back to the elevator, he saw the charming, well dressed doctor in the hotel gift shop, he was purchasing an expensive looking silk neck tie, and paying for it with US Dollars...

As he sat in his room waiting for delivery of the medicine, it suddenly dawned on him that the bell boy had probably gone to one of the many street pharmacy's to collect the Imodium, and that the charge for that would appear on his hotel account. 'Oh the joys of International travel,' he mumbled to himself. The bell boy delivered it in due course, and held out his hand for a few Dinars. Sparky spent a very uncomfortable night dashing between his bed and the toilet. By morning there was some improvement, but he knew from past experience that he wasn't clear of trouble. His meeting with the client was very important, and the key people would only be available in Baghdad that day,so postponing it for twentyfour hours was not an option. Ever resourceful, Sparky decided to pack a spare pair of underpants, complete with paper napkins and a can of deodorant spray in his brief case, along with the drawings and quotation relating to the project.

In the taxi taking him to the meeting, everything seemed reasonably stable, he'd had very little sleep the night before, and looked drawn and tired, but he was resolute and determined to see it through. There were eight people at the meeting, which started with the usual cup of thick sweet Arabic coffee, then it was down to business. Most of the issues were resolved quickly, and everyone seemed quite relaxed. There was still the matter of payment and training of the customers technicians to discuss, when Sparky suddenly felt an ominous sensation rumbling in his gut, he just knew what was going to happen, he asked to be excused so that he could use the toilet facilities. He stood up, collected all his papers together, put them in his brief case, then walked somewhat stiffly towards the door. He could sense rather than see that people were slightly mystified as to why he was taking his brief case with him to the bathroom.

He launched himself through the door and into a typical stand up Arab toilet, he tried to contain it, but was too late, Monty-zoomer was having his revenge, he had soiled himself. Panic ensued as he put down his brief case and carefully removed his trousers, he was now sweating profusely, but even so he couldn't help laughing at his predicament. After careful manipulation of the offending items, he washed himself down, thanking Allah for being kind enough to have provided a water tap which actually worked. Gradually he regained his dignity, and was almost ready to go back to the meeting, when he realised that he hadn't planned what to do with his discarded underwear. Thanking Allah once more for his inspiration, he removed the system drawings from their plastic folder and deftly replaced them with his soiled pants, and left them in the corner of the room. Then calming himself down, he mopped his brow with his handkerchief and walked confidently back into the meeting. Looking at his watch, he realised that he'd been out of the room for almost twenty minutes. Nobody said anything, and the meeting continued where it had left off. The issues were soon resolved, handshakes sealed the deal, and he was told to expect confirmation of the contract within a few days.

One of the senior engineers accompanied him down to street level where they hailed a passing taxi. There were already two passengers inside, one in the front and one in the back. Sparky gave the driver the name of his hotel, then sat back clutching his brief case, and tried to compose himself. Then it happened again, silently, but leaving a tell tale odour that he couldn't disguise. He looked sideways at the passenger next to him, and smiled. Now, Sparky couldn't understand Arabic, but he was sure that the man next to him, looked into the drivers rear-view mirror and said, 'This disgusting infidel and none believer, has just shit himself.' The three Iraqi's then talked excitedly amongst themselves, occasionally pointing fingers in his direction.

At the Ishtar Sheraton, Sparky gave the driver ten US dollars, and some Dinar, a massive tip, then turned towards the Hotel. At this point he didn't know whether to laugh or cry, so he did the British thing, and walked slowly towards the ornately uniformed doorman, head held high, brief case firmly griped in his right hand, and clenching his buttocks as hard as he could... but his agony wasn't quite over, as the elevator doors opened he saw that it was almost full to capacity, he backed off thinking to take the next one instead. But those inside smiled and beckoned him to come on board, he stood with his back to the rest of the passengers, and could see through the shiny surface of the doors that they were all looking sheepishly at each other, and at him. At the his floor he bailed out almost before the doors were fully opened, and was inside his room within seconds, he spent the next thirty minutes standing naked under the hottest shower he could stand, smiling to himself, and pleased that he had managed to survive the ravages of Montezumers-revenge, despite one or two close calls...

The contract was confirmed, and three months later,as part of the agreement, four of the engineers came over to the factory for training. Sparky greeted them upon their arrival, and took them into the board room where they were offered sweet Arabic coffee, and a tray full of sweetmeats. They expressed their thanks, and said they were all looking forward to being trained, and if possible, they would like to go to the Cavern and see the Beatles museum. Then Mustafa, the senior engineer stood up and said,'It is our tradition in Iraq to always bring gifts when visiting friends,' he then took an elaborately wrapped parcel from his brief case, and handed it across the table saying 'Mr Sparky this is special, just for you,' also and in keeping with tradition, Sparky opened his gift. It was his underpants, beautifully ironed and smelling vaguely of deodorant. Everyone burst out laughing, Mustafa concluded by saying, 'When we saw they were from Mark and Spencer's, we realised they were expensive, and should not be discarded.' It was a rare and special moment. The training was completed to everyone's satisfaction and before they left for Baghdad they were treated to a great night out in Beatle City.

The 1980s was an amazing decade in Sparky's life, he was in his forties, he had left secure employment in marine communications, hoping to make his name and fortune, but the venture had failed with almost catastrophic consequences. Within a year he had faced the prospect of loosing everything, recovered from bouts of heavy drinking, secured another job, worked hard to recover his situation and self esteem .and gradually regained his old *never say die or give up* confidence in himself. In the early 80s he was back to running and climbing, and was very physically very fit once again. Life began to stabilise and his relationship with his wife Mary became more harmonious. He worked hard, and offset this by playing hard at his passion of climbing and running.

In March 1984 he went to Scotland with a few of his Liverpool climbing club friends, together with three Greek mountaineers who he had climbed with during his time in Athens. The main objective was to do as much ice climbing as possible, the conditions in the Scottish mountains were superb. A number of weeks of alternate snow, and freezing conditions meant that many of the traditional Scottish winter climbs would be in good condition. That is to say that generally the ice and snow was stable, with minimum risk of avalanche, and to top it all, the weather forecast for that week was for high pressure to dominate the north of the country, meaning bright cold days, and freezing nights. They had booked into a superb bunkhouse in Glencoe, and from the very first day out everything went according to plan. They were up at the crack of dawn each day, and headed off into the hills, ticking off some classic routes. There were twelve of them all together, and they split into groups, some wanting to climb ice gullies, and others who preferred ridge walks with lofty peaks. The evenings were spent in the bar having a few beers, and planning the next days objectives.

Sparky was teamed up with his old pal Geoff, they had climbed together many times, both on hard rock routes, and exhilarating winter climbs in the North Wales and the lake District. The highlight of their partnership had been a successful accent of the Matterhorn via the famous Hornli ridge, on the on the 4th of September 1984.They were of very similar abilities as climbers, Sparky probably had the edge on hard rock routes, but Geoff was definitely a superior ice climber. As a team they complemented each other well, they were of a similar age, careful in their attitude to climbing, but ambitious, and both of them possessed a great sense of humour, especially at times of difficulty or danger.

Their Greek friends, Spiro, Costa, and Alexander were competent Alpinists with a number of classic accents to their name. Scotland was a revelation to them, and they loved every minute of it, their sense of humour and zest for life fitted in perfectly with the group.

For some time Sparky had wanted to climb Point Five Gully on the North Face of Ben Nevis, at 1344 metres (4409 feet) it was Britain's highest mountain. Point Five is an almost 1000 foot, vertical gully, which when blessed with a hard winter of snow and ice, is the most famous ice gully in Scotland, some say, perhaps in the world. In the 1980s its technical grading of 5, was one of the hardest winter routes in the British Isles. This fine climb attracted climbers from all over the world, and on this day it was in almost perfect condition. It was agreed that Sparky, Geoff and the three Greeks would drive up the A82 to Fort William early on the Thursday morning, all prepared and kitted out. From the car park they would walk up the glen passing the CIC hut, and then traverse across to the bottom of the climb. Unfortunately their early start was slightly delayed and it was mid morning before they eventually shouldered their rucksacks and set off up the Glen.

The fine bright start to the day gradually began to change, ominous black clouds were scudding across the sky, and light snow flurries came down from the north. The atmosphere was tense, as each member of the group had his own private thoughts about the task ahead, and the deteriorating weather conditions. But the surroundings were spectacular, they were all very fit, and very excited. Even so the progress was slow, there were no tracks in the snow, and their packs were heavy. It was way past noon when they finally cut across the snow slope to the bottom of the route. The Greeks would go first, they soon sorted themselves out and began climbing. Sparky and Geoff were impressed with their efficiency and progress, they were ready to start climbing once the last Greek was out of sight. Ice and snow debris came bouncing down the gully from the team above, nothing too dramatic, and at least it showed that they were moving.

Geoff lead the first pitch, which became steeper as he gained height, at approximately 30 metres and found a good placement for a peg belay.

The weather was closing in, and bitterly cold gusts of icy wind lashed his face as Sparky prepared to climb. He good placements for his ice axes and felt confident as he front pointed his crampons up nice compact snow. A quick look out of the gully towards the north, revealed a darkening sky, and the light was fading fast. It was now after two pm, they were way behind schedule and should have been half way up the route by now. As he reached a steepening section, a whooshing sound announced the arrival of debris from above, he put his head close to the icy wall and braced himself, as icicles and small frozen rocks slammed against his helmet, some of the fine powder snow found its way into his Berghaus Mountain jacket, and trickled down his neck. 'Looks like its going to be one of those days,' he mused to himself. He could now see Geoff as he continued to climb easily towards the belay, when he was less than two metres away from the ledge, there was a jangling sound of metal, and a curse from Geoff as he saw the rack of ice screws slide past him, and dis-appear down the gully. Sparky lunged sideways to try and catch them, but it was no good. Without moving up any further, Sparky secured himself with two excellent axe placements, then looked up incredulously at Geoff.

There was nothing to say really, it was potentially a disaster, ice screws were essential for their protection, to go on without them would be foolhardy. With Geoff paying out the rope, Sparky back climbed to the bottom of the gully. By now a misty cold gloom was descending on the glen, and it was hard to see the CIC hut. He cast around, desperately searching for the screws amongst the frozen and broken rocks and ice spoil which was coming down the gully. The light was fading fast now but then he spotted them, laying precariously on the top a small ice covered boulder four metres away. Cautiously, Sparky gently made his way towards the boulder, he didn't want to disturb the loose snow which had followed him during his decent, and with a deft and purposeful move he grabbed the large metal ring which held all the screws together... then clipped them onto a nylon sling across his chest...

Once back at the belay it was his turn to lead the next pitch. It was a steep and sustained chimney, and with the light almost gone it was hard to spot good placements for the ice screws, or anything else for that matter. But it was possible to bridge most of it, and by the time he reached the obvious belay position, he was climbing at the extreme edges of his ability. The available protection was hard to find, and minimal. There should have been some tell tale evidence of the Greeks ascent, but the increasing snow flurries, and passage of debris, had obliterated any signs of them having been there. He managed to place one good screw in a snowy cluster, and a channel peg in a dubious iced up crack. If they fell now,he doubted that any of it would hold them. He shouted down his concerns to Geoff and told him to climb with extreme care. Geoff was very good at that, he had the ability to move up difficult and thin ice with delicate placements of his axes and crampons.

As Sparky looked down towards him, he suddenly realised that their situation was very unsafe, a fall now would would almost certainly mean the end, for both of them, it was hundreds of feet to the bottom. This was the first time in his long climbing career, that Sparky had been confronted with a situation so dramatically uncontrollable. Holding ones nerve, and working as a team was the only way forward. For a fleeting moment he thought of his family and those who loved him, the classic climbers dilemma, should he really be doing such a dangerous thing, was it fair to the ones he would leave behind? Then he snapped back into the zone, negativity and fear were no help, so banish them.

When Geoff joined him, they both quietly ran through the process of checking everything, they new the belay points were poor, and they had no alternative but to get on with . This third pitch was known as the Rogue, and was considered to be the technical crux of the whole climb, it increased in steepness very quickly, and depending upon conditions at the time, it may often be overhanging near the top. Now the darkness was complete, and they both switched on their head torches.

With a nod of acknowledgement to each other, Geoff stepped up into the vertical abyss. Slowly and methodically he placed his axe picks delicately into the ice, and kicked his front points as deep as he dare into the rapidly steepening wall. Now on his own, Sparky switched off his head torch to conserve power and, was immediately drawn to the total blackness below his feet. The increasing gusts of wind howled around his legs like banshees, buffeting his body, and causing him to alter position to keep his balance on the tiny ledge, while frozen streams of debris rushed past him to the valley floor. But Geoff was climbing like a perfectly tuned machine, chipping, stretching, moving confidently, and managing to find the odd good placement of an ice screw or peg. This was classic Geoff, the man of Ice, in his element, and his progress made Sparky feel good, for the first time since he had recovered the fallen screws.

Then suddenly the moving light above him went out, Geoff had reached the overhanging section of the wall, and his head torch batteries had gone flat. Turning his own torch back on again, Sparky look up the gully, and instinctively tightened his hold on the belay stitch plate. Geoff was shouting down to him, but the banshees ripped his words away and scattered them to the heavens. Now in almost total darkness Geoff had no alternative but to continue moving upwards. The rope slowly moved through Sparky's freezing fingers, it seemed like it was an inch at a time, but at least it was moving. Then in a quiet moment whilst the banshees were gathering for another attack, he could hear Geoff grunting, and hacking his axes into the very core of the mountain, then there was silence.'Are you OK Geoff?' shouted Sparky, there was no reply, but suddenly the ropes moved upwards, he thought Geoff had fallen, but then he heard those wonderful, special words, that Climbers love to hear, 'I'm safe.'...

When Sparky finally joined him above the overhangs, he was drained of energy and emotion, it was the hardest thing he'd ever done.Geoff just looked through the light from Sparky's torch and said, 'Well done mate, a bit brutal eh?' They were still about two hundred metres from the summit, but the ground was less demanding as Sparky lead through on the next pitch. The weather was getting worse, violent gusts of wind buffeted them and whipped their climbing ropes up and down like snakes.

The snow was falling thick and fast, covering everything. It was hard to see more than a half a metre in front, whilst constantly scrapping it away from the eyes with the back of frozen Dachstein mittens. They guessed they had about a hundred metres to go, the guide booked advised that the top can often be corniced, and would require a leader to brake their way through to the summit slope. With this in mind Geoff disappeared into the swirling blizzard, the rope moved out steadily, then stopped.

'I've found a rope up here,' Shouted Geoff 'It must be the Greeks, what should I do?' 'Tie onto the bloody thing.' screamed Sparky at the top of his voice...

Fifteen minutes later Sparky was hauled over the rim of the mountain onto the summit by a snow covered Greek, who grabbed hold and hugged him with a vice like grip.'Efharisto,' he croaked Sparky as he collapsed onto the safety of the frozen summit.

Inside the summit refuge the world was eerily quiet, and surreal, the whole of the interior was covered in thick ice, but it felt amazingly warm, compared to the conditions outside. Their Greek companions had become worried when Geoff and Sparky failed to turn up within a reasonable time. So Spiro climbed back down and secured the end of spare rope with an ice screw, and attached a small Greek flag as a marker. Back at the top they took it it in turns to keep watch. They had actually broken through the cornice to gain the summit, but with the snow and the high winds they reasoned that it would have been almost impossible for Geoff and Sparky to see it.

Sparky and Geoff arrived on the top of the Ben at 2300 hrs. it had taken them nearly nine hours. As they sat around trying to hack frozen Mars bar's into edible bits with their ice axe's, everyone suddenly realised that the wind had stopped, and when they looked outside there there was a beautiful moonlit starry sky, and not a breath of wind. It was immediately agreed that they should descend back down to Fort William whilst the visibility and conditions were favourable. In these latitudes the weather can change without warning. After a careful retreat through fresh snow they eventually arrived back at the car around four am. exhausted but absolutely buzzing. A few minutes after setting off for Glencoe, a police car with a flashing beacon, pulled them over to the side of the road. Sparky lowered the window as the young officer approached. 'Gud mornin lads, are ye the boys who were up on the north face today?' he said with a smile. 'That's us,' replied Sparky 'We've just done Point Five, is there a problem?' The young constable looked a bit embarrassed and said 'Och no lads, the mountain rescue were following yer progress until the snow storm blotted you oot, then they saw some lights on the way doon, and just wanted us to check that it was yer good-selves, and not anyone else up there,'

They were impressed that the rescue services had been keeping an eye on them, Sparky thanked the officer and said, 'As far as we know we were the only daft buggers up there tonight.' The officer gave them a smart salute then wished them all the best... Their climbing holiday was over and it was time to go home.

Back in the real world, Sparky and company continued to make their presence known in the security business, his sales team were supplying the newly developed Micro-coms 22 Ghz links to CCTV security Installers, who in turn were engineering them into projects up and down the country. City centres and shopping precinct's were rapidly being installed with cameras, which transmitted the images back to central control rooms staffed with trained observers. Over the next few years, the streets and public places of Great Britain would become the most monitored of anywhere in the free world, and the size of its security industry grew enormously. The high tech solutions required to maintain this momentum were at the cutting edge of technology, and they would continue to grow year on year. Much of this expertise was home grown, developed in the software houses of an emerging young breed of high tech entrepreneurs.

Sparky continued with his overseas travels, attending and exhibiting at major security forums and shows from Istanbul to Bangkok, Oman and Cairo and many others. Then one day they received a very detailed and comprehensive technical specification to build highly specialised three-phase power controllers for the Iraqi state electrical generating department, the equivalent of the Electricity Board in Britain. The document was delivered personally to Micro-coms by his Iraqi business contact Khalid. After a very careful evaluation of the data and specification, it seemed that this was something the company could manufacture. The quantities involved were substantial, and the projected costings with resulting profit margins were very attractive and considerable. This was in turn supported with a water tight financial contract which would release payments against presentation of documentation to the bank, prior to releasing the goods for shipment to the customer. On the face of it this seemed like an opportunity that would be hard to turn down, it could transform the companies fortunes. But as often happens in life, things aren't always what they seem.

Before accepting the contract, Richard applied to the British Department of Trade and Industry for permission to build, and export these components to Iraq. In 1988 the DTI approved the contract and in due course an official order was received from the State Electrical Industries of Iraq, during the last quarter of that year. There was a lot of procurement and setting up of production facilities required before work could begin. It was a very busy time for the factory, and the mood amongst the employees was one of cautious optimism, the future looked bright.

At this time Richard considered that it was necessary to restructure the company a number of important issues had been brought to a conclusion, ending a period of much uncertainty, and amongst other things he thought it was necessary for a growing technological manufacturing company to have a strong and multi-disciplined board of directors. On the 4th of January

1988 he appointed a manufacturing director, finance director, technical director, and a sales director. Sparky was delighted.

Behind the scenes however forces were at play which were determined to bring the company into disrepute, and eventually see its downfall.

In April 1990 an ex-employee of Micro-coms gave the Mail on Sunday newspaper, a specification for a device known as the 'brain', which he claimed was capable of forming the link which could trigger a nuclear device.

HM Customs officers had recently seized a consignment of such triggers at Heathrow Airport, destined to be ship too Iraq. The informant claimed that these were the same type of devices which Micro-coms were actually building under the guise of a contract with the State Electrical Industries of Iraq.

NOTE: *The author feels that it will serve no purpose in this manuscript, to explain the background as to why the informant embarked upon his course of action to destroy the company. The reasons were historical,complicated, personal and emotional. Suffice it to say that his actions were to have serious consequences for Sparky and everyone in Micro-coms.*

The Mail on Sunday, then went on to claim that defence experts who were shown a copy of the documents, believed it would be possible to fit the device to a missile's nuclear or chemical warhead. They said that one major fear was that such a device could be lunched by the so called Iraqi super-gun, parts of which were allegedly impounded in Middlesbrough, Greece, and Turkey. When interviewed by the Mail, Sparky laughed off suggestions that the units could be used for nuclear detonation, adding that a licence had been granted by the British DTI, and that his company conducted its business in an ethical, honest and professional manner at all times, and they would never do anything illegal, or violate any government regulations.

NOTE: *Older readers may remember that after extensive examination into Saddam Hussain's alleged capability to deploy WMD, weapons of mass destruction, the UN investigation teams found not one single piece of evidence to support these allegations.*

All of these claims, counter claims, and suspicions, initiated by the ex employee, created a lot of distractions for Sparky and the other directors. But it would be fair to say that it was Sparky who seemed to be the one who had to keep on facing the music, so to speak. One evening when he arrived back at the factory after attending an exhibition in Birmingham, Sparky was met in the car park by his PA Vanda. She told him that two gentlemen from HM Customs and Excise were waiting in his office, they had been there all day, and had officially seized a number of files and documents, it was now almost five thirty pm, and most people were leaving for the day. He thanked Vanda and said she should pack up and go home.

The meeting in his office with the HMRC officers was almost bizarre,after the initial introductions, one of them, a short stocky character not very smartly dressed, and speaking with a strong Mancunian accent, began accusing Sparky of unlawfully selling and exporting 1.8 GHz video transmission equipment to the Iraqi military. His tone of voice was threatening and somewhat disrespectful, he said strange things like, 'I see you drive a BMW 5 series.' and 'Have you ever personally met Saddam Hussain?' They advised him that they were removing numbers of sales files for closer examination, and that his PA had a certified list of what they were taking. Sparky was not enjoying this at all, he was furious that without any prior warning they had the power to enter their premises, interrogate his staff, and impound important files. He denied that he ever had acted unlawfully in exporting anything to Iraq, and had never even seen Saddam Hussain, apart from on the TV, let alone met him.

The Mancunian then went into Vanda's office and used her phone to make a call, when he returned he advised Sparky that his superiors in Manchester would like to interview him that evening, and that Sparky should follow him in his own car, and would be accompanied by one of the HMRC officers. Sparky asked if he was under arrest, the Mancunian said he wasn't, but if he refused to cooperate, it could be very easily arranged... He spent all that night at the HMRC regional offices in Piccadilly Manchester, and he only met with one other person, who asked him the same questions. He was then kept in an office, which was sparsely fitted out with a scruffy old desk, and two uncomfortable chairs, but no phones. He repeatedly asked if he could make a telephone call, but it was declined. He continued to ask what grounds they had for detaining him, but all they did was ask him to admit that he had unlawfully exported restricted video transmission equipment to Iraq.

The convenience of the mobile phone, as it is known today was not generally available then. He had one in his car, and should have used it on the way to Manchester, but he had been too concerned about what was happening to him to think about it. He was convinced it was all a bad mistake, and that he would be home by the middle of the evening. In the early hours of the next morning someone else came into the office and said he was free to go. He was handed a large cardboard box which contained all the confiscated files. Incredulously, that was it, the man walked with him out of the office, into the elevator and accompanied him to the basement where handed him his car keys, then went back into the lift without saying a single word. Sparky was shaking with emotion, felt exhausted and he was famished, not having eaten anything since the previous lunch time... If this narrative sounds far fetched, and you think it is something which can't happen in Britain's green and pleasant land, then no one could blame you. But be assured, there are agencies within our realm who have dark and awesome powers, and if they believe the security of the nation is at risk, they are at liberty to use them.

A few days later stories appeared in the national press claiming that British firms were being investigated by Customs officers on suspicion of supplying high tech equipment to Iraq, which could be for used with nuclear weapons. One news paper even named Micro-coms as being one of those under investigation. It was a scary encounter, and despite the companies lawyers efforts to try and bring the Mancunian episode to court, or even to receive an apology they, eventually advised Sparky to put it all behind him. Two weeks later when Sparky was in Manchester on other business, he returned the building where he had been detained, but the car park was locked, and a sign said 'Offices To Let.' It occurred to him that the alleged Micro-coms *ex* employee must have been well pleased with the mayhem he was causing.

At around this time Sparky's relationship with his wife finally broke down, and they separated. He moved out to a small apartment close to the factory and buried himself in his work. It was a hard time for all concerned, there was bitterness and recrimination, these things are rarely anything else but traumatic. However life has to move on, and a few months later he moved in with his new partner, Kay. It was time to rebuild and find a way forward.

In August 1990, now aged forty nine, Sparky was unwittingly involved in a saga which would change the world as we knew it for ever. He was in Iraq, finalising the details for the supply of more equipment, to expand the use of their video links in the Baghdad Teaching Hospital. Everything was settled, there were no problems, and that night he packed his bags in readiness for the flight home the following morning. The date was the 2nd of August, and as he went down for breakfast, he decided to check with the Air France office in the hotel complex, just to make sure there were no problems with his flight. The Air France rep looked at him with surprise and said, 'Haven't your heard the news sir, the airport is closed until further notice, the Iraqi army has invaded Kuwait, we have no Idea when we will be able to fly, and all overseas telephone calls are currently unavailable. ' For a few moments he could not grasp the importance of what she had just said. He went back to his room, and switched on the TV... there were no foreign channels available at all, not even the usual Iraqi ones, there was just background music. He opened up his suitcase and took out his Sony short-wave world radio. It was always spot tuned to the BBC Overseas Service, within a few minutes he had all the news he needed. Iraqi troops had entered the State of Kuwait and were fighting their way across the city.

The true impact on him and hundreds of other expatriate businessmen. and families, would take a few days to unfold. Iraq succeeded in taking over control of Kuwait within two days, and it would take seven months before they were removed by a United Nations-authorized coalition of forces led by the United States. But all of this was in the future, what would happen now was the question on everyone's mind. Most observers and analysts were of the opinion that Iraq was sabre rattling, in order to teach Kuwait a lesson for allegedly stealing its oil by extending its pipe lines into the Iraqi desert oil fields.

The next few days were conducted in an almost surreal atmosphere, nobody believed it would last very long, and things would soon get back to normal. Ex-pats, including Sparky, went about their business as normal. The hotel swimming pools were full of people who did not expect to still be there, so they were making the best use of some relaxing down time until they could go home. Even Sparky's visits to the British Embassy seemed to endorse the feeling that it would all be over soon. How wrong they all turned out to be. Hotel guests congregated in the public rooms, the bars and cafés around the pool, and walked around the gardens in small groups talking over the situation they found themselves in. Sparky joined in and tried to gain any snippet of news from other sources. In the end his best source was his Sony radio, and the BBC. What he heard convinced him that there would be no rapid resolution to the problem. The UN were putting pressure on Saddam to leave Kuwait or face sanctions, Saddam wasn't interested, and this sort of rhetoric could go on for days or weeks.

After five days of pointless speculation, Sparky made some plans of his own, he decided to take a taxi to the Jordanian border, and if refused permission to enter, he would divert to the Turkish border and enter via Curkurca, he reasoned that he was more likely to find sympathetic sanctuary in Turkey, rather than Syria or Iran. During his many visits to Iraq over the previous couple of years, Sparky used a Jordanian Taxi driver called Ahmed, he was big gentle man, married with four children, spoke excellent English, and had a wicked sense of humour. Ahmed would normally have taken him to the airport on departure day, but this time he'd opted to use the Air France Shuttle bus. The taxi drivers would often cruise around the hotels touting for fares, Sparky hoped Ahmed would turn eventually up. In the meantime he took his passport and some money and decided to walk over to the Turkish Embassy. As he was leaving the hotel he met a fellow Englishman he'd become friendly with, called John Johnson. John was an engineer working for the Dutch truck manufacturer DAF, and was in Baghdad training one of their distributors. He was a really nice person, and although he had travelled a bit, he hadn't done much in the Middle East, and it seemed to Sparky that he was a bit anxious and worried about what was going to happen. He told John his plan, and asked if he fancied joining him, John was delighted.

It turned out to be amazingly easy to obtain a Turkish entry visa, there was a small photo booth outside the Embassy, and for a few Dinars they were in business. They completed a simple form, handed over their passports and some money, ten minutes later they were walking back to the hotel smiling and laughing. The next part of Sparky's plan was to attend the British Embassies weekly briefing, to check on what the British government were planning to do for them, if anything.

Just before they reached the hotel Ahmed pulled up alongside them and blasted his horn. 'Mr Sparky, what you do here, you be in England now,' he smiled, they jumped in the cab, and Sparky told Ahmed to drive into the hotel grounds and park. He arranged for Ahmed to take them to the Embassy at seven that evening, then he asked Ahmed if he would take them to the Jordanian border the next day, and how much it would cost, 'OK Embassy tonight, I tell you price then, Inshallah Mr Sparky.'

The Embassy meeting was packed with businessmen, wives, children and Embassy staff. The assistant ambassador gave them the official government statement of how things were proceeding with the Kuwait crisis, and assured them they were doing everything possible to secure exit visas for all those Brits who wanted to go home, which was nearly everybody who wasn't an embassy employee. People were asking various questions, and there was quite a bit of chatter amongst themselves. Sparky raised his hand to ask a question, he introduced himself and said,'Is there any chance the Embassy can organise a bus to take us to the border, I'm a businessman, and need to get back to my factory, I haven't even spoken to them since the day of the invasion.'

They were told that the chances of securing passage for a coach full of people at the moment were very slim, things may improve, and they were working hard to make this happen.

There was quite a bit of discussion at this point, but then Sparky put his hand up again and said,' Well in that case I would like to inform you that I am leaving in the morning in a taxi for the Iraqi Jordanian border, and my friend here is coming with me.' There was a stunned silence, then the Embassy man said,

'That's very interesting, but we would strongly advise against it, it could be a risky business once you leave the outskirts of the city, and reach the desert road. We have no intelligence regarding approval for such an action, and are unsure about Iraqi troop deployment at the moment,' Sparky thanked him, and said,' I accept it may be risky, but I would prefer to take my chances.' The meeting then erupted, as people asked more questions, and Sparky found himself surrounded by other businessmen who were asking him about his taxi arrangement,how much it would cost, and if they could come with him.

In the end Sparky gathered together fourteen more people who wanted to give it a try, they all agreed to meet at the Ishtar Sheraton two hours later to find out if he had been able to arrange enough vehicles... outside Ahmed was waiting as arranged, Sparky told him what had happened and he said he would make some calls and meet him again outside the hotel. When Sparky collected his room key from reception, the assistant gave him an envelope, inside was a message from his agent Khalid. Written on the back of his business card, it simply said, *'Get out as soon as you can.'* Later, it transpired that Khalid was making a dash for the border with Turkey, 210 miles north of Baghdad, and had come to collect him...

Ahmed excelled himself, with the help of his cousins, he was able to provide six limousine's, and the price would be five hundred US dollars per person. They would drive them to within a hundred metres of the border post, then wait in a Wadi for one hour, after that they would return to Baghdad. The closest crossing for the Jordanian border was 500 Km due west over the desert from Baghdad, and would take six or seven hours. Ahmed insisted they should be ready to leave the Sheraton no later than two in the morning.

It was a long way, and a risky enterprise for all of them, the drivers, if caught could go to jail, or worse. Sparky and companions risked being refused exit, then maybe taken back to Baghdad, and possibly held in detention. They may be challenged by Iraqi army patrols, and sent back to Baghdad, or worse. Finally they had to trust that these people they had never met before, may take take their money, then abandon them in the desert, or worse. Everyone agreed to take the chance, the next few hours, and more would prove to be very interesting. What they had failed to realise was that once at the border post there was still another 100 KM to go before reaching the Jordanian capital Amman, assuming of course that they would be allowed to enter the country. But that important point was yet to present itself.

Back at the hotel Sparky packed his last few things, making sure he had his money, and passport readily available. Well before time he was at reception checking out. He was slightly concerned that there maybe a problem, perhaps the authorities would want to prevent people leaving. Especially since the were strong rumours that the borders were going to close. The hotel receptionist's were just great, there were no problems checking out. Sparky had the feeling that they knew it wouldn't be long before restrictions would be imposed. He used his Amex card to settle his account, asking them to issue him with five hundred US dollars cash. These were anxious moments, would Ahmed and his cousins honour their agreement, or would they decide it was too risky, even though the money was more than they could earn in months of usual daily taxi work. As the agreed departure time approached the rest of the budding escapees began to arrive, one by one they gravitated towards Sparky, checking and confirming that everything was still on track. The hotel receptionist's must have realised something unusual was happening, but they remained cheerful, and when it finally came for them all to leave, they shouted their goodbyes,telling everyone to come back and visit them soon. Sparky was amazed that the Iraqi authorities had not restricted the movement of the stranded foreign businessmen, and expatriate residents.

There were more armed guards to be seen than normal, but they displayed no obvious hostility towards anyone, and in fact they all looked rather bored.

At around two a.m. on the morning of the 8th of August 1990 their fully loaded cavalcade pulled away from the Ishtar Sheraton, as the guards gave them a half hearted salute. The streets of Baghdad were almost deserted, and it wasn't long before they were heading westwards out of the city passing north of lake Habbaniyah into the desert, and towards the Iraqi border post. Sparky, John and Tony were with Ahmed in the lead vehicle. It was quiet, and nobody spoke as they sat back looking ahead through the car's bright headlights. Wrapped up in his own personal thoughts, Sparky reflected on the events of the past days, he was worried about the future and what would happen to the Iraqi sales contracts his company were processing, if the conflict escalated into a more serious phase. They had been driving for more than than two hours, and as the dawn light was lifting the darkness off the desert floor, they saw a number of Iraqi army trucks up ahead, parked by the side of the road. Ahmed instinctively slowed down,and flashed his rear lights to the others behind.'Maybe problem Mr Sparky,' said Ahmed, his voice low and hesitant. 'Just keep driving, nice and steady, eh my friend,' replied Sparky.

As they drew closer head lights flashed on and off, and an armed soldier stepped into the middle of the road with his Kalashnikov over his shoulder, raising his hand indicating they should stop.'Keep calm Ahmed,' advised Sparky, 'Inshallah,' croaked Ahmed as he came to a halt winding down his window. A rapid and aggressive sounding conversation began, and Ahmed handed over some papers to the guard, who took them back to the trucks. It was very quiet and still, the morning light had increased, and they could see at lot more trucks. Two other soldiers went along the road and collected more paper work. Small groups of armed soldiers stood around, smoking and talking, occasionally pointing at the cavalcade of limousine's. There seemed to be no hostility, but these were tense moments, everyone in the cars was keeping their own counsel. Eventually an officer came towards Ahmed's vehicle accompanied by a soldier, they returned all the paper work, then bizarrely the officer gave a salute, and waved them all on.

They were very relieved, and pleased to be moving towards the border once again. It was difficult to understand why the patrol had let them go, maybe the officer had no orders to detain foreigners, or maybe they were on another mission, and had no facilities to look after them, or take them prisoners. Whatever the reason everyone felt a huge relief and a lot more relaxed. Just as the last Limo cleared the road block, two soldiers stood in the middle of the road behind them firing their Kalashnikov automatics rifles into the air, laughing as they did so. *'Having fun thought Sparky?'*

The journey continued without further incident. Now the sun was well over the horizon, the road ahead was straight as a die, and seemed to go on forever as Ahmed turned on the air con. Nearly five hours after leaving the troops behind, Ahmed started to slow down and said, 'Not far Mr Sparky, soon we stop.' As they reached a bend in the road, the terrain ahead changed. There were sand dunes, and what looked like a dried out river bed, Ahmed tuned off the road and parked twenty metres further on in a crescent shaped area which had been flattened out by the parking of previous vehicles.

This was it, their ride was over and it was time to walk out and the confront the guards. Ahmed explained that it was only a short distance to the border, 'We wait here for you, one hour, then we go Baghdad, Inshallah.' With the luggage unloaded, everyone was ready, they shook hands with the drivers, and said their goodbyes with a variety of phrases both Arabic and English. As Sparky lifted up his suit case from the desert sand, Ahmed walked towards him, hand outstretched, looking very sad and uncomfortable he said,'Goodbye my friend Mr Sparky, *Baaraka Allahu fik* for everything you have done for me, may Allah take care of you all, Inshallah.' It was strangely precious moment, as the heat of the Arabian sun beat down on this disparate band of men, only moments away from possible freedom. What would happen to them all, what would happen to their country, where would everyone end up?

The sun was now very hot, as shimmering waves of heat slightly distorted their view of the border check point. Stretching towards them was a low level wooden board walk, leading to a door and a window with a sliding panel. They all stopped some six metres away and put down their bags. Sparky looked about him, and almost laughed. What a strange, somewhat bizarre sight they made, a dozen or so English Business men, standing outside in the searing desert heat, some in slacks and loose shirts, others in lightweight suits, and two gentlemen wearing three piece pin stripped jackets and trousers, pure white shirts, collar and tie. Both of them clutching their leather brief cases, and looking as though they had no intentions of putting them down.

Someone said, 'Might be best if we give all our passports to Sparky, rather than stand in a queue.' It was no problem for him, he wanted to progress things as quickly as possible. So there he stood outside the sliding window with sixteen British passports in his hand. He could see the guard inside, but there was no acknowledgement or movement, the guard simply sat at his desk, smoking, and occasionally turning to talk to a colleague. After a few minutes the window slid open, and the guard motioned for Sparky to hand over the passports he was holding. No word was spoken, and window was immediately closed.

The sun was now climbing to it's zenith, there was no shade, or rest places, and everyone was finding the heat difficult to cope with. Looking around Sparky took note of the five metre high security weldmesh fencing which formed the physical border. It stood, looking formidable, and stretching as far as the eye could see between Syria to the north, Jordan to the west, and Saudi Arabia in the south. Thousands of Kilometres of territorial ownership and a statement of power. He further noted that twenty metres to the west from where he was standing was sentry post with a huge set of double gates, and on the surface of the desert lay a large diameter pipeline supported every ten metres or so by substantial concrete cradles. The pipeline was disappearing towards Jordan. 'Must be the way out of here,' he mused, then it dawned on him, if that's the way they have to go, how were they going to travel down it? Every twenty minutes or so, large trucks were checked in and out of the gates, some coming from Jordan, and others returning back down the pipeline highway towards Jordan.

It was almost noon when the guard opened the door to the board walk, shouted something they couldn't understand and motioned Sparky to come forward. Before he reached the threshold, the guard threw all the passports into the sand and said, 'Imshi go,' as he pointed towards the double gates, then closed the door behind him. Sparky handed out the passports, and as he gave John his, he nodded towards the gate and said,'lets get out of here.' The sentry had been watching the the board-walk proceedings with interest, but when Sparky and John arrived at his post, he looked surprised, and slightly confused. There then followed an animated negotiation with the guard, who of course spoke no English, French, German or anything else but his native Iraqi dialect. It was obvious what these strange, sweaty, baggage laden men wanted. They needed transport to Jordan. There was no chance at all of calling a bunch of Taxi's, it would have to be the Trucks. As they stood around, now joined by other members of the group, various people tried to communicate with the friendly but amused guard. He was offered cigarettes, money, and smiles as an inducement to secure passage on a truck. He refused everything, until one of the Brits showed him some quite smart promotional company ball point pens, which were left over from an exhibition. This seemed to do the trick, and the guard happily accepted a handful, putting them strait into his trouser pocket.

The next truck leaving Iraq, was a monster, a massive cargo truck. The guard spoke to the driver and then turned to Sparky and nodded his confirmation that a lift was on offer, but only for two people. Scrambling around to the passenger side, where the driver had opened the door, they lifted up their bags and followed them into a large cab, shouting out good luck to the others, saying they would wait for them later... what was to happen over the next few hours was quite extraordinary. Elated at finally leaving Iraq behind, they sat back in the huge passenger seats and tried to let it all sink in. The road ahead was strait as a die, and seemed to go on for ever. The driver a jovial looking man, with very bad teeth, bad breath, and a definite case of sympathetic ophthalmia, crunched his way through the gear box and headed west at a rapidly increasing speed. It became obvious to Sparky that the oil pipeline road was a conduit, supplying Saddam Hussain with essential supplies, trucks were passing each other in both directions every half and hour or so.

As far as they could tell the driver was a Jordanian called Tariq. After a short while they noticed numbers of burnt out trucks laying on either side of the road, which was black topped and only single width, built half a metre or so above the floor of the desert. There was only just enough room to pass. Then Tariq switched on his radio, turned up the volume and began singing loudly to the catchy upbeat Arabic music. This seemed to have the effect of making him drive even faster, Sparky squirmed as he saw the speedometer was touching 70 kph and rising. Heading towards them from the west was another truck, Tariq stopped singing, gripped the steering wheel, then put his arms out in front of him, in typical formula one fashion. He assumed a position in the centre of the highway, and pushed the accelerator pedal to the floor. The speed increased as John covered his face with both his hands, as the on coming truck seemed to be carrying out the same manoeuvre.

Sparky looked sideways towards Tariq, who retuned his gaze, and laughed. For ever afterwards he was convinced that he had said,'Chicken.' as the speedo read 130kmph, and still rising. There was nothing the pair could do, maybe this was their fate, *obliterated on the oil-pipe highway,* somewhere between Iraq and Amman. But at the very last moment both drivers veered slightly from their suicidal lines, and the trucks scrapped past each others wing mirrors with centimetres to spare.

The game of chicken were repeated a number of times during the hair raising hundred Kilometre drive. The surrounding desert terrain had hardly changed since leaving the Iraqi border, but ahead they could see some sort of a settlement with a walled area and a tall white pole displaying the national flag of Jordan. Their wonderfully crazy cross-eyed Tariq, crunched back down through his gears and brought them gently to a halt outside a high wall. Sparky offered him some money, but he was having none of it, he just smiled and said,'Allah Akbar,' They shook hands with him, then climbed down stiffly and somewhat unsteadily from the cab, onto the soft hot desert sand. Outside the cool interior of the truck, the late afternoon heat hit them like a blast furnace. But they didn't care, they had survived and were now starting the next stage of their great escape. *Eat your heart Steve McQueen.*

There was a wooden door in the brick built desert wall, and Sparky was first to go through to the other side. The sun temporarily dazzled his tired eyes, but as he took stock of the situation, a very attractive auburn haired young lady, pushed a microphone towards him, said something about CNN Television, followed by, 'Hi have you just come from Baghdad in a truck?' The next few minutes were a blur, as he struggled to compose himself.'Yes I have,' he replied moving up the path towards a substantial looking building. No sooner was he over the shock of meeting a nice young American TV reporter, when he was confronted by a distinguished looking smartly dressed man walking down the path to meet him. 'Welcome to Jordan,' he said in a cultured middle eastern accent, 'I'm the minister for tourism.' Well, Sparky always thought that's what the man said... They had apparently arrived at the Jordanian customs post of Ruweished,this day was getting more bizarre with every minute. Gradually the rest of the escapees arrived safely, and like Sparky and John they were asked to fill in a simple form, pay a few Dollars, and have an entry visa stamped in their passports. The British Embassy in Baghdad had alerted their office in Amman to expect the arrival of the 'Baghdad sixteen' as they were to be called later. Michael Phillips the assistant military attaché in Jordan was also there to greet them, together with an air-conditioned bus, stocked with quantities of nice cool fresh water, and decorated with Union Jacks. It was around three pm when their bus eventually left on the 80 KM drive to Amman, eventually arriving shortly before eight pm that evening. The mood on the bus was one of great relief, most people sat quietly watching the countryside slip bye, and probably contemplating the events of the past few hours. During the course of the journey the two be-suited gentlemen with the leather brief cases, told them that they had been in Baghdad for nearly a month. They were from Oxford University, and had been conducting a study into the cities traffic control systems, and road networks. They were contracted to write a report, recommending the improvements necessary if Baghdad was to stop itself from coming to a stand still, in the not too distant future. The study had been ordered by Saddam Hussain himself. The Oxford men divulged that the authorities had been very helpful during their stay, providing them with a complete set of the most up to date, and detailed plans of the whole city and its environs. The reader can draw their own conclusions as to how useful and important this would be to the British Government, and others in the future...

The sun was setting as the bus weaved it's way through the busy suburbs of Jordan's capital, Amman. It had been a long drive, and a long day, but it was far from over. As the bus pulled over to the side of the road and stopped, their embassy man Michael Phillips, stood up at the front and told them that they should prepare themselves for a warm reception. The news was out about their departure from Iraq, they could expect a welcome from ex Pat Brits, and a very hectic time with the world press and TV, who were eagerly waiting to hear their story. The hotel had a block of rooms reserved for them, but it was up to individuals to make their own booking. Five minutes later the bus pulled up outside the Intercontinental Hotel. Almost immediately a frantic group of media people surged towards the front exit door of the bus, and as soon as it opened the questions began. Everyone on board was anxious to leave and stand on firm safe ground again, but a bottle neck formed inside as people were being delayed from stepping of the bus. Sparky could see this may take some time, and he wasn't really in the mood to answer questions, besides which he wanted to check into the hotel, and make sure he had a decent room. He nodded to his friend John, and said,'Come on mate, lets leave by the back door.' They skirted the throng of journalists, reporters and camera men, which included the BBC's intrepid Kate Ade. As they headed for the hotel entrance, an English voice shouted,'Where you from mate?' 'Liverpool replied Sparky with a smile as he moved inside the hotel. On the 9th of August Sparky was to see his picture on page three of the Today newspaper, the caption underneath read HOMEWARD BOUND for Liverpool. It showed Sparky dressed in his favourite Hawaiian shirt, KD slacks, well worn leather deck shoes, and clutching his beloved and well travelled leather Pilot case. It was alongside another half page picture showing him and nine of the escapees standing behind all their luggage inside the hotel lobby, Sparky was still clutching his Pilot case.

It was mayhem at the reception desk, and rooms were going fast. Sparky and John agreed to share a twin bedded room, and this speeded things up considerably. After dumping their bags, they tossed a coin for the shower, and John won. Sparky took this opportunity to make a call back home, he was politely advised that there were no lines available, the worlds press appeared to have commandeered all outgoing communication, and it stayed that way for the rest of the night. There were no mobile phones readily available for international use in those days, and satellite phones were extremely expensive. It was still old fashioned journalism, reporters had to file their stories to their news editors using the good old land-line telephone system. It would be almost twenty four hours before Sparky managed to make a quick call, whilst rushing to catch a London bound BA flight from Rome International the next day. In the meantime the now famous group of so called Iraqi Hero's were to spend their first night of freedom in a haze of alcohol, food, and never ending interviews.

Sparky never really understood how it happened, but it appeared that the British Press Corps had booked the main banquet room of the Intercontinental, and they were all invited to join them as their guests.

It was well into mid evening by this time, but the offer of food and sustenance needed no second thoughts. The whole table and room was buzzing, there was almost certainly some form of introduction from somebody, but Sparky couldn't remember who it was. After hours on the road, and having covered hundreds of kilometres in the stifling dessert heat, they were all famished, and dehydrated. It wasn't long before most people started to feel the effects of unlimited amounts of free alcohol, and superb Arab food. It seemed as though there was a reporter or journalist to cover every other guest in the room.

But Sparky's opinion could have been influenced by the fast moving and excited atmosphere, and was probably distorted by too much to drink. The outcome was that the press built up their valuable copy, the Baghdad sixteen had a fantastic night, and as far as he could remember, no one disgraced themselves. They all agreed however to check out the next morning, and go strait to the airport and catch the next available flight to anywhere at all, no matter where it was, they just wanted to leave Jordan, and end up any where except Iraq...

After breakfast the next morning, a fleet of happy taxi drivers took most of them to the airport. Sparky and John agreed to keep together if possible and managed to secure the last two seats on a flight direct to Rome, with an onward connection to Heathrow that day, if they could make it on time. Others ended up in Cyprus, Stockholm, Istanbul and Moscow. It had been an amazing encounter for all of them, everyone had performed really well under difficult circumstances, there was no panic, and no complaining. They all took each others contact details and pledged to meet up at the first available opportunity. But life doesn't always work out that way, and they never did. Sparky and John would remain in contact for some time afterwards, since they both lived in the Lancashire/ Merseyside area, and Sparky exchanged Christmas cards with a number of the group for a couple of years. Their Alitalia flight was late taking off from Amman due to airspace congestion, and circled Rome airport for some time before completing a bumpy landing.

Their main bags were booked through to the BA flight, but they doubted if they would see them any time soon. With only ten minutes to spare they ran, pushed and shouted their way through the terminal and the BA departure gate. Sparky saw an opportunity and made a collect charge phone call to his partner Kay, just hoping that she would actually be at home. She was, but John was screaming at him to hurry up, so when she answered he just said,'Leaving Rome now, BA, Heathrow,' and slammed the phone down, he wasn't even sure she had heard the message. Breathless, they presented themselves to gate staff. It seemed as if crew were half expecting them, and they were definitely the last passengers to board the flight. Feeling a bit embarrassed, they made their way down the aisle to their allocated seats. Then something really amazing, and completely unexpected happened. Passengers were standing up,clapping and cheering, some even reaching over and shaking their hands, or just touching them as they passed.'Well done lads, great stuff,' shouted one man, and others joined in. Their secret was out, the whole plane had copies of the British daily newspapers from the The Mail, Guardian, Mirror, Today and possibly others. The two sat down, really embarrassed now, but it was a wonderful feeling to be going home to good old Blighty, and in the company of friendly natives.

Miraculously their luggage rolled off the escalator, and they soon cleared customs and immigration. Kay was waiting in the arrivals hall, he just knew she would be. Totally reliable, totally dependable and lovely. They may both have shed some tears... Sparky recovered and introduced John, he lived in Wigan, so there was no problem taking him home, on their way to Liverpool, before they left, John phoned his parents. The motorway was quiet and they had an excellent journey through to Wigan, John's parents insisted they go in for a cup of tea, so they spent a pleasant half hour telling their story. His mum and dad were just lovely, and delighted to have their son back home in one piece, safe and sound. His mum kept thanking Sparky, and giving him a hugs. In truth Sparky had been very pleased to have someone with him, John had shared everything with him, from the moment the idea was born, to the final dash for a flight in Rome. It was all very special. Later they met up again for an evening out, and kept in touch for a while, he was a very nice man with great parents.

The following day Sparky went to work, and as was his habit, he was the first to arrive. Gradually the factory came to life as people clocked on, and normality resumed. Vanda rushed into his office, smiling and crying at the same time, they had a quick *mutually concessional* hug, then she brought two cups of strong coffee and got on with the big catch up. He told her his story, occasionally interrupted by colleagues and staff who came to congratulate him, and say they were pleased he was back. Richard however was not there, having left for a holiday in France a few days before Saddam invaded Kuwait. The news from Vanda was not good. The UN had placed a total freeze on all Iraqi overseas assets, and investments, all their bank account were frozen.

It was really bad news for Sparky and his company. The current order they were manufacturing for Iraqi state electricity was now in crisis.

There was a deposit of seven hundred and fifty thousand pounds lodged in the Iraqi's London bank. The contract was based on the release of funds against presentation of the appropriate documentation. In other words Micro-coms were paid prior to shipment of goods, and the factory scheduled its production to fit that contractual condition. The company was already over extended on its credit with the suppliers of parts required to fulfil the order. These creditors, and others were now closing ranks. Demanding their money. They knew Sparky had been detained in Baghdad, they watched the unfolding daily news about the crisis in Kuwait, and quite rightly took the view that things would get worse before they got better. How right they were.

Richard returned early from his holiday in France, and a board meeting was con-veined to review their overall situation. It was not good news, with the collapse of the Iraqi job things were dire. Financially they had been sailing close to the wind for some time, not really keeping their head above water. They would now have to pull together, Richard was experienced in raising venture capital, but he had played those cards on previous occasions and wasn't sure there was much help waiting in the wings. Sparky tried to interest other investors, most observers were complimentary about the company and its products. They could see there was great potential, but it needed risky investment, and the smart money doesn't do risky. In a wild moment of inspiration he contacted the offices of the famous business tycoon Richard Branson. He was advised to send a telex to their office outlining their problems, and what it was they were looking for.

Sparky put together a comprehensive explanation, detailing the company's history and where it was now. He stressed the point that they were an innovative small British company,working at the cutting edge of their technology. All they needed was some help to steer them out of stormy waters. Three days after he sent the telex, his desk phone rang, and Wendy their switchboard operator told him, in a rather incredulous voice, that Richard Branson wanted to speak to him. Even Sparky was impressed, and took the call with some hopeful anticipation.

In the event, a very friendly and charming Mr Branson said he was unable to invest in Micro-coms. He understood their dilemma, sympathised with it, but at the end of the day Micro-coms was unfortunately too small to include in his acquisitions portfolio. He sounded genuinely sorry, he wished them the best of luck, and said he would put the word out in financial circles. But nothing ever came of it at all.

As he put down the telephone Sparky realized he was alone, everywhere was unusually quiet. He sat for a few moments thinking about what had just happened, and had the feeling that he'd been here before, his life was about to take another nose dive, he could see no way out. He felt sad, and emotionally drained. Over the ensuing months numbers of avenues were explored, none of them produced any satisfactory results. There were companies interested in their acquisition, but they had the luxury of time on their side, and could wait until the condition's and price were right.

As expected Iraq did not give up its occupation of Kuwait, holding on for seven months. A UN backed coalition to expel Iraqi troops from Kuwait began with an aerial bombardment on 16 January 1991. This was followed by a ground assault on 23 February. It was a decisive victory for the coalition forces, who liberated Kuwait and advanced into Iraqi territory. The coalition ceased their advance, and declared a cease-fire 100 hours after the ground campaign started. Aerial and ground combat was confined to Iraq, Kuwait, and areas on the border of Saudi Arabia.

During their retreat Iraqi military forces set fire to 700 oil wells as part of a scorched earth policy while retreating from Kuwait. The fires started in January and February 1991 and the last one wasn't extinguished until November 1991.

In mid 91,Richard eventually agreed a deal for the sale of Micro-coms to a security equipment manufacturer. Sparky and the other directors were still employed, and steps were taken to put the company back into profitability and give it a future. By this time Sparky had become disillusioned with what was happening, he was lacking enthusiasm and still felt emotionally bankrupt. Together with others, he had given everything he could, but it was time to move on. In the autumn of 1991, after securing a sales position with a small Satellite Receiving tech company in the south of England, he resigned. It was a poor decision, and although the first few months were actually quite exciting, with numbers of visits to Saudi Arabia, it soon became clear that Sparky was not able contribute to the companies core business of Satellite TV down links. He was under the impression that they had employed him to broaden their sales base, by moving into CCTV microwave transmission systems, and associated security equipment. His relationship with the owner gradually deteriorated, until one morning when he arrived at their offices, he was made redundant. It was a surprise, and he was shocked at first, but there was nothing he could do, except go home and look for another job.

He put feelers out through his contacts, and secured numbers of interviews. Two of them offered him employment, but both required him to move overseas, which in itself wasn't a problem, but he didn't fancy West Africa, or Saudi Arabia. Then in the summer of 92, he was offered a superb position with a Derbyshire based security manufacturing company called G-Technics. Sparky new their MD, Peter , they had met many times on the international exhibition circuit, he liked him, and loved their product. Peter had developed a unique magnetic sensing cable which picked up mechanical vibrations when attached to certain types of surface, the cable turned these into electrical impulses which were analysed through a special processor. Typically this cable could be attached to high security fencing as used in prisons, or the surface of bank vaults. Any unauthorised physical attack on these structures would be interoperated as hostile, and an alarm would be activated. It was ingeniously simple but very cleaver, and Peter had established his company as market leaders. They were almost a household name for this type of application, both in the UK and numbers of overseas outlets.

In the early 1990s China was beginning to emerge from its isolationism, and was hungry for cooperation with foreign companies. Peter wanted a piece of this vast market, and needed a dedicated person with overseas experience, and technical knowledge to promote his company throughout China and South East Asia. He invited Sparky to come and discuss it with him, during the interview he suddenly asked Sparky if he could pick up two salted peanuts, with a pair of chop sticks. Sparky picked up three at once, and immediately got the job. Well it was a bit of fun, he had already decided to offer him the position, starting on the following Monday. For Sparky it was a job made in heaven, it was absolutely perfect for him, he could hardly believe his good fortune, and was still smiling when he arrived back home in Merseyside.

His time spent working for Peter were amongst would be some of the most enjoyable working years he had ever had. The company was relatively small, only forty or so employees, but there was an enthusiasm which made going to work a pleasure. The office facilities and training room were all maintained to an excellent standard, and it seemed as though everyone took a pride in the product. Most importantly, it worked exceptionally well, was reliable, and the after sales technical support was second to none. Peter's motto was that the 'Customer is King.' He instilled in everyone the belief that they were all salespeople for the company, no matter whether they were engineer's, production staff, admin or the all important cleaning lady. He firmly believed that customers judge the company by the way they were dealt with on the phone, or when they came to visit the factory. Sparky felt completely at home right from the first day he arrived. Peters ideals resonated with him, and for the first time in years he was able to see a way forward. The big bonus was that they were financially stable, something he had not enjoyed for a long time.

The first week was taken up with technical product training, introduction to all the staff and sales meetings with Peter. The task ahead was not an easy one, it would involve extensive overseas travel, and numbers of weeks away from home. The UK government were very supportive of any British companies who wanted to expand into world wide markets. There were financial incentives in the form of overseas trade delegations. Companies who signed up for these had to pay their expenses up front, but could then claim back more than fifty percent of the costs upon completion of the tour. China and South East Asia were high on the list, and Peter had already signed up to join a number of them.

One of Sparkys roles was to act as product training and support manager for existing and newly appointed distributors in his territory, attending local and regional seminars and exhibitions. All this was right up Spark's street. He'd been doing it for years, and was excited at the prospect. He had only been in the company for three weeks, when Peter came into his office one day, and said, 'Ever been to Papua New Guinea?' no I haven't he replied, 'well your going there next week,' said Peter with a smile.

Their Australian distributor Wormald Security, had a substantial operation in Papua, they protected private residences and commercial organisations. Their biggest job was the security of a huge goldmine in a remote mountainous area north west of Mt Hagen, in the central highlands. It was called Porgera, and at the time it was the largest open cast gold mining project in the world. The site was enormous, and was protected by a five metre high perimeter fence constructed of prison grade weldmesh. Wormald had originally installed Geotechnics product on the whole of the fence. But the local indigenous tribe were very hostile, they had existed for generations in the highlands, and had never had contact with white-men until the surveyors arrived prospecting for gold in the late 1980s. They considered the mountain where the mine was situated to be sacred and holy. They violently opposed the presence of the mine, shooting at the workers with poison darts and arrows, and numbers of people had been killed. It was a dangerous place to be, and was patrolled twenty four hours a day by armed guards wearing Kevlar body armour, and carrying high velocity automatic rifles. The Papua New Guinea government were anxious to continue mining the gold, the country stood to benefit considerably from the proceeds. At the same time they were trying to reach an agreement with the local tribe, but progress was slow.

Sparky's brief was to fly out to the capital Port Moresby and conduct a training session with their agents Wormald. He was then to fly up to the mine by helicopter and conduct a survey of the equipment on the fence. The locals had been attacking anything they could gain access to. The owners needed solutions, they desperately needed to detect intruders, and protect their employees. 'Seems like a walk in the park,' mused Sparky as he read through the reports and telex messages from down under.

The plan was to fly to Kuala Lumpur in Malaysia for a stop over before moving on to Port Moresby. In Kuala Lumpur he met their Malaysian distributors, and spent a few days with them. They had not been operating very long, and were still trying to establish themselves. It was a pleasant and somewhat civilised start to his trip. They were a very professional company, who had appointed a smart Chinese manager called Michael Tan. Sparky was well received and duly impressed with the offices and sales facilities that were available. He gave some product training and discussed strategy for future visits. Reviewed the potential market for their products in Malaysia and Singapore, the opportunities looked very exciting, but it needed a lot of work.

The fight down to Port Moresby was on a small turbo prop,aircraft. It was noisy, bumpy and took hours. At one stage on the flight a large Dutch backpacker deciding that he was tired, lay down in the isle and fell fast asleep, the cabin crew gave up on their attempts to wake him, and left him where he was.

Sparky was met at the airport by Harry Taylor the local Wormald Security Manager. He was a lean and fit looking man in his mid thirties, casually dressed, with a relaxed manner, endorsed by his cool Australian accent, Ray-ban shades and deep suntanned face. He liked him for the outset. On the way to his hotel, he was struck by the obvious physical security which surrounded all the residential houses, and some of the commercial properties. Everywhere he looked there were high fences, topped with coils of vicious looking barbedwire, monitored by CCTV cameras at the gates, and on each corner of the property. This was serious defensive protection, which seemed out of place amongst the sunshine, blues skies, abundance of lush vegetation and exotic flora. 'It's the wild west out here mate,' drawled Harry, 'Violent crime, and robberies happen all the time.' Later Harry was to explain some of the reasons behind his statement, but in the meantime Sparky took it all on board, and realised this was a society under stress.

The entrance to the hotel grounds were heavily guarded, firearms being worn openly. Harry sorted things out at reception, and suggested they met up for dinner in a couple of hours time. 'We'll go to the Moresby Yacht Club just down the road, its as safe a place as any,' said Harry. 'Sounds great,' replied Sparky, 'Tell me exactly where it is and I'll stroll down there to meet you if you like?' he added. ' Not on your life mate, it'll be dark by then, and not safe, so I'll come and pick you up at seven, OK?' Harry was right on time, and as Sparky slid onto the passenger seat he noticed a pistol laying in the centre of the Jeep's console. The drive to the Yacht club was less than one hundred metres, and took less than two minutes.

His introduction to the delights of Papua New Guinea had only just begun. The following day was Sunday, and Harry invited Sparky to spend the day down at his Bungalow. 'I've got cold beers, a pool table, and my girlfriend is a great cook, she'd be pleased to meet you, on account of you being English,' Smiled Harry. 'She thinks you guys are sooo polite and gentlemanly,' 'That's me alright,' taunted Sparky. It turned out to be a great day, Harry's girlfriend was an attractive local girl, and she was a great cook. During the course of the afternoon Sparky learned a lot about the political and sociological problems the country was going through. As a British possession it was placed under the authority of the Commonwealth of Australia in 1902. Following the passage of the Papua Act in 1905, British New Guinea became the Territory of Papua, and formal Australian administration began in 1906. Although Papua remained under their control it was still a British possession until the independence of

Papua New Guinea in 1975. They were at the time of Sparky's visit, still a newly emerging nation.

Many of the indigenous hill tribes still clung to their old ways, they did not understand or want intergeneration. Those who came down to the coastal areas found themselves marginalised,there was little or no work, and discrimination was rampant. A breeding ground for discontent, civil disorder and violence. Harry explained that it was not unusual for people to be attacked whist in their cars, typically this may happen at traffic lights or road junctions, and women in particular were very vulnerable. Wormald had developed a panic alarm alert system, for use in Port Moresby, basically it was a wide area radio based paging network. Anyone under attack could activate the panic button on a transmitter, a signal would be flagged up in a central control-room on a large screen city map, and with its location identified, a rapid response team would be despatched to the scene. It was claimed that they could have a unit on the scene. within less than five minutes. *It is important to remember that that these events were taking place in the very early 1990s.* When he went to bed that night, Sparky now had no doubt that he was in a very volatile environment. Caution and alertness should be his watchword.

On the Monday he met the rest of the Wormald Security team, and conducted a practical training course, with a general discussion about the Geoqtechnics product range and back up services. Everyone seemed to enjoy Sparky's easy going style mixed with his typical northern humour. Harry had booked them on the next available flight leaving for the mine at 10am the following morning. He told him take the minimum of personal items, tooth brush and paste, and comfortable clothing. It was more important to take his site survey kit and camera, and although the were staying overnight, they wouldn't know if there were any bunks available for them until they arrived. In the worst case they may even be *Hot Bunking.*

The following morning they boarded a large Russian built, and operated transport helicopter. Sparky was excited, he had been out on helicopters to oil rigs in the north sea a number of times, but not as big as this one. It was possible to reach the mine by road, but the route was torturous and dangerous, winding through the mountains and rain forest. It could take up to a couple of days, and longer if the weather closed in. Even helicopters could be grounded when visibility was down, and this happened to Sparky and Harry, after approximately half an hour they had to divert to one of the way stations in the forest, and wait for the weather to improve. The chopper was full of mine workers going out to begin another two week stint in the inhospitable environment of Pergola. The majority of people were from Australian or New Zealand, they signed on knowing the dangers and hardships they could expect, and they were very well paid, far more than was possible back home, or in other mining operations. Later, one of the Australian security guards told Sparky that he was earning and saving so much money, that he planned to retire within five years, if he survived that long.

The big helicopter was very noisy, and it was almost impossible to have any sort of conversation with anyone. It looked as though it had seen better days, the tell tale signs of long and hard service were showing, Sparky hoped it had an up to date airworthiness certificate. Their stop over was in a small jungle clearing, on a concrete landing pad next to a small well constructed building which contained tables, chairs, and a self service food and coffee stand. They were on the side of steep hill, which afforded spectacular views of the forest canopy. The screeching of monkey's and a wide variety of undistinguishable sounds added a sense of remoteness to the whole experience. The mist which had grounded them, swirled around the helipad blotting out the sun, coating everything with a heavy dew. It felt clammy and oppressive. Sparky had the distinct feeling they were being watched, and not just by the animals or birds. He moved back inside the building, 'no point getting stuck with a poison dart or an arrow,' he thought to himself. 'I've only just got here.'

Minutes later the PA system announced they would be ready to leave in five minutes. Forty-five minutes later the chopper descended rapidly to the main landing area situated in the middle of the site. After only fifteen minuets on the ground it had disembarked it's new arrivals, and loaded those workers who were going on leave, or were terminating their contracts after making enough money to retire! Once outside the helicopter Harry told Sparky that everyone on the site walked very quickly or ran, moving targets were harder to hit, well that's what they all hoped. It was noticeably cooler here than at the way station. The mine was located at the head of the Porgera valley in the rain forest covered highlands at an altitude of 2,200 to 2,700m, in a region of high rainfall, landslides, and frequent earthquakes.

After registering their details with security reception, they were issued with passes, told not to loose them, and must wear them at all times. The guard took them to meet the mines security director a huge bear of a man, who Sparky guessed was an Afrikaner. Peter De jong, was a long-time employee of the mining company, serving with them on projects all over the world. His last assignment had been in the diamond mines of Kimberly.

Over coffee Peter, a quietly spoken and jovial man, showed them detailed site plans, and in particular the perimeter fence, which was constructed to a very high specification, and was topped with austenitic stainless steel barbed coils, impervious to corrosion, and possessing razor sharp barbs. Since the fence was proving almost impossible to climb or penetrate, the tribesmen were now trying to physically wreck anything they could, and were shooting arrows and darts at people within the PIDS zone. (Perimeter Intruder Detection System). CCTV cameras were interfaced with the Geoqtechnics sensor, which were programmed to activate each time a physical attack on the fence took place. The security control room could then pinpoint the exact location of the intrusion anywhere around the perimeter. But now the sensor cable and its associated analysers were being put out of action on a regular basis, the situation had become critical.

Accompanied by two heavily armed guards sporting high powered automatic rifles and powerful binoculars, Harry and Sparky carried out a complete survey around the fence line. In three separate areas they came across Geotechnics electronic analyser boxes with holes in them, and some with arrows sticking out of both sides. The sensor cables had been cut, and in one section the the tribesmen had lit a large fire alongside the fence. It had been a scary few hours, and although they had not actually seen anyone on the outside it didn't mean they weren't there. Everyone was pleased to be back inside the accommodation modules. The following morning, they reported back to Peter De jong, and Sparky gave him an overview of what they had seen. He explained that it would be necessary for him to consult with his factory so that a full upgraded proposal could be offered. Peter fully accepted this, but stressed that a solution and response was required as a matter of grave urgency, then rising from his chair, dwarfing both Harry and Sparky he shook hands, and repeated his request for a very rapid reply.

It had been an amazing visit to Papua New Guinea, Sparky had never been anywhere quite like it before. The overt threat of violence, the obvious visual confirmation of how serious things were, this could be seen everywhere, around the perimeters of residential homes well as commercial properties. But it was a fascinating place and he was pleased to have made the visit. At that time nobody could have foreseen that more than thirty year later, PN would become a popular tourist destination, advertised on the world wide web, offering luxury hotels, self contained apartments, and exciting coastal activates such as sailing and scuba diving off the reefs. Within a few days of Sparky faxing his survey report, photograph, drawings and plans, to the team at the factory in Derbyshire, they came back with a detailed proposal. The solution was expensive and would involve Harry and his engineers in a lot of hard work, but Peter De jong would eventually place a contract with Wormald to carry the work.

Over the next few years Sparky would travel extensively throughout China, Hong Kong, the Philippines,South East Asia, Indonesia, Malaysia, Singapore, Thailand, South Korea, and Taiwan. He successfully set up a network of distributors, who in turn were successful in gaining numbers of large and small contracts for applications such as: Airports, Prison's, Petrochemical refineries, Power stations, land borders, Container terminals, Environmental Recycling Plants, and dozens of small but important installations. Geotechnics continued to expand, and develop new and exciting electronic equipment for use in PIDS environments. Then Peter decided to appoint a general manager, his brief was to manage and reorganise the company, and expand their customer base. This turned out to be a disaster for Sparky, when after only a few months of the new man being on board, Peter made Sparky redundant. This move was not directly attributed to the new man, but Sparky was always convinced that it was him who had persuaded Peter to get rid of him. Sparky was completely devastated, he could not believe that after all his hard work, spending months every year away from the UK, travelling thousands and thousands of air miles that it should come to this. Many of his distributors were equally shocked, they contacted Peter direct, and pleaded with him not to let Sparky go... but it was to no avail, and Sparky left. He kept in touch with various people in the company, and a few months later he learned that Peter was diagnosed with terminal cancer. Sparky was really upset, despite the redundancy issue, he still regarded Peter as the best boss he had ever worked for. He never understood his decision, but he also never held it against him. Shortly before Peter died Sparky visited him at his home near Ashbourne Derbyshire, they had a good natter and a cup of tea. During the visit Peter asked Sparky if he had screwed up his life by making him redundant. Sparky said it was a hard decision to understand, but praised Peter for being the best boss he had ever worked for. A few weeks later Peter sadly passed away, and his company continued under new ownership, which Peter had already negotiated.

With his now extensive contacts in the security industry, it wasn't long before he secured himself another position working for an integrated security systems company in Middlesex north London. They designed and installed high end access control, time management and perimeter intruder detection equipment, which could be controlled over dedicated private Local Area Networks or LANS. Although it was a small company it employed high quality technicians and a system design engineer. Sparky new the owner, having met him on numbers of occasions at various security exhibitions. He was in need of another salesman, and Sparky fitted the bill. The salary was below what he had been used to, but there was a bonus scheme based of sales turnover paid every quarter. The deal included a company car, and expenses. The offer was to include UK and Overseas sales territories. But Sparky was fed up with travelling all over the world, living out of VIP airport lounges and hotel rooms. He wanted stability, and some sort of a regular home life. His Derbyshire cottage was now refurbished, it was in a lovely location and he was very comfortable living there. During his time with Geotechnics he had continued running and climbing, keeping himself very fit. Derbyshire was the perfect place for him to live. After a bit of wrangling he was offered the job, and it was agreed that he cold work from home. At that particular time this was not the norm, employers usually liked people to be based at one location. In time of course this would change dramatically, especially when the Internet became more widely established.

When he joined the company, his computer skills were at best very basic, which was true of the majority of his friends and business associates at that time. But his new boss was very focused on the future and had invested a lot of money and effort in to embracing this new world, he could see that it was the only way forward. Sparky was issued with his first laptop computer, and was encouraged to become proficient in its use. There was no shortage of help and tuition, his boss was particularity skilled as a tutor, as were all the other members of staff, they were only to pleased and ready to help Sparky the newbie.

The range of equipment they sold was designed and manufactured in Europe, it was of high quality, with innovative technology. The company had an established customer base, which was ready for expansion, and it didn't take long for Sparky to make his mark. In the beginning everything went well, the engineers were always very helpful, and he quickly became good friends with them all. However after a while he realized there was a problem between the boss and some of the staff, there were tensions with undertones of dissatisfaction. Enquiries and orders grew at a steady rate, but Sparky became frustrated with the boss, who always examined every quotation in minute detail before it was allowed to be submitted. In some cases he insisted the customer pay fifty percent of contract value with purchase order. This caused all sorts of problems for Sparky, as his customers refused to have such conditions placed them, some even told him they would go elsewhere rather than agree to what they thought of as an unfair request. This made Sparky suspect that the finances of his new company were not very healthy, which was endorsed when he realized they were being chased by suppliers for the payment of overdue accounts, and he had not been paid any of his quarterly bonus's. He had been working with them for almost a year, and as Christmas approached he had a meeting with his boss to ask why he had not been paid. He apologised, said it was a complicated issue involving a number of factors, but that he would sort it out very soon. Sparky new this was a poor excuse, either he hadn't got enough money to pay him, or had no intentions of doing so.

At the start of the new year two important things happened. Through his contacts in Malaysia, Sparky was sent an enquiry for a very large integrated security system for the Malaysian government, worth almost three hundred thousand pounds. It was absolutely perfect for them, just the sort of systems they excelled at. After a number of weeks of hard work, numerous telephone calls and telex messages, his Malaysian agent sent one of his senior engineers to the UK to work on the final proposal prior to submission. Confidence was very high, the Agent was well placed, highly respected, and had every reason to believe he would secure the contract. With their specification and proposal agreed, the engineer went back to Kuala Lumpur... Sparky expected that the good news would only be a few days away. But life can really be difficult at times. One morning they woke up to the devastating announcement that the Malaysian currency, the ringgit, had been devalued. News from his agent was dire, all government contacts were on hold until further notice, their bid was now pointless, everyone involved was deflated and disappointed. All that work for no reward.

A couple of weeks later Sparky took a telephone call from a large Railway Systems Turn Key Solutions company based near Bristol in the west of England. The result of this conversation was to have far reaching effects on both his life, and that of the company he was working for. As the conversation unfolded Sparky could hardly believe what he was being told. He was asked to confirm that they could supply a fully integrated security and access control system capable of working over private dedicated LAN's. The man on the other end, we'll call him Colin, then told Sparky that his company already had a contract to supply a huge new railway system, including rolling stock, railways stations, control centre, and all infrastructure for the new Chek Lap Kok Island, airport rail link, to be known as Hong Kong International Airport. Currently under construction to replace the infamous Kai Tak.

Colin confirmed they had signed the contract, which was worth many millions of pounds, but at the very last moment they realised they had completely overlooked the specification to supply the access control and security system. In their original proposal they had included an estimated capital sum to cover that part of the bid, but now they had the approval to go ahead someone realized they had not been out to tender for that part of the contact. To make matters worse they were required to meet with the client in ten days time for detailed discussions about the implementation of the work.

Then Colin told him that due to the urgency of the the project they would not be going out to general tender at this time, so long as Sparky could confirm to them that they were able to offer a solution within the next few days. It was Thursday afternoon, but Colin said he would send an overall requirement by email, and that the full tender documentation would arrive by special courier the following morning, once Sparky confirmed that they could do the job and were interested.

The initial information via email showed that this was exactly the sort of job they were capable of doing, his boss had reservations about contractual conditions, but in the end Sparky rang Colin and told him to go ahead and send the courier with the full specifications and terms of supply. The following few days saw them all burning the midnight oil, working hard to complete the proposal within a week. When the calculations were completed the job it was worth just short of a million pounds. A huge amount of money for such a small company. It is beyond the scope of this narrative to dwell to long on the full details of what transpired over the coming months. They were awarded the contract, the European factory were excellent with their technical support, and with delivery of equipments. An experienced project engineered was employed to oversea the job in Hong Kong, he set up a local office, and rented a small apartment. As the job proceeded more equipment and services were added to the contract and its value rose to well in excess of one and half million pounds and rising all the time.

Prior to the commencement of the Check Lap Kok project, his boss employed an experienced overseas salesman. Barry was a really nice man, who had been in the access control business for many years, Sparky got on very well with him, as did other members of the team. Some eighteen months had now gone by and Sparky had still not received and bonus payments at all, despite his frequent requests. All he got was a promise which was never fulfilled. Frustrated and becoming more and more disenchanted with the situation, he consulted an employment disputes specialist who advised him to write a letter outlining the facts of his case, including copies of his original contact with the company. He should set a time limit for a response of one week, after which time if his boss had not responded he would have no alternative but to take the matter to court. The meeting which followed with his boss was short and terse, he said he would work something out and advise him of the outcome.

The following week Barry phoned and asked Sparky to meet him at Leicester Forest Services on the M1 motorway. They met up in Barry's car, and looking very uncomfortable, Barry handed him a letter advising him that had he been made redundant, there was a payslip showing his salary to date, together with the tax rebates commensurate with redundancy. The letter also offered him the use of the company car for a period of eight weeks, but exclusive of any fuel expense. There was also separate letter regarding his bonus payments, it contained an offer of final settlement which was far below that which Sparky was entitled to. Especially considering the bonus he expected in connection with the Hong Kong contract. Barry was unimpressed with the way Sparky had been treated, and the fact that his boss had lacked the courage to carry out the deed himself. They sat for a while, Sparky feeling angry by what had happened, and the much reduced bonus payment offer. Barry then said that in his opinion the company was about to go under. He advised that the Hong Kong engineer had not been paid for two months,and the rent on the office and apartment were now overdue. Within a few weeks of Sparky's redundancy the company folded, allegedly owing large amounts of money to suppliers, VAT, and members of staff. Sparky sent a recorded delivery letter agreeing to the bonus payment, with a copy to his solicitor. He then made a vow to himself that he wouldn't work for anyone else again, he was sick of being at the bad end of companies failures. He decided from now on to work only for himself.

It was late spring time, so Sparky decided to go camping and walking in the mountains of Snowdonia, he needed time to clear his thoughts, and forget recent events. The year was 1998, he was fifty seven years old, out of work, but very fit. He lived in a lovely old stone cottage, was running up and down mountains and climbing well. He had some saving to see him by, so life wasn't so bad really. The weather was glorious, sunny days and warm nights, a perfect interlude on his own, in the environment he loved most of all. By the end of the week he had formulated a plan for his future. He smiled as he looked westwards towards his favourite mountain,Tryfan, packed his tent and drove back home to Derbyshire.

Sparky decided to work as a freelance consultant, covering communications and security. He called his company Com-Sec-Services, ordered a few hundred business cards, and printed stationary, opened up his large contact list and hit the telephone. The reaction from the people he talked to was very encouraging and within a couple of weeks he had his first consultancy assignment. The client was the Garda in the republic of Ireland, they had a requirement to write a specification to cover perimeter protection and microwave video transmission systems on a new training facility to the south of Dublin. They needed an independent report specifying a suitable system. It involved a visit with site survey, and writing up of the report. This would then be included with the tender documents for those companies bidding for the work. All together it involved a weeks work and two trips to Dublin. It was perfect for Sparky, and had a bonus that he was working with people he had known for some years. It was the start of more things to come. During a visit to Liverpool he called in on his old friend Richard, who had started a new company selling and installing fixed microwave links. They had distributorship agreement with a number of manufacturers, and business was booming. Richard suggested Sparky could be useful to them for radio mast surveys, and installation of the hardware, with commission on any sales made as a result of referrals.

In order to be a mast technician it was necessary to attend a four day course in Lancashire, the rules and regulations did not permit none qualified personnel from performing this work. It was just up Sparky's street, after all he was a climber, and very fit. It would be another string to his bow. The course was quite expensive, and when completed would mean an investment in a considerable amount of specialist hardware to carry out the work. He passed with flying colours,and was qualified to climb masts in excess of 100 metres. The investment was well worth it, and was paid back very quickly from the resultant work. One of the main requirements was to survey lines of sight. That is to say if a new microwave radio link was to be installed between one point to another, the supplier had to prove that there was a clear visual line of sight between the two, or sometimes even more locations. Mapping software could often be used using a computer, and sometimes this was satisfactory. But before a final decision was made, it would be necessary for someone to climb to the top of the mast, look towards the other end of the link, and confirm that there were no obstruction which would prevent the radio signal reaching the mast. These obstructions could be hills or mountains, or maybe apartment or office blocks which stood within the direct line. Some of these links were quite short, in the region of four or five kilometres,others may extend out to twenty-five of thirty kilometres. In both cases a good pair of binoculars were essential.

Within the first year Sparky was doing well, earning more than he had done for a while. His customer base was growing, and he was securing a good reputation for his work. He never turned down an opportunity, so long as it did not clash or coincide with other commitments. The work was varied and interesting, and he was more than satisfied with his life.

Never the less it was It was hard going, and there was no time for holidays, but he offset this by managing numbers of weekend camping trips, where he could go walking or climbing.

As the new millennium of 2000 approached, there were numbers of crazy theories forecasting doom, and the end of the world as people knew it. This was actually good business for Sparky who was asked to survey, and check out all manner of installations, just to make sure they would all work on the strike of midnight in the year 2000.

One cold Saturday November morning in1999, he was working in his office sorting out paper work and accounts when the phone rang and his pal Richard came on and said, 'What are you doing tomorrow?' 'Not a lot as it happens,' replied Sparky. 'Well how about going to Manchester airport, and collecting a ticket for a flight to Cairo?' Sparky smiled, just the sort of thing he expected from Richard. 'No problem, what's the job.'. 'I'll email you the details.' replied Richard. It turned out to be a survey for Bank America who were making plans to safeguard their European and Middle East ATM services, in the unlikely event of a major problems on the stroke of midnight, 2000. They had hundreds of thousands of transactions taking place all over the region every hour of the day, and incredibly in the late 1990s all these services were routed through their Cairo headquarters. They wanted to install a microwave data link from an Egypt Telecom satellite ground station, situated on the coast, twenty-five kilometres Northwest of the city, to a signal mast on top of the Hilton Hotel in Cairo. Sparkys brief was to climb to the top of each location and confirm that there was line of sight between them. Richards email advised that he would be met by a representative of Bank America, who would have cleared the approvals to access each site, and assist him in any way he could. All sounded pretty strait forward to Sparky, and as he packed his special holdall which contained his mast climbing harness, hard hat, binoculars, compass and other bits of equipment, he thought, 'it would be quite nice to be in sunny Cairo, instead of freezing cold Derbyshire.'

He was met at the airport by a Frenchman called Gaston, a slim smart looking man in his mid thirties, he spoke excellent English, and seemed very organized. Before setting out for the sites, they went for a coffee, and Gaston gave Sparky a set of plans with details of both locations. Sparky then explained how the survey would be conducted. He would climb to the top of the mast on the Hilton Hotel, and try to visually locate the other end of the link, using a compass bearing and binoculars. He would then fix a powerful strobe light on top of the Hilton mast, then drive to the other end at the satellite ground station. But when he reached the top of the Hilton mast ,the pollution and heat haze made a visual sighting virtually impossible. However Gaston told him local conditions would improve later in the day. The twenty-five or so kilometres drive to the coast was noisy and congested, but eventually Sparky could see the Egypt Telecom facility appearing out of the dusty haze. It was huge, with half a dozen enormous Satellite Dishes, all aligned in different directions, and one massive signal mast standing way above everything else. 'That's what you have to climb mon ami' said Gaston with his eyes looking skyward. 'Impressive.' said Sparky, trying to sound cool. It was a really big mast, nearly sixty five metres high, or over 200 feet in old money.

They cleared the security gate and parked the car underneath a long corrugated sun shelter. It was just after two pm, and the heat was intense, but the haze seemed to be clearing slowly as Sparky sorted out all his climbing equipment. Meanwhile Gaston was talking to a stocky looking gentleman dressed in an immaculate white, short sleeved shirt with epaulettes and grey KD slacks. Gaston introduced him as the duty engineer in charge of the site, after a few pleasantries the engineer asked Sparky if he was actually going to the very top of the mast on his own, or was Gaston going with him... 'On my own,' said Sparky.

He had brought with him a selection self arresting safely devices, any one of which should be sufficient to protect him during the climb. The mast stood on a huge four cornered base, mounted on large concrete blocks. It looked like a smaller version of the Eiffel Tower in Paris. A system of vertical ladders led to a series of platforms, which became small and smaller as the lattice structure rose up to an ever diminishing top section, which from ground level was difficult to see. Sparky scanned the mast from top to bottom with his binoculars, it was reassuringly well built, but he could see that it did not have a rail lock safety system, which were installed on most UK masts of this size and, smaller. The rail lock was almost completely foolproof, if a climber fell the mechanism automatically locked into place, preventing any chance of downward movement.

Sparky had now prepared all his equipment, checked it twice, put his hard hat on and walked towards the first set of steps. As he took hold of of the ladder he looked around him, and was surprised to see a couple of dozen people outside the main office block, all eyes turned on him. He was looking forward to the accent, and so with a cheeky touch of his hard hat, he gave the audience a sharp salute, and began his climb. This would in fact be the tallest mast he had ever climbed, during his time as a mast technician. He was wearing a body harness with two special nylon slings attached to either side. On the end of each sling were large spring loaded hooks. The technique was to basically climb hand above hand, clipping one of the hooks into the ladder rungs as far above his head as he could reach, then move upwards, releasing the one which had been previously placed. This way there was always one secure sling protecting him at any one time. These were over specified pieces of equipment, which were strong enough to lift a double decker London bus. Well that's what the instructor had told him when he'd attended the training course in Manchester.

With steadily growing confidence he moved smoothly up towards the top section, which was terminated with a slender steel pole fitted with high intensity aircraft hazard warning lights. There was a cooling breeze coming off the Mediterranean Sea, and Sparky was feeling very relaxed, his breathing was slow and steady, he was in his element, loving every moment. His safety equipment was the best that money could buy, the mast was in excellent condition, and he was at the top. He secured his harness to the pole, and braced his feet firmly on the brackets which supported the hazard lights. Leaning back he let go of the mast and removed his binoculars from the special pouch on the waist belt of his harness. The binoculars in turn were attached to a safety lanyard in case he had to let go of them. With his compass he took a reciprocal bearing from the one he had had taken on top of the Hilton, then focused his lenses. The visibility was not five by five, but it had improved, just as Gaston predicted. He swept the skyline, looking over the top of the sprawling Cairo suburbs. After a few moments he spotted a high intensity flashing beacon, it could be the mast on the Hilton, he smiled.

Then out of his pouch he took a small metal box with a rubber antenna attached to it, clicking a switch on the top of the box he kept his eye on the flashing beacon over 25 Km away. Microseconds later the beacon stopped flashing, he then depressed a small green button, and through his binoculars he could see the beacon flashing again. He repeated this process four times, until he was satisfied that he was looking at the signal mast on top of the Hilton Hotel. He carefully stowed his precious binoculars, and VHF transmitter, secured the pouch then carefully reversed his way back to the base, and a smiling Gaston. 'Well mon ami, you ave ze visual confirmation for ze link none,' 'Mais quie Gaston of course.' replied Sparky.

As the reader will have noticed, the year 2000 arrived and the world did not come to a standstill, communication satellites did nor fall out of the sky, all the doom merchants were wrong. Basically things carried on as normal, mankind was still trying to wreck the planet with pollution, exploitation, and selfish disregard for nature. But there were many good people who continued to do their best, working and fighting hard to try and put things right. All was not yet lost, and there was a new millennium to look forward to...

He had already been to Nepal twice before, the first visit was in 1983, with climbing friend Paul Deketalere, and again in 1989,trekking to Everest Base camp with Colin and Jo...

But early in the year 2000 Sparky read an article in his Fellrunner magazine about the Everest Marathon which was to take place in November of that year. Billed as the highest and hardest Marathon in the World, it would start close to Everest Base camp in a place called Gorak Shep, at an altitude of 5184 metres, and run the full Marathon distance of 26.219 miles to the famous hillside trading town and Sherpa Capital of Namche Bazar at 3446 metres. In order to acclimatise all the contestants would be required to undergo a gruelling 16 day trek to the start, passing through some of the most spectacular mountain scenery in the world. The race was first run on Friday the 27th of November 1987, and since then it had been repeated seven times, every two years. The whole reason for its existence was to raise money to support the Everest Marathon Fund, which was created to promote health and education in rural Nepal, one of the poorest countries on earth. Those seven races had raised over £290.000 so far, helping to provide hospitals, schools, clean water, and improved sanitation.

He had been mountain and fell running for some years now, and the prospect of taking part in the ultimate *hill race*, in the shadow of the worlds highest peaks was more than he could resist. In the spring of 2000 he sent off his application form, and was duly accepted. They would leave Heathrow on November the fifth, then trek to Gorak Shep where the race would start on Sunday the twenty sixth of November. After the race they would spend a few days in Kathmandu before flying home on the second of December. The originators, and organisers of the race, were a company called Bufo Ventures, they operated trekking holidays in Nepal. With a base in the English Lake district, and an office in Kathmandu, their whole organisation was simply superb from start to finish. Everything from the flights, hotels, porters, support staff and marshals throughout the race, which including fully qualified team of British doctors. The cost of £2,000.00 for everything was excellent value. All Sparky had to do now was make sure he was fit enough. It was a huge undertaking, and required him to dig deep into his financial reserves and physical commitment. It also meant that he would not earn any money for a least a month whilst he was in Nepal.

Runners from eleven different countries had signed up for the race, including a team of formidable local Nepalese .There were 60 entrants, and these were split into three separate trekking groups, taking different routes, but all ending up in Namche Bazar. After taking a few days well earned rest the whole cavalcade would then trek to the start at Gorak Shep, altitude 5400m and lying in the shadow of Mount Everest. A team of porters carried all their equipment, which included each runners personal kit-bag containing sleeping bag, spare clothes required on race day. Plus tents, food, and cooking equipment. Before leaving Kathmandu race director Diana Penny Sherpani and her team sorted out all the last minute arrangements, and held a number of group meetings so that everyone knew what to expect, and who to ask if they had any problems... Then they were off on their adventure.

The Everest region lies to the east of Kathmandu, and Sparky's group had the thrill of flying into small landing strip at a wonderfully named village called Tumlingtar. The locals village people came onto the field to greet them with garlands of flowers and prayer flags, whilst the children ran around excitedly asking for pens and sweets. After unloading all the baggage and equipment, they were soon on the way to their first overnight camp. Everyone was pleased to be on the move at last, there would be a chance to get to know other members of the expedition over the next couple of weeks. In Kathmandu everyone was paired off with a tent buddy, Sparkys was a great guy called Jeff Fielding, a jewellery shop owner from Bury in Lancashire. At 56 he was three years younger than Sparky, and was a keen Fell runner. The two of them hit it off immediately, with Jeff going on to finish in eighteenth place in a very creditable time of 6 hours 7 minutes, giving him and overall place of third male veteran.

The other two groups started at the head of the famous Jiri trail, which had been used for many years by Everest Expeditions on their way to base camp in the Khumbu region. It would pass through some truly stunning scenery, and with the passage of countless climbers it was generally a more developed trail than Sparky and friends were on. But all the routes provided sufficient time and altitude to help everyone acclimatise. The golden rule in high altitude trekking is to walk high during the day, and descend to a lower point for the overnight camp. There were no cushy options for anyone, during the day it was generally hot and sunny, but as soon as the sun dipped below the mountains, temperatures plummeted rapidly, as everyone dived into their day packs to find down jackets and warm hats. Altitude was not the only problem threatening the health of the runners.

Nepal is a truly fantastic country, but a very poor one, and trekkers needed to be aware that illness is never very far away. Chest infections, bad coughs and colds, and severe stomach bugs to name just a few. The squalor, and the virtual lack of basic hygiene, had taxed each and everyone of them. No one was immune, despite taking all necessary precautions, it's a lottery. Sparky was to arrive at Namche Bazaar with a gradually deteriorating chest infection, which had started somewhere back on the trail. It was hoped a few days rest would help, but on the trek to Gorak Shep it became worse and the doctor advised that he should descend back down to Pheriche and rest. A decision as to whether he could start the race from there would be made on the morning of the start. In the event he was allowed to run, completing the 18.7 miles to the finish in Namche in a time of 6.48.53, which included the Thamo loop. Not the Marathon distance he had come there to challenge, a huge disappointment, but life sometimes plays these tricks. He had however had a wonderful time in the company of some exceptional people, the memories and experiences were priceless and would be there forever.

The race was won by the amazing Nepalese runner Hari Roka, his forth win, in a record time of 3.50.23 hours, he was followed by ten of his countrymen, with Garry Owen's of Great Britain gaining twelfth place in a time of 5.20.00 hours. There was much more to this adventure than has been written here, too much to include in the confines of the main narrative, but it is recorded in another journal entitled *Everest Pilgrimage.*

After his return from Nepal Sparky was still unwell from the chest infection which had almost prevented him from taking part in the race. But eventually he was back to normal and concentrating on continuing to build his business. As the new year of 2001 unfolded things were going very well, and he was managing to do more than just keep his his head above water. There were a number of customers who had overseas contracts over the coming months,where Sparky's experience was required. Not only did he feel comfortable but he also felt confident that he would have no problems earning his crust of bread. But life often teaches us to not to count our chickens before they are hatched. On the morning of September the 11th 2001, Al Qaeda inspired suicide terrorists crashed two passenger planes into the twin towers of the World Trade Centre in New York, killing 2,886 people and injuring more than 6,000. On TV a horrified and stunned world watched the atrocity as it happened, unable to comprehend what they were seeing. It was the most devastating single peacetime attack on a civilian population in the history of mankind. It is no exaggeration to say that this devastating event would change the World for ever.

As everyone tried to make sense of what had happened the situation, was further complicated by the decision of the United States to blame Saddam Hussein for this outrage, and eventually US President George Bush Junior declared war on Iraq, and on the on March 20th 2003 he unleashed his *Shock and Awe* attack on Baghdad, and once again the whole World watched with horrid fascination as US Bombers lit up the night sky with wave after wave of unremitting devastation and terror.

The history of these events are well documented for anyone who needs to know more. But the aftermath would affect people and businesses all over the Globe for a long time to come. There had never been anything quite so far reaching. With the spectre of terrorism now potentially threatening everyone lives there was an atmosphere of uncertainty, governments, corporations, and institutions were unsure of what the future would be.

Over the next few months Sparky saw his forward business plan start to unravel, customers were reluctant to go ahead with their security plans, hesitating to make the decision. His income was not yet affected, but he was never the less concerned about the future.

Sitting at his desk one morning he was reading through a security magazine, and spotted an advert describing a position for a salesman with a company called Senstar. They were looking for someone with experience in Perimeter Intruder Detection Systems. Sparky knew Senstar well, they were a Canadian manufacturer of a range of PIDS for numbers of applications, but the jewel in the crown was their underground buried cable detection system, known as Perimitrax. At that time they were the world leaders in this technology, there was nothing else on the market to equal it. Senstars reputation was first class, and they claimed to have installed more of this type of system worldwide than any of their competitors. Sparky had always considered them to be the best, and held them in high regard, the job was based in the UK out of their Evesham offices in the beautiful English Cotswold's, close to Shakespeare's Stratford upon Avon, and he already knew the UK's Managing Director. He went for the interview, and was offered the job.

Now aged sixty one, but still only feeling fifty one, Sparky was delighted to have secured this position, it was perfect for him and with luck and good management should take him to his retirement at sixty-five.

An added bonus being that he did not have to relocate, they were more than happy to let him work from home, visiting the head office as required. He was allocated a sales territory which included the whole of Ireland, North and South, another bonus which pleased him very much. He had a good track record on the emerald Isles with many excellent contacts. Sparky's time with Senstar was most enjoyable, he loved the products and the people he was working with. It wasn't long before he secured some business, life was good, he was kept busy and gradually built up a useful list of new contacts. The company attended numbers of trade exhibitions, and Sparky once again enjoyed the hustle and bustle of meeting new people and explaining how their products worked. It's what he'd been doing for many years, and he loved it.

On the domestic front Sparky was also enjoying life, lots of fell running, climbing and camping, he felt very fit and in truth was looking forward to retirement in 2006, with the added prospect of travelling extensively to South East Asia, Australia, New Zealand and Patagonia with his long time partner Kay. But in the meantime he continued to work hard and save his money to fund any forthcoming new adventures.

2006 arrived soon enough and Sparky officially retired in July of that year. The Canadian Vice President of the company asked him if he would be prepared to stay on for a least another year, it was a tempting offer, which he almost accepted, but the lure of new adventures and the freedom to seek them out won the day. Kay retired in the August, and the rest of that year they enjoyed touring in the Scottish Highlands, and numbers of camping trips to North Wales and the Lake District. It was all very enjoyable, and he wasn't sorry he'd decided to retire.

In the early part of 2007 Sparky was approached by a number of his past clients asking him if he was available for some consultancy work. Never one to miss an opportunity he accepted a number of these, especially if they were short term jobs involving week or so of his time. During the next three years various projects became available, and he was able to accept those which fitted into his now very busy retired life. The money was very useful, but he began to feel that he should start to scale down the work, after all he was supposed to be retired, and was approaching *his three score years and ten.*

In the meantime they continued to enjoy travelling, and in 2008 they booked the trip of a lifetime to Patagonia. They had both wanted to visit this stunning part of the world since they were teenagers. One rainy afternoon whilst walking around the delightful little town of Ingelton near Carnforth they went into a small travel agent called Walks Worldwide, and came out with a pile of information about small group holidays in South America. Basically these trips were for keen and fit walkers who wanted to explore this amazing continent in the company of like minded people, trekking off the beaten track, but with the benefit of having an expert local guide for the duration of the trip. It was just what we were looking for.

Eventually they decided on a trip to Patagonia. It is a sparsely populated region located at the southern end of South America, shared by Argentina and Chile. The whole area comprises the southern section of the Andes mountains, as well as the deserts pampas and grasslands east of this southern portion of the Andes. Patagonia has two coasts: western facing the Pacific Ocean and eastern facing the Atlantic .The Colorado and Barrancas rivers, which run from the Andes to the Atlantic, are commonly considered the northern limit of Argentine Patagonia. The archipelago of Tierra de Fuego is sometimes included as part of Patagonia, and most geographers and historians locate the northern limit of Chilean Patagonia, at the Reloncavi Estuary.

Since he would already be in Argentina,Sparky decided to attempt to climb Cerro Aconcagua, at 6,962 metres, its the highest mountain in the Western hemisphere. After completing their tour of Patagonia, Kay would return to the UK, and Sparky would make his way Northwest and join his climbing expedition in the famous Argentinian wine growing area of Mendoza, before travelling onward to Aconcagua itself.

After lots of planning and preparation they flew out to Buenos Aires from Heathrow during the first week of February 2008. After a couple of days enjoying the sites and sounds of this vibrant and exciting city, it was time to move on and fly to Calafate 1,200 miles south west of BA, situated on the Southern Shore of Largo Argentino. Here they would meet up with their guide and the rest of their fellow travellers. During the trip they would use a minibus, and some local transport. Accommodation would be in tents, hotels, *pensions* or Hosteria's, depending upon the itinerary and where they were trekking to. Everything was well organised, and their group comprised a total of eight trekkers plus a professional guide called Sylvina, a very experienced lady mountaineer and trek leader. Her English was excellent, and her knowledge of all the mountains and surrounding areas was impressive.

For their first trek they took a local bus to the town of El Chalten, on the edge of Los Glaciares National Park, next to Mount Fitzroy. From there they walked for three hours along a beautiful trail which gave them superb panoramic views of Mount Fitzroy, this was on Sparky's tick list, he had always wanted to climb it, ever since he had seen pictures of it in climbing magazines when he was a teenager.

Their camp site at Capri was already set up for their arrival, they had good quality mountain tents, and a large communal tent used at meal times and for general socialising. The Argentine national parks were well managed, with strict rules covering the protection of the ecology. It was forbidden to pick flowers or plants, no dogs were allowed, and everyone was asked too respect where they were walking. Everything taken into the parks, had to be brought out when leaving, including all rubbish. It was very impressive. During their stay at the Capri Lagoon Camp site, they had visited water falls and lakes, gazed in awe at the impressive massif of Cerro Torre with its 3,128 metre granite needles, which was on Kay's tick list, she had waited more than thirty years for the moment, originally inspired by photographs in a book shown to her by her dad.

On their last day at the camp they visited the Torre glacier and practised ice climbing with with crampon and axes. After three days they returned to their base hotel in Calafate. From here they took a trip to the magnificent Perito Moreno Glacier, one of the last remaining advancing glaciers in Argentina. As it pushes forward gigantic ice rock continually fall and crash into the waters of channel, a unique experience.

Departing El Calafate early in the morning they drove to Torres del Paine National Park in Chile, passing through the spectacular landscape of the Patagonia steppe, there was an abundance of wild life, choiques (rheas) and flamingos amongst magnificent scenery, the cameras were working overtime. After clearing Chilean immigration they eventually reached their next Camp site, passing the incredibly dazzling turquoise Noredenskjold lake with guanacos and wild horses grazing nearby. Their tents were pitched near lake Pehoe, their views towards the famous towers and horns of Los Cuernos, as the setting sun seemed to be setting them on fire, was simply breathtaking. The whole area was simply atmospheric, everywhere there were stunning mountain ranges, deep valleys, rivers and lakes. The wind is a constant reminder that the wild waters of the Southern Ocean is the only thing which separates the tip of South America from Antarctica. It blows nearly all the time.

The following day they would do their first trek in Chile, walking through the Valle Ascencio to the foot of the impressive granite massif of El Paine, a distance of 10km up steep rough terrain, which would take up to eight hours round trip. As a climber Sparky was really excited at the prospect of this day out. The history of how these spires were eventually conquered is the stuff of legends. But in 1963 Don Whillans and Chris Bonington made the first accent of the formidable Central Tower of Paine, an amazing feat of endurance and rock climbing ability, overcoming ferocious storms up 7,000 feet of vertical granite.

During their approach to El Paine the towers were mainly hidden from view, but after clambering over large boulders for an hour or so, they arrived at the Mirador Las Torres to be rewarded with the beautiful sun lit spectacle of the three massive granite monoliths of Torres del Paine (2,900 metres) dropping sheer to the lake below.

Sparky stood in complete awe, the size and location mesmerized him, he stood transfixed, trying to work out the routes the original climbers had forced up these terrifyingly steep granite faces. It was the sort of climbing he would love to have done in his younger years, but all he could do now was look, and dream. This was his own totally magic moment, never to be forgotten. They were so lucky that the weather had been kind to them, the area around Torres del Paine has it's own micro climate, a few miles away there can be beautiful sunshine, but the Towers can be engulfed in horrendous storms with unrelenting winds which can last for many days. It had been the most demanding day of their trip so far, but the rewards were worth the effort. Back at the camp site most people retired early after dinner, retreating to the warmth their cosy sleeping bags.

They stayed at the Pehoe camp-site for another two days, trekking through lush green forests, spectacular glaciers and beautiful lakes or Largos, The weather continued to remain fine and sunny during the daytime, with minus temperatures once the sun dipped below the western horizon. Yet again the whole experience more than exceeded their expectations, everything about the trip so far had been just perfect, great company, good food and amazing scenery, they were very happy.

It was now time to leave this wonderful area and drive south to Punta Arenas, here they boarded a ferry to sail the Straits of Magellan across to the port of Porvenir, where another minibus was waiting for them. Sparky for one was very excited, he was in the famous waters of the Magellan Straits, heading for Tierra del Fuego Island and South to Rio Grande. They could now see the South Atlantic Ocean, in his seagoing days Sparky had sailed these waters, and made passage round the dramatic and unpredictable Cape Horn before heading up the West Coast of Chile. He had often stood on the bridge of his ship looking at the rugged and inhospitable shoreline, and used to say to himself, 'One day I'll go and visit this amazing place.'... Dreams can come true.

From Rio Grande they drove south and stayed overnight at an Estancia, where they were treated to a superb traditional lamb asado (barbecue) and local wine. The next morning they visited the enormous wool sheds, (wool is the main business of the Patagonian Estancias). The size of their estates are huge, covering hundreds of square miles, with thousands of sheep to look after. To everyone's delight they were shown around by genuine Patagonian gauchos, resplendent in their leather jackets, hats and gauchos trousers, real working men these, not Hollywood look a likes, Sparky thought they were great, and some of the ladies seemed quite impressed as well. At midday they left the Estancia and continued their journey south eventually taking a mountain track to stay overnight at a refuge in the Tierra Mayor Valley. After dinner their guide took them to see the devastation caused by the introduction of Beaver farming, which was developed in the hope of providing an alternative livelihood for the local people. It was a failure, and the Beaver population grew out of control, causing considerable damage to trees and rivers. The local authorities were working hard to rectify the situation.

The following day was their last time on the road together as they drove towards Ushuaia, the most southerly city in the world. The road took them alongside the Beagle Channel, with spectacular views of the Chilean Andes. As they checked into the Ushuaia hotel there was a feeling of regret that this wonderful and amazing trip was now at an end. That night would be their last meal together as a group, but there was still time to explore the city, and the surrounding area the following day, before leaving for their flight to Buenos Aires in the evening...

They took a trip on a motor yacht into the Beagle Channel, in the mistaken hope of seeing some penguins, only to be told it was too early in the year, and they should come back in June or July. But the trip was worth it, they saw all kinds of wildlife, and all the time the Andes looked down on them from across the Chilean border. Ushuaia is a thriving bustling city, with a fair mix of tourist shops, bars bistros and designer outlets. Numbers of large cruise ships were in the port, no doubt providing prosperity for the local people. Sparky loved the fact that if you looked up the main street, at the end of it were snow capped peaks of the Andes. The Argentinian people were friendly, and there were no outwards signs of hostility towards British people, there was the occasional graffiti proclaiming their right to the Malvinas, which was only to be expected. That evening at a very busy and noisy airport they said goodbye to some of the people who they had trekked with over the past few weeks, promising to keep in touch, but typically never did.

In BA they were back at the hotel they had used on their arrival, Sparky retrieved his heavily loaded mountain rucksack from the porter, and transferred some of his other stuff to Kay for her to take back home. The following day they were taken to the airport, Kay to International departures, and Sparky for his internal flight to Mendoza. They said their goodbyes, and Sparky promised to be careful, after all Aconcagua is a big mountain....

Sparky's Aconcagua
Summit Attempt
6,962 metres

———— • ————

Walks Worldwide were also organising Sparky's trip, and their agent in Mendoza were Grajales and sons. They had been involved in mountaineering expeditions for many years, employing very experienced guides, and had an excellent reputation. The flight to Mendoza was uneventful, and with time to relax and think things through, Sparky was keen to get started. It was a big undertaking, but he was feeling very fit after his Patagonian trip and was looking forward to meeting everyone. After arrival he checked into the Mendoza Hotel, pre booked by the agent. A meeting had been arranged with their guide in the hotel bar for 2pm that afternoon.

When Sparky arrived in the room he introduced himself to the other members of the team. There were two Americans, a German, four Swedish climbers and him. Their guide was called Salvador, a tall imposing bearded man in his early forties, with a deeply tanned face. He had a calm and confident look about him, Sparky liked him immediately. Salvador welcomed everyone and then introduced a very attractive young lady called Anita. She was a fully qualified Mountain guide who was to accompany them on their Aconcagua trip, she was to be learning the Aconcagua route from Salvador, and would summit with some of the team. He then outlined the itinerary, they would leave in the morning and stay overnight at the ski resort of Penitentes 2,500 metres. The following day there would be a short drive to the trail head, and their trek to base camp would start there. After the meeting Salvador visited each team member separately, and carried out a complete check of all the equipment , making sure they had the right boots, clothing, sleeping bags etc. He was very thorough, asking questions about climbing experience, any notable accents, and experience in winter conditions. Salvador and Sparky hit it off right away, he had climbed many times in Snowdonia, the Lake District and Scotland, as well as the French and Austrian Alps.

That evening the team went into Mendoza for a meal and a few beers, a great way to get to know each other. They were going to be on the mountain together for nearly a month, and it was important for them to get along with each other. The Swedish guys, Lars, Sven, Harry, and Erik were all close friends who worked on overseas IT contracts together, they had some winter climbing experience in Norway, but they were mainly skiers. The younger of the two Americans Dave,was from New York, he was 27, and had been backpacking in South America for almost a year, he was also a climber. The older American, Bob, was a retired eye surgeon from Jacksons Hole in the USA, he was a very experienced mountaineer, having climbed most of his life, but had failed to Summit Aconcagua via its North face three years earlier. He had just arrived from Africa where he had been performing free eye operations in the remote areas of several East African countries. At 69 he was the oldest member of the team, after Sparky. The German, Peter, had also failed to reach the summit of Aconcagua twice before, he was a retired factory worker who had just turned 65, a keen mountain walker, but the only mountaineering he had done was on Aconcagua. A mix of people, with one objective...get to the summit.

Aconcagua Sacred Pyramid
of The Incas
Keeper of Mysteries
and Dreams

――――◆――――

After leaving Mendoza they drove for three hours through arid but picturesque scenery, they climbed slowly up the mountain passes to a height of 2,500 metres to reach their overnight stop at the ski resort of Penitentes where they would stay at the Ski lodge. It was large building, and at this time of the year was almost deserted, their small party of International summit hopefuls and a few staff providing the only sign of life, an early night was had by all. At 0700 after breakfast they immediately set off along the road to the the National Parks HQ at Los Horcones and the start of the walk to Base Camp. The park Ranger examined their permits, gave them a short talk about the need to be responsible about the environment, and issued them with rubbish bags. These would be checked again when they came back down the trail to make sure all bags had been removed from the mountain, it was impressive to see that ecology was high on their agenda, something which Sparky had noticed during his Patagonian trip.

Mules were waiting to carry all the expeditions bags and equipment to base camp, allowing the climbers to walk without heavy loads, that would come later. After a group photograph by the side of a small lake, they moved off to start their adventure. They had been walking for around fifteen minutes when the unmistakable sound of a helicopter interrupted the tranquillity of valley. Salvador told them this was the daily run from the Ranger HQ to base camp, delivering the camp doctor and acting as an evacuation service for any injured or unwell people. ('Very comforting' thought Sparky, 'Just hope I'm not one of them'). The trek was reasonably easy taking around four hours. It was hot and dusty, as they passed high alpine lakes, walked through green desert valley scenery enclosed between the beautiful steep mountains of the Andes. It became increasing barren as they gained altitude, but eventually they arrived at the private Camp Grajales, at an altitude of 3,620 metres. It was a close but peaceful distance from the main halfway point, Camp Confluencia, where most trekkers were staying. It had been a long day, and after eating a superb meal cooked by the Grajales Camp boss Pipa, most people sat around and chilled out looking at the scenery and taking photos.

The next day was a walk to view the imposing South Face of Aconcagua, first climbed by the legendary Tyrolean climber Messner. They reached the Plaza Francia at 4,200 metres, the same altitude as the main base camp. Looking up at the massive panorama of the South Face they felt overawed by its size, and as they watched, a number of avalanches could be seen crashing down the sheer slopes. There was a fierce wind bowing up the valley as they returned to Camp Grajales for a second night.

The main Base Camp plateau was their next objective, and would be their home for the next two or three weeks. It was to be a long hard day, the temperature had changed considerably, made worse by a strong headwind sweeping down from the plateau, and the effects of altitude were being felt as they struggled up some of the steep sections. At one stage they were caught up by the mules carrying all their kit. Two of them decided to kick off and started running back down the mountain. The Boss Muleteer and two other horsemen gave chase, encouraged by the cheers from Trekkers. It was like a wild west show, and they all enjoyed the diversion, until it dawned on them that it may be their bags which were trying to escape, the boss soon had things under control. It probably happened all the time.

After nearly eight hours of walking, the fluttering flags and brightly coloured tents of Base Camp were a welcome sight, they were now at 4,200 metres, the sun was setting behind the Andes, and the temperature plummeted to well below freezing. They soon discovered that it would drop down to minus 20 degrees or more, on most nights. Sparky was amazed at the size of the camp, he had not expected to see so many people. Not all of them had come to climb, many of them were with trekking companies. Their Grajales Camp was well organised, and their tents were already in place. Once they were settled in they were called to the dining and kitchen tent, proudly displaying the Grajales name and house flag. Their camp boss, Thomas, introduced himself, he was a big man, sporting a long black beard, with his hair drawn back into a pony tail. He welcomed them all, and explained the camp rules, times of breakfast, lunch and dinner, he was in ultimate charge, and whatever he said was law. However he looked like a jovial sort of man, and turned out to be an excellent cook.

Sparky walked around base camp, to familiarise himself with everything. First on his list were the latrines, there were two of them, which had to serve all residents of the camp. In keeping with the Argentinian ethics concerning ecology in their National Parks, the latrines were airlifted out of the camp every day by helicopter, and replacements installed. This and other aspects of the Park Rangers work was to protect the environment of the area, and it deserves considerable acclaim.

The Aconcagua Base Camp was more like a small tented village, with numbers of trekking and climbing companies providing large Base Camp tents for their clients to relax in after a day on the mountains, there was even a pub, which played disco music in the evening, complete with flashing lights. It was all a bit much for Sparky, and although he knew the revenue to the National Parks was essential, he was still disappointment to find so many people in such a remote and ecologically sensitive area. However he wasn't there to criticise, he'd come to climb a big mountain.

After a well deserved rest day, the preparation for their summit attempt began in earnest. To aid with acclimatisation they climbed the nearby 5,000 meter Cerro Bonete, from Base Camp it looked like a massive undertaking, but it was not a technical climb and the ascent was quite straightforward. They shared their lunch on the summit with a group of German climbers who were also intending to attempt Aconcagua. The round trip took them six hours, and they were back in time for a relaxing time with a lovely cup of tea supplied by Thomas and his team. After evening meals when the sun had gone out of sight, it became bitterly cold, and most people retired to a warm sleeping bag and a few more pages of their book.

Over the next three days they carried equipment and food to set up Camps, 1 Plaza Canada at 4,700 metres, here they rested and had lunch before continuing onwards to Camp 2 Nido de Codores (the condor's nest) at 5,400 metres. At this point they were now high above the surrounding mountain peaks. It was a very windy place, but provided them with stunning views of the spectacular snow covered Andes. After all this effort they then retreated back down to Base Camp, all part of the acclimatisation cycle, *climb high and sleep low is the rule*. Once back down the other rule was to eat well, and rehydrate as much as possible.

During a much needed rest day, they checked all their personnel equipment and prepared for the summit.

The following day they moved up to Camp 1 for an overnight stay, it was a cold but beautiful night with high pressure holding steady, the stars were clearer than Sparky had ever seen them before. All the group were going well and the guides seemed pleased with the way everyone was performing. After breakfast, which was a boil in the bag concoction followed by a mug of steaming black coffee, they made their accent to Camp 2. The weather seemed to be holding and the site was bathed in sunshine. A wonderful day for taking pictures. In the afternoon Salvador called them all together for a discussion. It was his opinion that because they were all fit, with no altitude problems they should not go for a Camp 3 overnight stay, but make an earlier start the following day and go for the summit. He asked for everyone's opinion, which in retrospect was the wrong thing to do. They were not really in a position to make that judgement, they had no real understanding of the distance or the route conditions which they would be faced with. Unfortunately they all agreed, and It would turn out to be an almost disastrous decision...

At 5am, after a somewhat sparse breakfast, they were all kitted up with their crampons, ice axes and down clothing ready to go. It was still dark with the stars shining brightly, but no moon to light the way. Crunching their way across the frozen snowfields, they were all quiet and contemplative. This was why they had come, and they were now on their way. The climbing became steeper and zigzagged through rocky outcrops making the going slow and precarious in the dawn light. Five hours later they arrived at Camp Berlin, there were numbers of tents pitched on what seemed to be quite inhospitable ground. By this time the party was not walking together, as some people seemed to be struggling with the cold and steepness of the route.

After a rest and some energy bars they made a short scramble up a rocky slope behind the camp, then continued along a gently sloping path which led to the ruined Independencia hut at

6,250 metres. At this point three of the Swedish team, and the American Surgeon Bob decided they did not want to proceed any further, Erik was the only Swede willing to carry on. One of the guides accompanied them safely down to another camp. By this time they had all been climbing for more than six hours, and the weather was deteriorating with heavy dark clouds scudding across the horizon. Their objective was to make a long steady traverse over a ridge with its open side sloping steeply all the way down to Base Camp. It was just possible to make out the colours of the tents. At the end of the traverse they would reach the infamous 'Canelleta', a large steep gully which came down from the summit ridge above. After a nervy and careful passage across the ridge they reached the 'Canelleta', and took a rest. They were now a party of six, Sparky, Erik, Peter, Dave, Salvador and Anita. The gully was full of fresh snow, which was not ideal, it would have been better if it had been frozen, making an ascent with crampons and axes much less strenuous.

After some food and water it was time to set off, they were now only a few hundred metres from the summit ridge and a successful ascent. Anita went first with Erik and Peter. Dave and Sparky followed them with Salvador at the back. After only ten minutes Dave was having difficulty making headway, the soft powdery snow collapsing with every move. It was one step up then two steps back. Sparky was having a similar problem and his energy levels were getting low. Eventually Dave declared he could go no further, so the three of them retreated to the base of the gully. Once back on the safety of the ledge below, Dave sat down in the snow and refused to move. Salvador decided to belay him to the mountain, and suggested he wait there until Sparky and he were at the top of the gully, once there Sparky could join the others with Anita. But it was not long before Sparky was in trouble, slipping backwards and making no progress. Salvador was behind encouraging him to keep going. But Sparky knew he was beaten, he had no energy left, and felt awful. He looked at the guide, and shook his head, he could not go on. The emotional trauma of his decision overwhelmed him, his shoulders began to shake, and he started to cry. Salvador seemed devastated by his decision, he had always been convinced that Sparky would make it,his disappointment and compassion was obvious. They retreated down to the base of the gully and joined Dave.

Salvador produced some more energy bars and isotonic drink, Sparky was grateful for the chance to put something back into his body. Dave was not interested, he seemed vacant and remote, not answering any of their questions, just staring out wards towards the mountains. Salvador contacted Anita on his walkie talkie and updated her on their situation, she confirmed they were all OK, and were about to start the summit ridge. The weather was getting worse, snow flurries stung their faces, and the wind was gusting strongly from the west. Eventually they persuaded Dave it was time to move, reluctantly he stood up and followed Sparky. Away from the shelter of the gully conditions on the traverse were now decidedly tricky. The wind buffeted their clothing and made every step feel insecure, half way across Dave sat down in the snow and closed his eyes, he didn't want to carry on. Salvador decided to tie him onto a rope for his protection, but insisted that Sparky continued on his own.

This was the best decision, since it would be easier to try and hold one person in the event of a fall than two. They made it to the other side and Sparky was starting to feel stronger, Dave was staggering about like a drunken man and by the time they reached Camp Berlin he could hardly walk, and the light was fading fast.

The encampment tents were all battened down, with no sign of anyone. They both held Dave steady whilst Salvador prepared to give him a shot of Adrenaline, and between them just about managed to pull Dave's trousers down far enough to expose one of his buttocks. It must have been a bizarre site, almost surreal. With a swift movement the needle was plunged into its target, but as they were trying to pull Dave's pants back up, he suddenly opened his eyes wide, looked around him and ran off across the site shouting loudly. He collided with a number tents, and a chorus of 'Shut up', and numbers of obscenities filled the camp. A few people poked their heads out to see what was happening, then shot back in to get out of the freezing wind. Sparky caught up with Dave and settled him down. In the shelter of some large boulders Salvador managed to contact the guides down at the camp where they had taken the Swedes and Bob. One of them immediately started up the trail to join them.

The radio started to crackle, and Anita's voice was just recognisable, she said they had made the summit and were descending, but Erik had become almost uncontrollable, accusing her and Peter of stealing his money...another victim of high altitude and physical exhaustion. This was a potentially a serious situation, so Salvador told her he would come up the trail to meet them. Sparky assured him he would take care of Dave until the guide arrived. Driving snow and screeching winds continued to batter them, despite the shelter of the boulders. Then suddenly it died away, the night became quiet, and they could see the loom of the guides head-torch. When he finally arrived he was plastered in thick snow. Two hours later they reached the camp and collapsed into a tent where Bob was sitting up reading a book. Dave immediately fell asleep, dead to the world without a single care. Some hours later the summit party arrived, but when Erik was taken to his Swedish friends tent, he refused to enter it shouting that they were not his friends, it was soon sorted out and an eerie calm brought peace and quiet, while people tried to get a bit of sleep. It had been an amazing and eventful day, it was almost twenty four hours since they had left camp 2. It seemed as though Aconcagua, Sacred Pyramid of the Incas, Keeper of Mysteries and Dreams, had been showing her authority, and this time had spared them from any serious harm, or worse.

Two days later they left Base Camp, having said their farewells to camp boss Thomas and others, then they took the long winding tedious trek down to the Los Horcones Ranger HQ. It was nearly the end of their trip. A Grajales mini bus was at the roadside to greet them and take them back to Mendoza. Everyone was exhausted when they arrived at the hotel, so it was agreed they would meet up the following evening for a farewell dinner and a few beers. Sparky phoned Kay and told her he was OK, but obviously disappointment at not making the summit. Sometimes life is like that, it just wasn't meant to be.

He had lost more than ten kilos in weight, his face was blistered from the sun and snow, and he looked like a survivor of a shipwreck. A very long shower, a shave and a hair cut soon put things right, and the next day he enjoyed walking in the warm sunshine around the Mendoza shops and market place. That evening they all met up with Salvador and Anita, who treated them to a slap up meal and more than enough wine and beer. Sparky was delighted that Peter had finally reached the summit, while Erik couldn't stop apologising for his summit madness. Dave said he did not remember anything at all about his actions on the 'Canelleta', or anything about the Adrenaline jab, or coming down the mountain. So he certainly had a story to tell when he finally arrived back home. Bob the surgeon from Jacksons Hole finally conceded that maybe it was time to cross Aconcagua off his list of things to do. There were no recriminations about the decision not to establish camp 3. At least everyone arrived back down safely, and those who feel the urge can always return to the mountain for another go. Sparky enjoyed the whole Patagonian, and Argentinian experience, it had been truly fantastic. Now it was time to catch the flight home, take a rest, then plan the next adventure.

The Next Two Years
2008 to 2010

———— • ————

After returning from South America Sparky settled down to completing work on his Derbyshire cottage, and immersed himself in rock climbing and Fell running. He participated in numbers of races in the Lake District and North Wales, including his favourite big mountain race to the summit of Snowdon and back, over the years he had competed in it more than ten times. His local running club was thriving and he ran with them a couple of times a week. No more adventure holidays were planned for the rest of the year, but looking forward into 2009/2010 they came up with an ambitious trip which would take them to Hong Kong, Sydney Australia, New Zealand and the Cook Islands in the Pacific. By purchasing a round the world ticket well in advance they could cover all these destinations at a very economic price. The plan was to leave the UK at the end of December 2009 and land in Sydney on New Years Eve. Sparky's long time friend and climbing partner Colin was living in Sydney with his wife Kate and young son Harry. He was working for one of the worlds leading professional camera manufactures. They planned to join them for the New Year Celebrations and stay for a couple of weeks before flying down to New Zealand, where they had booked a camper van for a month.

For Sparky 2009 was a busy year, he did some consultancy work, and saved all the money for their forthcoming trip. He joined Kay on numbers of walking trips in Yorkshire and the Lake District, they were both fit and were excited by the thought of what was ahead of them in 2010.

They left Manchester airport on the 29th of December 2009, bound for Sydney via a stop over in Hong Kong, choosing to stay not too far from Chek Lap Kok airport at the lovely resort of Silver Mine Bay, a nice quiet area, with a friendly hotel. The next day they took a trip to see the big Tian Tan Buddha situated in the Lantau North Country park. It was a misty damp day, but this did not affect the spirit or enthusiasm of the visitors. It was very busy, and the steps leading up to the Buddha were crowded with mainly Chinese people. It was a trip Sparky had wanted to do for a long time. It is an incredible place to visit, there is so much to see, and is well worth the effort of climbing up the many steps, as Tian Tan looks down peacefully watching over you.

That evening they boarded the flight for Sydney, arriving on the morning of December 31st 2009. Colin was there to meet them, and it wasn't long before they reached his apartment for a reunion with Kate and Harry, there was lots to talk about. In the afternoon they went for a drive around the local area, and were shown where they would come later in the evening to enjoy the New Years Eve celebrations. As the time arrived it was a special moment, watching the end of the year, and the start of a new one, thousands of miles away from home in the company of special friends. The fireworks display was amazing, and the crowd of people were making the most of the occasion, together with their families and children. It was a great experience. As the count down to midnight finished and the new year was born, Sparky was blissfully ignorant of the fact that by the end of 2010 his whole life would change forever, and would never be quite the same again.

Colin and Kate were excellent hosts and looked after them very well, Taking them out on sight seeing trips, as well as daily visits to the beach. Harry really loved his time in the crashing surf, and would swim out quite a long way to catch the best rollers. Colin went with him most of the time, but it was Harry who was fearless in the sea, and Kay thought he was the bravest of them all. It was great to see them all having such a fun time, after all that's what Oz is all about!

On a couple of occasions Sparky and Kay went into the city on the bus to do some exploring, and also give Kate a break. It was such an easy place to be, and they enjoyed it. On a business trip to Canberra, Colin took them with him and dropped them off at the Parliament building. It was an impressive place and worth the effort. The continuing presence of the Aboriginal peoples protest in the grounds of the Nations Parliament created a slight blight on what was otherwise an enjoyable day. Colin and Sparky went out one evening to photograph the Sydney Harbour Bridge, an opportunity to take some iconic images. They both set up their cameras on tripods and clicked away at numbers of locations and angles. The main difference, apart from the quality of their images, was that Sparky's camera cost about £500.00 but Colin was using one of his companies top of the range systems which cost in excess of £30,000. Needless to say Colin had the best results.

On January 10th they said goodbye to Kate, Colin and Harry as they boarded their flight to Christchurch New Zealand. They'd had a great time, thanks guys.

The trip to New Zealand, the Cook Islands, and their eventual return via a three day stop over in Hong Kong was absolutely fantastic. The six weeks were full of wonderful places, great people, and unforgettable memories. To do them justice they deserve a more detailed travelogue of their own. The author has therefore decided to pick

some of those memories for inclusion in Sparky's story,
and hopes that the reader may be sufficiently inspired to
make a similar journey themselves...

On arrival in Christchurch they picked up their camper van, which was to be their home for the next four weeks. It had been ordered months before on line, at very good rate, so they were a little apprehensive as to what they might find. They needn't have worried, it was fine, a Toyota High Ace, well fitted out, and perfect for two people. They drove to the nearest camp site and set about checking things out, then went to a local Super market and stocked up with as many provisions as they could think of.

Christchurch is a delightful city,vibrant, clean and well ordered, with lots to see, and nice friendly people. Such a shame about the terrible earthquakes which caused so much widespread damage... Leaving Christchurch they drove south to Akaroa before moving on to Lake Tekapo, a delightful camp site on the shore of the Lake. They were soon beginning to enjoy the freedom on the roads, the further they travelled the less traffic they saw, often driving for half an hour without seeing another vehicle. It was also becoming apparent that the Camp Sites were excellent, there was no need to phone ahead to book, they just turned up and always had a pitch. They were immaculately clean and well organised, best of all the camp fees were very reasonable, especially compared to back home in the UK. One feature they all offered was the use of good cooking spaces and free use of pots and pans. This was especially useful to backpackers or touring cyclists.

There was no hurry to get anywhere, and if they liked it they stayed, or moved on to the next area. The roads were in very good condition, even on the steep mountain passes and remote valley's. Navigation was easy, it wasn't necessary to have a GPS, just look at the maps, and watch out for the road signs.

Mount Cook was top of their tick list, the drive into the valley was spectacular, although it is not easy to see the mountain without walking up to one of a number of superbly positioned Alpine huts. Mount Cook Village is a delightful place tucked in at the foot of the mountain. The famous Hermitage Hotel and the Sir Edmund Hillary Alpine Centre are with out a doubt the main village attractions. The Alpine Centre in particular is extremely well presented, with lots of original pieces of equipment used on Sir Edmunds successful Everest expedition. Boots, crampons, rucksacks and lots more. There is also a fascinating display which records the history of Mount Cook, and stories of the early 1930s climbers who pioneered the most incredibly hard Alpine style routes on and around the Mount Cook massive.

The Hermitage Hotel has long been synonymous with the Kiwi spirit of adventure. Its history is packed with stories of flood, fire, triumph and tragedy. Since first being built in 1884, The Hermitage has stood as a perfect escape destination for generations of Kiwis and international travellers, spell-bound by the Mount Cook region.

Milford Sound was next on the list, and they stayed in Queens-town before taking the amazing road journey to the sound. It descends steeply for many miles, until reaching a single track road through a tunnel carved through a mountain of granite. The construction was a huge undertaking at the time, it was hand drilled and blasted by teams of tough construction workers, many of whom were killed during the years it took to complete.

Once down at sea level there are regular boat trips to take visitors out into the sound. It's awe inspiring, with huge rock walls towering as much as three thousand feet from the sound high into the mist. If the weather permits it is sometimes possible for the boats to leave the sound and enter the Tasman sea. The Skippers take their boats right up to the massive cliff walls,nudging them with their bows, and depth of water below them is many hundred of fathoms. A dramatic and very memorable excursion. The one draw back can be the infamous sand flies, they are like no other flies you will have encountered, when in season they are very persistent and annoying and do not respond to normal insect repellent.(Unless you buy the locally produced deterrent).

Retracing their route back from Milford Sound they made their way to Wanaka Lake, camping near the shore line, with Mount Aspiring as their back drop to the west. It was yet another stunning location, and they stayed a while to do some local walks. They had been on the road for nearly three weeks now, and it was time to drive north and catch the ferry from Picton across the Cook Strait to Wellington and North Island. They drove up the Haas pass on the western coast of South Island, where they encountered landslides and deep gorges. It made for interesting driving, eventually stopping in Franz Josef, a small town at the bottom of the Franz Josef Glacier. On the spur of the moment they went into the Air Safaris office and booked two seats for a flight the following morning to take them over the glacier, and Mount Cook.

When they woke up the next day there was beautiful clear blue sky, not a cloud in sight, and no wind. It was absolutely the most perfect day for their trip. The Air Safari minibus picked them up outside the office together with two more passengers and drove them the 8km to the airstrip. Upon arrival the staff allocated their seats, and Sparky was delighted to have one next to a window. With the sun beating down on on them they took off and did a circuit of the town, before gaining altitude and heading for the mighty Franz Josef and Fox Glaciers. They had incredible views as the pilot flew close to the ice, then headed for the rugged Westland National Park, before traversing the face of Mount Cook. The visibility was superb, and they flew round a couple of more times, getting slightly closer with each pass.

Then they the flew over the Mount Cook National Park before returning to the air strip. Everyone was more than satisfied, and very impressed by the whole experience. Once they landed the pilot told them they were so lucky with the weather, it was the best flight he'd made in more than two weeks.

From Franz Josef they headed north to Picton and the ferry. The road took them along the spectacular coastal highway with superb views over the Tasman sea before heading north-east to Picton. They arrived around lunch time, bought a ticket for the ferry then walked around in the warm sunshine enjoying all the sights. The Ferry loaded up and departed for Wellington around 1800 hours. They sorted out a comfortable place to sit, and settled themselves down for the crossing. As the sun began to sink towards the horizon, a long thin cloud formation began to gather, splitting the sky into layers which partially obscured sections of the sun. Over the next half an hour the spectacle constantly changed becoming more dramatic as the sun continued to go down. Sparky couldn't resist the opportunity, and took twenty or more images until the cool sea breeze chased him inside to the warmth of the saloon.

It was dark as they approached Wellington harbour, and the crew were busy preparing the ship for docking. With about twenty minutes to go before entering the harbour, the Southern Ocean suddenly decided to show its mighty power, and a shrieking squall stormed in from the east. The motion of the boat told Sparky that the captain would have his work cut out trying to enter Wellington safely, passenger were gathering at the saloon windows, staring out into the darkness as huge waves crashed over the ships bows and deposited tons of water on the bridge deck. The captain came on the PA system to advise the passengers that they would be unable to berth for the time being, and would hove too off the harbour until the wind abated.

As suddenly as it had blown up, the wind dropped, the sea state was turbulent, but there was a window of opportunity, and the captain skilfully took it. Half an hour later they were tied up and vehicles were disembarking. It was now raining, and gusting winds spread the showers horizontally across the concrete surface of the quay. Sparky was driving, and Kay had the guidebook to the location of their camp site. With the rain, and car headlights dazzling them it was difficult to see the road signs. After a couple of abortive attempts they eventually found the site entrance. It led them into large high sided quarry which had been converted into a well protected caravan and camper park. They drove around until they found an empty plot, parked, switched off and opened a bottle of wine. It had been a long day, but they were safe and secure as they listened to the rain lashing down on top of their camper.

After two windy and rainy days in Wellington, they headed north to the Tongariro National Park and found a very nice camp site. They decided to walk the Tongariro Crossing, a distance of nearly 20 km one way, with a minibus at the end to bring them back to the camp site. The following day they took the camp bus to the start of the walk. Tongariro National park has three live volcanoes, Tongariro, Ngauruhoe, and Ruapehu. All three are liable to erupt at any time. However an early warning system is in place which monitors all volcanic activity, making sure it's safe for trekkers and visitors to venture into the park. The crossing takes between five and six hours, it was a challenging journey but there were a well marked series of board-walks and trails which took them over all the high points of the walk. The smell of sulphur was never far away, with pools of boiling lava bubbling up right alongside the trail.

It was a barren and grey landscape, similar to what we have seen of the moons surface. But it was enhanced by numbers of vivid green lakes and well formed impressive peaks. They climbed up the Mangatepopo valley towards mount Tongariro and Ngauruhoe before reaching the summit of the Red Crater, at an altitude of 1886 metres, eventually making a very pleasant and welcome descent down the other side, and their rendezvous with the camp bus and fellow trekkers.

It had been a very enjoyable and relaxing stay, and Sparky had made friends with the camps tame Raven who followed him wherever he went . It would jump up on his shoulders whilst he was walking through the site, and even tried to establish its self in their camper.

After a few days they decided to head north towards Auckland,stopping at Lake Taupo, and visiting the lava pools of Rotura. At this point they decided they had driven enough, and were in need of some R and R. So they headed over to the east coast where they came across the fabulous Waihi Beach Camp site. It was set out amongst the trees, and was almost idyllic. So they decided to camp there until it was time to return the camper van to Auckland, where it would be collected by the hire company, and where they would transfer into an apartment in the centre of Auckland itself, but that was four days away. So they just chilled out, on virtually deserted, white sandy beaches. The weather was warm, sunny and ideal for sitting around reading and swimming. There was a fresh water stream running through the site which was full of quite large eels. They were completely unconcerned about the intrusion of humans, and the kids would to pick them up and hold them for a while, before putting them back in the water.

They were sorry to leave but all good things come to an end, and they delivered the camper as instructed. The guy who collected it gave them a lift into Auckland and dropped them outside their apartment. When they stepped inside they could hardly believe their eyes, it was beautiful, with a large airy lounge, a fully fitted kitchen, great shower, and a window looking out on the main street, which was only a short walk from the harbour with all its yachts, cruise ships, bars and restaurants. Once again the wisdom off booking well in advance had paid off, it was cheaper to stay there than a three star hotel up the road. So a great time was had enjoying the sights of the 'City of Sails' (as it's known).

Then it was on the move again, this time from Auckland to the Cook Islands in the Pacific Ocean, staying for a week on the small island of Rarotonga. Their plane touched down around midnight, and as they cleared customs they were greeted by an elderly gentleman playing south sea island songs on a battered old Ukulele. This turned out to be the owner of the accommodation they had booked (well in advance of course). Apparently he had arrived on the Island to work for the New Zealand Government as a civil servant, fell in love with a local girl, got married and never left, and that had been more than fifty years ago.

Yet again they were delighted with their accommodation, which was a bamboo and rattan lodge on stilts, almost on the beach, simply but very adequately appointed with all necessary items to make them comfortable. They were very tired and went to bed strait away. In the morning things got even better. They walked out onto the verandah in the cool of the early morning freshness, to be confronted with the sight of a magnificent blue lagoon only ten metres from their front door. The words paradise immediately came into Sparky's mind. Rarotonga was almost circular, and was protected from the ocean by a coral reef which circled the whole island, and was some 150 or more metres wide, thus providing a perfect place to swim safely, and was probably home to thousands of sea creatures. The tide went out each morning and returned in the afternoon. If they weren't chilled out when they arrived, they certainly were by the time they had to leave six days later.

This was now their time to return home, so back to Auckland then a late afternoon flight to Hong Kong. This time they were in a very nice Chinese run hotel on Hong Kong Island. The main reason for their second visit was to find out how things had changed since the handover of the territory back to China. Sparky visited Hong Kong many times on business in the old days, and knew the place well. They went everywhere using trams and the MTR, even on the bus down to Aberdeen Harbour. They went to the top of the Peak, and to Causeway Bay, where Sparky used to stay in the famous Excelsior Hotel. Once used in a James Bond 007 film. They walked miles, and also took a night time cruise to view the impressive skyline with its millions of twinkling lights.

The overwhelming verdict was, that since the hand over the whole place had changed for the better, it hadn't not lost its old magic, its was still essentially the exciting Hong Kong he loved, but it had been given a face lift, and even the people seemed happier. Finally back home in good old GB, they eventually wound down from their absolutely fantastic trip, and resumed a normal existence one again.

Sparky continued running, and enjoying the wide open spaces. On the last weekend of July 2010, he ran the Snowdon International Summit race yet again, and put in a time of 2 hours 16 minutes, not his best performance, but then he was 69 years old after all....

'A Reason to be Cheerful'

———◆———

He awoke early that June morning, around six fifteen, it was in fact his birthday and outside there was a clear blue sky - it was going to be a beautiful day.

Wearing his old baggy T shirt and long shorts, he padded down the stairs to the kitchen and made his customary coffee, walked through the conservatory and opened the doors onto his patio where he was immediately greeted by a post dawn chorus from the Blackbirds and Thrushes as they contested first place on the 'songbird airwaves'.

He sat down in his favourite eastwards facing garden chair, closed his eyes and allowed himself to be completely absorbed. The warmth of the early morning sun and fresh clean air bound everything together.

When he opened his eyes they were filled with a wonderful panorama of hills, dales, farms and sheep. 'It's about as perfect as it could be' he thought. However, after sitting for a few more minutes he sensed rather than saw the clouds following the rising sun over the eastern horizon.

Suddenly it seemed as though the light was fading, and a chill made him shudder as the symphony of birdsong gradually diminished, trailing off to an occasional tweet and staccato chirp.

Almost instantaneously his own mood changed and he found himself transported back five years, to a time when an even blacker cloud had affected his mood, black clouds with far more serious consequences.

Then he had been having his morning shave, when he noticed a swelling or lump on the left side of his neck which had not been there the day before. After a couple of weeks he was concerned enough to see his G.P. who said " It's probably just a cyst, but to be on the safe side let's get you over to the hospital for a biopsy". The results from that one action were to change his life forever.

All his life he had been an active athlete, running and climbing mountains, walking and trekking over the high passes of the world, and now at the back end of his sixties he was still in great physical condition.

But this black cloud had no mercy and quickly pulled him deeper and further into its terrifying centre. 'Malignant cancer in the throat, with a tumour on the left tonsil,' advised the oncologist, and aggressive treatment would be required immediately.

The cloud became his very dark place, so dark at times that he wasn't sure he could cope, he had visions of him never running again in the dales and hills he loved so much.

The people who loved and cared for him were in the same dark place, but they were always there to help him fight, their love and encouragement never ceasing and never wavering.

The dark place did not give ground easily, and for some time held him fast in its awful grip. Gradually, and sometimes it seemed barely perceptible to him, there came a slender sliver of golden light, challenging the darkness, and gradually winning!

As the sun kissed his face once more, the birds began to sing again, and the dark cloud passed over.

In the house he put on his running shorts and vest, and as he laced up his fell shoes in the porch, he looked around him and he knew why he had a 'reason to be cheerful'...

The end...

Date 16th of December 2019.

Sparky is still around, still enjoying mountains, walks, cycling, and easy paced runs around his new home on Merseyside to the north of Liverpool in England.

Lightning Source UK Ltd.
Milton Keynes UK
UKHW010824130420
361614UK00001B/40

9 781916 377936